THE BIRDS OF BUCKINGHAMSHIRE

THE BIRDS OF BUCKINGHAMSHIRE

Edited by

Peter Lack

and

David Ferguson

Illustrations by

Kim Atkinson
Philip Burton
Jane Cross
Crispin Fisher
David Mead

THE BUCKINGHAMSHIRE BIRD CLUB

First published in 1993 by The Buckinghamshire Bird Club.

British Library Cataloguing-in-Publication Data.
A catalogue record for this book is available from the British Library.

ISBN 0 907823 12 2

Printed and bound by Biddles Ltd., Guildford and King's Lynn.

CONTENTS

INTRODUCTION

This book aims to summarise the status of the birds which have occurred in the present county of Buckinghamshire. The boundaries of the county have in fact changed very little for several hundred years. It is a medium-sized more or less rectangular county situated in the midlands of England approximately 80 km from north to south and 30-40 km from east to west. Most of the county lies between the Rivers Thames in the south and the Great Ouse in the north with the major dividing line of the Chiltern Escarpment running southwest to northeast between them. To the north of this, about two thirds of the area, the landscape is predominantly mixed farmland with a few scattered woodlands and with a rather low human population density, except in Aylesbury and MIlton Keynes. The south, occupying the remaining third, is more wooded, especially on the Chilterns themselves and today is much more densely populated.

The population of the county is now about 500,000 with the majority in the urban areas in and around High Wycombe, Beaconsfield and towards Slough (itself since 1974 in Berkshire), Marlow, Amersham and in recent years increasingly in the administrative capital of Aylesbury and the new town of Milton Keynes. In between are some areas which, for southern England, have a very low population indeed.

Ornithologically the county has not been very well served in the past partly because there are relatively few well known birdwatching sites, at least in national terms. Also it was not until the advent of the Buckinghamshire Bird Club (hereafter referred to as the BBC) in the early 1980s that there was a co-ordinating body able to cover the whole county effectively. The southern part had been very well served by the Middle Thames Natural History Society for many years previous to this but, until 1975 when a very active group of birdwatchers was formed, the north of the county in particular was too far away from this Society's main recording area. Indeed until the 1970s there were very few people and hence birdwatchers at all in the northern part of the county. The growth of Milton Keynes brought both many more people and the development of some excellent new birdwatching sites to the area.

There have been a few compilations of the birds of the county, most recently by Fraser and Youngman (1976), and together with the more recent records compiled by the BBC in the 1980s these form the basis of this book. Two complications have been the geographically minor, but ornithologically quite important, boundary changes, in particular Slough and its immediate environs which were in the county until 1974, and that a small part of the Tring Reservoir complex is actually in Buckinghamshire rather than Hertfordshire. We have tried to ensure that all the records quoted have been recorded within the confines of the county as it stands today although a few old records from boundary areas may have slipped through.

We have also tried to be as consistent as possible over assessing records of less common species. All recent records have been vetted by the BBC's Records Committee but a great many earlier records have had to be accepted as they stand.

During the early 1980s the Club took over the running of the fieldwork for an atlas of the breeding birds of the county. This continued for several years and the resulting maps are published in this book to give an indication of the status of the county's breeding species. Full details of the methods used and some comments on the interpretation of the resulting maps are included below.

The book starts with some introductory chapters on the history of Buckinghamshire's birdwatchers, the main habitats to be found and a short essay on migration within the county. All these and the main bulk of the book, the species accounts, have been written by a variety of birdwatchers and scientists who have an interest in the birds of the county and who are credited with their texts. Authors of the species accounts were asked to follow certain guidelines when writing and to use material from Buckinghamshire where possible in preference to that from other areas. In particular the simple repeating of general information which appears in other books is avoided although some has been necessary to put the Buckinghamshire information into context.

It will be obvious that the species accounts vary considerably in length. The longer ones mainly result from the particular species having been the subject of a special study in the county, often by the author of the text concerned, rather than that the species is particularly common, or rare. Where possible the editors have tried to retain the sometimes distinctive styles of these and the other authors. The result is that the book is a compilation of knowledge about the birds of the county and knowledge of the birds in general which was gained in the county. The bibliography contains the majority of significant references about the birds of the county, and serves in part as a complement to the much earlier very full bibliography in Hartert and Jourdain (1920) which listed all the old references to individual records up to that date.

There have been several particular surveys of birds in addition to the county breeding survey referred to above, and which have been mentioned specifically where relevant. Most of the national bird surveys which have taken place, largely under the auspices of the British Trust for Ornithology, have included the county. These include the ringing scheme and its associated recoveries, the Common Birds Census, the Nest Record Scheme and several shorter term ones including single species surveys. The National Wildfowl Counts organised by the Wildfowl and Wetlands Trust have been carried out regularly on the major water bodies for many years. The BBC has also run some surveys of its own and in particular a Garden Bird Survey which started in the winter of 1986/87 and continues. Particular surveys of wintering plovers and more detailed studies by individuals working in the county are also noted where relevant.

ACKNOWLEDGEMENTS

A book of this kind cannot be produced without the help of a large number of people, and in the case of this particular work the rather long gestation period has meant that even more people than usual have been involved.

We would like to thank the following:

The succesive county recorders Ron Youngman, John Marchant, and Andy Harding have been responsible for compiling the annual reports on which much of the book is based. The latter two in particular, together with the present county records committee, (JM, AH, Andrew Moon, and Chris Ward) have been instrumental in ensuing the accuracy of the records given here.

Alan Knox was chairman of the Buckinghamshire Atlas Working Group which co-ordinated the county breeding survey from 1981 to 1986 and whose other members included Trevor Brooks, Crispin Fisher, Jim Knight, Peter Lack and Robert Morgan.

Andy Clements and subsequently Peter Stevens acted as Managing Editors during the earlier stages of compiling and writing.

John Pemberton did much of the initial editing and typesetting.

Trevor Brooks was co-ordinator of the records coming in to the county breeding survey and was responsible for compiling the maps.

Arthur Brown has organised and co-ordinated the Club's Garden Bird Survey for several years.

The wildfowl counts used in the species accounts were kindly supplied by the Wildfowl and Wetlands Trust.

The species accounts were written by different authors. In many cases, the author's initials are given at the end of the account. Where no initials are given then the account is of one of the rarer birds and was written by a combination of John Marchant and David Ferguson, with help from Andy Harding.

The authors of individual species accounts are:

Philip Burton (PJKB)
Susan Cowdy (SC)
David Ferguson (DMF)
Rob Fuller (RJF)
Darrell Hamley (DBH)
Andy Harding (AVH)
Jim Knight (JK)
Henry Mayer-Gross (HM-G)
Robert Morgan (RAM)
Jim Rose (JER)
Peter Stevens (PJS)
Norman Stone (NHFS)
Richard Tomlin (RJT)
Phil Whittington (PAW)
Chris Young (CEY)

The population estimates were compiled and calculated by the second editor who also drew most of the graphs.

Chris Smith and Angela Fuller gave valuable comments to Rob Fuller on the Habitats chapter; he also wishes to thank Peter Lack, Kate Rowland, Jill Royston and Jonathon Spencer for providing information for this, and to thank Liz Murray and Su Gough for drawing the figures.

Warren Claydon provided much information for the Migration chapter.

The vignettes which are scattered through the text are by Kim Atkinson, Philip Burton, Jane Cross, the late Crispin Fisher, and David Mead. We would particularly like to thank Jane Fisher for allowing us to use her late husband's drawings.

The main cover drawing was painted by the Rev. John Hull, with the Hobby and Swifts added by David Mead.

The photographs of various habitats in the county were taken by Sandy Macfarlane, as was the Cormorant photograph. The gulls photograph was taken by Mike Wallen.

In the later stages Jim Rose acted as the vital link between the editors and the committee of the Buckinghamshire Bird Club, while Arthur Brown was responsible for liaising with the printers and for most of the marketing.

A special thank you goes to Susan Cowdy who kept us all going, and another to the late Crispin Fisher who was one of the instigators of the Buckinghamshire Bird Club, the county breeding survey and this book.

Finally we thank Buckinghamshire County Council for some substantial sponsorship to make the book a reality.

To all these, and particularly to anyone we have inadvertently left out, we are very grateful.

ORNITHOLOGISTS, COLLECTORS AND FIELDWORKERS IN BUCKINGHAMSHIRE THROUGH THE YEARS

Susan Cowdy and Peter Lack

Early Records

The first explicit mention of birds in Buckinghamshire seems to be in the Domesday Book of 1085. It is stated there that William the Conqueror held two eyries of Hawks in the county: firstly, Manno the Breton owned some land in Chalfont St Giles which 'included woodland to feed 600 swine and in the same wood was a falcon's eyrie'; and, secondly, at Chalfont St Peter, Bishop Bayeux owned some woodland which held a 'hawk's eyrie'. We can only guess at the species involved.

We know of no other mention until the beginning of the sixteenth century when a letter to Cardinal Wolsey stated that the timber for St George's Chapel in Windsor Castle came from Dreynford Wodde at Agmondesham (the present day Brentford Wood at Amersham), where there 'hath been this twenty or thirty years an Ayreye of Goossehawks contynually there bredying. By mysorder they were put from there' (quoted by R.H.Tighe in Annals of Windsor -- see Fraser (1953)).

Hawks seem to have been the major interest because the first mention of a collector in the county was at about the same time. In 1530 Thomas Hawtry, the owner of the Chequers Estate, together with Edward and Harry Hampden and other 'evil-disposed persons, riotously with force and arms entered Frith Wood and caused the tree wherein the Goshawk bred to be scaled and so took out of the nest all the said keyries of young hawks and bore them away to hitherto keep at their wills and pleasures'. Sir John Hampden, as Sheriff, reported the matter to his royal master the King (Henry VIII), and added that he had caused the nest to be kept under continuous watch, at not little cost to himself, with the object that the young hawks should be taken and delivered 'to the commodity and pleasure of your Royal Highness'. This was by no means the end of the story though; for when Hampden sent messengers to collect information on the spot, 'Thomas Hawtry with a dozen others issued out of an ambush on the Ellesborough road and beat and grievously wounded the messengers'. After this, all the accused were summoned to appear before the Court of the Star Chamber, although the upshot of the affair is not told (Jenkins 1967).

A whole series of observations which were made during the late 18th century were recorded in a manuscript which was found in Dinton Hall near Aylesbury. The notes were started in 1772 by Sir John Van Hatten and were continued by a grandson, the Rev. W. Goodall, into the beginning of the nineteenth century. Hartert (see below) later saw this treatise and verified the statements made in it and used them in his two later papers on the birds of the county. Unfortunately this manuscript cannot now be found and must be presumed lost.

It is, however, from about the middle of the nineteenth century that we have a rather better idea of what occurred in the area. There was still considerable persecution going on, as an addendum to the book Aedes Hartwelliana (Smythe 1864) explains. Admiral Smythe lived in Hartwell House and there is a chapter describing the persecution in *A Defence of Birds*. The author discusses the 'vexed questions about birds and bird-murderers'. He denounced sparrow clubs and gives a list of innocuous species which became a quarry for sparrow club heroes, and there is a vivid description of the holiday pastimes of the 'Aylesbury street-arabs'.

Reasons are also given for the rapid thinning of bird communities while their enemies are on the increase. The problems faced by the birds of the time included such as:

> 'Predatory cottage urchins, hobbety boys and idle adults.
> Shrikes and the tribe of butcher birds.
> Sparrow clubs and Sunday bird-murderers.
> Supplying taxidermy's demands, and the associated wilful waste.
> Assarting of wood, groves, spinneys, coppices and the like.
> Aylesbury street-arabs' holiday pastime.
> Birds' nest plunderers, and birds' egg collectors.
> Buzzards, kestrels and hawks in general.
> Carrion, Hooded or Gor Crows.
> Dogs, cats, rats, fitchets and weasels.
> Fire-arms, bows and arrows, stones and sticks.
> Hard frosts, sudden storms and severe winters.
> Mongel sportsmen and small class poachers.
> Owls and strix-hooters of all sorts.
> Poisoned food, bird-lime, gins and springes.'

It is a wonder that there were any left!

Mid nineteenth and early twentieth centuries

The first attempt to write about all the birds of the county was a book *The Birds of Berkshire and Buckinghamshire* published in 1865, written by Alexander W.M. Clark Kennedy, 'an Eton boy'. This is a wonderfully interesting book, especially when one considers that the author was only 16 years old when it was written. It is unique too in that the illustrations are the first hand-coloured photographs used in a book on birds. Clark Kennedy's ardent wish was to see the ornithology of each British county represented in a book, but he himself did not do anything very much more ornithological in his life. In compiling the book he was in contact with many Buckinghamshire ornithologists of his day, in particular the Rev. Harpur Crewe of Drayton Beauchamp, but most of the records and observations concern the southern part of the county and across the River Thames in Berkshire.

In the following 50 years there was no concerted effort to compile records from the county although there are various individual reports of less common birds in such as The Field (see below). However, in 1905 Ernst Hartert, who was Curator of the Tring Museum from 1903 to 1930, wrote a paper, in collaboration with the Hon. Walter Rothschild, on the birds of Buckinghamshire as a chapter in the *Victoria County History* (Hartert & Rothschild 1905). They wrote then: 'compared with many other counties the number of collectors and field-ornithologists is small, and it seems to us that the country people generally are less observant than they are in some other parts of England'. Ernst Hartert was reckoned by Richard Meinertzhagen to be the best ornithologist of his day, and one who had a great sense of humour and was a charming companion. Rothschild (later Lord Rothschild) himself was the owner of Tring Museum and he too admired and appreciated Hartert's matchless curating and unflagging industry. Despite his travels all over the world in search of exotic flora and fauna, Rothschild's first interest was in the local Tring area and he and Hartert wrote several papers on the natural history of the nearby areas including the bird one noted above.

Rothschild too was evidently a remarkable man. He was extremely diffident and shy and either had nothing to say at all or gave vent to trumpeting: altogether a charismatic enthusiast who was very generous to all who came his way.

In 1920 Hartert wrote a second major paper on the birds of the county, this time including the Tring Reservoirs, most of which are in neighbouring Hertfordshire, and this time with Pastor F.C.R. Jourdain. Apart from some detailed notes about the birds known from the area, this paper is remarkable for the list of 185 references from 1827 to 1920 which Jourdain compiled. These include many odd records from The Field and all other journals and magazines which he could find. The paper included notes from their own observations, those of Clark Kennedy and from several birdwatchers of the day including Rev H.D. Astley, A. Heneage Cocks, Alan F. Crossman, Heatley Noble, Charles Wilson and Edwin Hollis. The last named was Curator of the Buckinghamshire County Museum in Aylesbury from 1908 to 1941, who was a keen collector and taxidermist and who made a very fine collection of birds and eggs from the county during his term of office. Sadly during the Second World War the bird skins became rather badly moth-eaten and were destroyed by a subsequent curator.

A rather different book was written in the late nineteenth century by the Rev Hubert Astley called *My Birds in Freedom and Captivity*, described by the author as 'only a homely account' of the birds in the gardens of his beautiful home, Chequers Court near Ellesborough (Astley 1900). He too was an extraordinary man for his time. He was one of the first people to put up nestboxes, and these attracted many species, including Redstarts which are decidedly uncommon there today. He was also one of the first bird protectionists and calls on the county magistrates to enforce the bird protection laws and to bestir the county police. In addition to local observations he travelled on the continent and in Egypt, and gives graphic descriptions of extreme cruelty to birds. He was particularly fond of wagtails. For example he bought 200 Blue-headed Wagtails from a man in Naples for 5 francs, then opened the large flat cage to the amazement of the bird seller. He had found that the townspeople bought the birds as 'flycatchers', clipping their wings and letting them run loose in their yards and rooms. A more local story was from his schooldays at Eton in the 1870s. At that time there was a ghastly old woman, 'Old Mother Lipscombe', who sat by the school gates selling fruit and local wild birds' eggs, and he lists many of the species she had for sale.

A final string to his bow concerns what may be the first ringing of any birds in Britain. He had a considerable bird collection and in June 1899 he obtained some nestling White Storks from Leadenhall Market, and then..

'..I bought some silver rings, on which I had the year and the name of their English home engraved, and slipped one on to the ankle of each bird. This was not easy, for the ring must not be too large for the stork's leg, and yet large enough to go over the foot. Of course one might have them made with a snap which would close for ever, when shut to; but it would be a more costly business.'

The birds spent the summer flying around Chequers, roosting on the chimney pots, then, in September, flew away, never to be seen again.

1920 - 1980

From 1920 after the publication of the paper by Hartert and Jourdain (1920) annual reports of birds seen in the county were published as part of the annual report of the then newly started Oxford Ornithological Society. These reports covered Oxfordshire, Berkshire and Buckinghamshire although reading through them it appears that Buckinghamshire was still relatively unrecorded compared to the others.

The reports continued in this way, many compiled and edited by Bernard Tucker, until that for 1953. As with present day county reports and books, the bulk of them consists of a list with notes of the birds seen during the year. However, the newly fledged society also organised several special surveys of particular species covering all three counties, especially during the 1930s. The Great Crested Grebe, Redstart, Tufted Duck and Pochard among others received such a survey. Full details of the results of these surveys are published in the annual reports and form an important record of the distribution of the species at that time. The status of several of the species has changed substantially since.

In 1947 Miss K. Price, who had previously been editor of the Oxford Ornithological Society report, compiled an annotated list (usually 2-3 lines per species) of the 'Birds of Buckinghamshire' as part of the centenary volume of the Buckinghamshire Archaeological Society (Price 1947).

The status of each species in the county was summarised although it was not nearly so detailed as the earlier papers by Hartert and his colleagues. In the introduction to the paper she adds:

'Reading through old county reports one is struck by the number of birds that were shot for identification or out of stupidity; this is now fortunately a rare thing, but it means that there is an element of doubt concerning a number of recent records.

It was not until about 1925 that we began to get reports of birds seen at sewage farms. It will be noticed that a good many species, especially waders, have so far only been met with on Slough sewage farm. Others are seen there almost annually but hardly ever recorded elsewhere in Buckinghamshire. The Chiltern Hills, in the western part of the county, is the only area where Stone Curlew, Cirl Bunting and Wood-lark are found. The Wryneck only breeds in the south-eastern part of the county.'

Unfortunately for Buckinghamshire ornithology Slough Sewage Farm is now not in the county as it was excised during the boundary changes in 1974 and put in Berkshire, as were some of the reservoirs nearby.

After 1953 the Oxford Ornithological Society ceased to report the birds of Buckinghamshire and the annual reporting of records was taken over by the Middle

Thames Natural History Society. However, until 1974 it only covered the area south of the Chiltern Escarpment with the north of the county not covered at all. From 1974 the report covers the whole county and it carried on in this format until the Buckinghamshire Bird Club took over the report for 1980. This has continued ever since.

The period of the Middle Thames Society stewardship of the county records also saw updates of the county list largely at the instigation of A.C. Fraser. *The Birds of the Middle Thames*, covering southern Buckinghamshire was first published in 1954 (Fraser 1954), was revised in 1967 and again in 1976 when, in collaboration with Ron Youngman, who was then County Recorder, it became a fully annotated list of birds of the whole county (Fraser and Youngman 1976). The opportunity was taken also to include the results of the BTO Atlas of Breeding Birds (Sharrock 1976) as it affected the birds of the county.

There were a few other groups active in the county during the latter part of this period. The Amersham and District Ornithological Society (now the Amersham BIrdwautching Club) continues to record birds in an area within about 10 km of Amersham, and served then, as it does today, as a focus for many of the birdwatchers in its vicinity.

At the end of 1974 the Milton Keynes Natural History Society spawned a monthly bird bulletin. Mirroring its parent body its area of interest spread farther out than just Milton Keynes and actually covered much of the north of the county. Over the following year or two this bulletin became larger and in 1977 became the North Bucks Bird Report, and the group whose activities centred on the publication formed themselves into a more formal group, the North Bucks Birders, in 1980. During the late 1970s they passed their records for the county report to the Middle Thames Natural History Society but other contact between the two groups was minimal largely because of the distance involved, 80-90 km.

There have been one or two other publications relating to the birds of the county in this period. In 1934 Godfrey Harrison published *A Bird Diary* which includes references to birds in the Amersham/Beaconsfield area, and is illustrated by wood engravings by Robert Gibbings. From his home at Little Missenden he visited Shardeloes Lake where he saw (probably the first) Canada Geese in 1934, commenting that he hoped they would disappear! He and his wife were keen bird mentors (but not collectors) and he writes vivid accounts of the behaviour of different species. He delighted in the common species: 'the Reed Bunting with his black head, singing his ridiculous song', and recalling how he and his wife were in full enjoyment of 'that existence for which ornithology is only an education and a discipline - the unconscious consciousness of the companionship of birds; seeing hearing and interpreting is a pleasure and a delight untold'.

The second is a more well-known book, *The Goshawk* by T.H.White, who was a schoolmaster at Stowe School and a knowledgeable ornithologist and falconer. This eloquent and absorbing book was written a few years before 1939 but publication was withheld for 15 years because as the author wrote: 'There was a guilty secret that had to be concealed at all costs'. This concerned a pair of Hobbies breeding in the area where he lived. White explains: 'The secret was the hobbies, one of the rarest falcons who migrate to breed in England, so rare that one must not tell anybody about them and particularly not in print. All the names in my book are real names. Any unscrupulous ornithologist had only to identify the place or me and then diminish the number of English nesting Hobbies by one pair'. The book was eventually published because an airport was built next to the site (now Silverstone Racing Circuit on the Buckinghamshire/Northamptonshire border), which caused the 'lovely hobbies to clear off on their own accord'. The book is a delight to read.

In more recent years the county has benefited from the fact that the British Trust for Ornithology headquarters was situated in Tring, only just outside the county boundary in Hertfordshire, from 1963 until 1991, and also the Bird Room of the British Museum (Natural History) moved to Tring during 1971. This has resulted in several eminent ornithologists making their homes in the area and there have been several detailed studies of particular species and areas as a result.

1981 to the Present

Birdwatchers did not really have a focus for their interests over the whole county until 1981 as there was no specific bird club covering the county. During 1981 a group of people in the middle of the county decided that a county bird club was needed to co-ordinate all activities and this resulted in the founding of the Buckinghamshire Bird Club. This had its first public meeting in Wendover in October 1981, since when it has met 6 or 7 times each winter and has organised many field meetings both in the county and farther afield throughout the year.

From its start the Club took over the production of an annual report on the birds of the county from the Middle Thames Natural History Society and produced the report for 1980 as a starting point. This annual report has always had the full co-operation of the North Bucks Birders and, until the society folded in 1989, the Middle Thames Natural History Society bird section.

The other societies mentioned in the previous section also continue to flourish and all provide their records for the compilation of the county bird report. The North Bucks Birders hold regular monthly meetings, as does the Amersham Birdwatching Club. There are also two RSPB Members Groups in the county, the North Bucks group based in Milton Keynes, and the Aylesbury group.

The result is that the county is probably now covered by birdwatchers as well as it ever has been. Having said that there are many places which are still only rarely visited, and by the standards of some counties it is still rather poorly covered. It is also one with relatively few sites which are considered as top bird watching sites, certainly in national terms. Perhaps the most important site, and noteworthy also for being completely artificial, is Willen Lake in Milton Keynes which regularly attracts large numbers of birdwatchers and has a reputation for attracting many of the less usual birds which are recorded.

BIRD HABITATS IN BUCKINGHAMSHIRE

R J Fuller

The northern and southern extremes of the county of Buckinghamshire are conveniently formed by the valleys of two of England's longest rivers - the Great Ouse and the Thames. Between these rivers lies a rich variety of landscapes. The general contrast between the open farmland north of the Chiltern escarpment and the heavily wooded country to the south is immediately obvious from any map of the region, but a journey through the county from north to south will reveal many other, more subtle, changes in the landscape, some of which are associated with the geological formations which run mainly on a south-west to north-east axis.

This chapter is a general account of the Buckinghamshire environment and its most distinctive ornithological features. It is a personal view, emphasising the most significant elements of the landscape in determining the character of the Buckinghamshire avifauna. Hence, farmland and woodland receive close scrutiny but little attention is paid, for example, to our relic fragments of heath and bog. This approach should not be taken to imply that any habitats, nor indeed specific sites, not mentioned in the chapter are bereft of ornithological interest. Wherever possible I have tried to assess the effects on birds of recent changes to habitats and land-use in the county. To set the habitats and their birds in perspective I first sketch out the main geographical variations in the Buckinghamshire landscape.

Geology, Landscape and Drainage

Buckinghamshire can be divided into eleven regions, of unequal area, each with its own distinctive landscape, although not always distinctive bird-life (Figure 1). The differences between these regions are ones of geology, soils, topography and drainage. The main rivers and canals are shown in Figure 2.

The oldest geological formations are those in the north of the county where boulder clay deposits overlie Jurassic formations - Oolite, Cornbrash and Liassic north of the Great Ouse, with vales of Kimmeridge and Oxford Clays to the south. The land north of the Great Ouse is predominantly arable farmland but with several substantial areas of woodland. To the south, there are fewer large woodlands but the farmland becomes more mixed with much permanent pasture.

A low range of hills, rising to some 190m at Quainton and Brill, marks the region where the Jurassic Portland and Purbeck Beds meet the overlying Lower Greensand of the Cretaceous. The hills on the Bedfordshire border, in the vicinity of the Brickhills, have the steepest slopes and are rather different in character to those south-west of Stewkley and Wing. The latter hills mark the watershed between the Great Ouse and Thames drainage systems. Claydon Brook and the River Ouzel drain the northern clay vales. To the south, the River Thame flows the length of the Vale of Aylesbury whilst, in the extreme west, the headwaters of the River Ray just reach into the county. The largely drift-free Kimmeridge and Gault Clay of the Vale of Aylesbury forms a narrow plain between the Portland and Greensand hills and the

Figure 1. Regions of Buckinghamshire following Reed (1979). The pre-1974 county boundary is marked with a broken line.

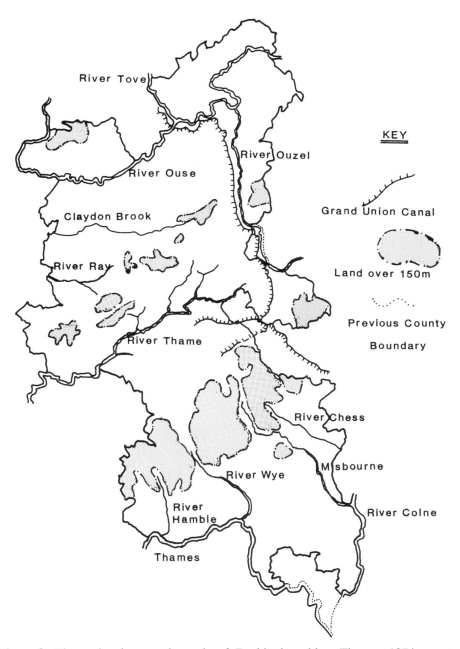

Figure 2. The main rivers and canals of Buckinghamshire. The pre-1974 county boundary is marked with a broken line.

Chalk escarpment of the Chilterns. The mixed farmland of the Vale is virtually devoid of woodland.

The highest points in the county (260m) occur along the Chiltern escarpment which is breached by three gaps at Princes Risborough, Wendover and Tring. The escarpment follows a somewhat convoluted path with 'headlands', as at Bledlow, Whiteleaf, Coombe Hill and Boddington Hill, interwoven with valleys and 'bays', for example at Great Kimble and Dancer's End. East of the Tring Gap there are tracts of relatively open downland at Pitstone Hill and in the Ivinghoe Beacon complex of chalk hills. Scrub is rapidly covering some of these downs through lack of grazing. To the south-west, the escarpment is far more heavily wooded but pockets of fine chalk grassland still cling to the slopes between Wendover and Princes Risborough.

The chalk plateau of the Chilterns is partly covered with clay-with-flints and other superficial deposits. The dip slope is dissected by many valleys, mostly dry, running to the south-east. The unique character of the Chilterns is vested partly in the topography of these valleys, and partly in the mixture of beech-dominated woods and arable farmland. Only four streams flow down the dip slope of the Chilterns: the Hamble, Wye, Misbourne and Chess.

In the extreme south-east of the county (the Burnham Plateau) the chalk gives way to Tertiary Reading Beds and London Clay, these often covered with glacial drift and Thames gravels. With the exception of Milton Keynes, the greatest landscape changes during the present century have been in the south-east where the influence of London

The Vale of Aylesbury near Dorton. Since the late 1970s drainage operations and grassland improvement have virtually wiped out the damp meadows which were characteristic of this region. Recent declines in number of breeding Curlews may be linked with this habitat change.

has pushed inexorably westwards. This urban and industrial transformation, superimposed on complex soils, has created diverse landscapes. In less than 10 km one can travel from the relative tranquillity of Burnham Beeches, through the housing and factories of Slough, onto the Thameside meadows, many of which have been altered by mineral extraction. The distribution of urban areas is shown in Figure 8.

Farmland

Farmland forms the fabric of the countryside so it is appropriate that it should be considered before other habitats. I first describe the main crops in the county and the birds associated with them. There have been enormous changes in Buckinghamshire agriculture over the last three or so decades and the effects of these on birds are outlined. But farmland consists of more than just crops and grass. Farming has created a mosaic of habitats and vegetation including ponds, hedges, shelterbelts and copses. Without hedgerows and trees, our countryside would be immeasurably poorer, both as landscape and wildlife habitat. Therefore, I conclude with an account of hedgerows and their importance to birds.

Crops and grassland: some statistics

There are more than 1200 square kilometres of crops and grassland in Buckinghamshire representing some 63% of the county's land surface. Overall, the agriculture of the county is mixed but there is considerable local variation. For example, the distribution of permanent grassland is patchy with some parts of the county carrying extensive tracts, such as the headwaters of the Rivers Thame and Ray. Elsewhere, the permanent grassland is mixed into a finer-grained mosaic of arable and grass. Many of the permanent grass fields north of the Chilterns exhibit fine ridge-and-furrow. These relics of medieval ploughing, so well described by Rackham (1986), date largely from a time when the Buckinghamshire countryside would have been starkly different from that of today. Much of the land north of the Chilterns was then worked as 'open-field' or 'strip-cultivation' with few hedgerows.

Over the last 20 years the crops of Buckinghamshire have been dominated by grassland, wheat and barley each covering at least 100 square kilometres (Figure 3). The area of wheat has recently increased, at the expense of grassland, but the barley area has been relatively stable. Other crops of some significance, in terms of their areas, are oats and oilseed rape. The former has declined since the mid 1960s (although it now seems to be increasing once more) while the area of rape has dramatically increased. Two other notable trends concern horticulture and orchards both of which have declined appreciably over the last 20 years. These broad statistics mask many changes in grassland and crop management of considerable significance to birds; for example the ubiquitous improvement of grassland through drainage, artificial fertilizers and reseeding. The ornithological effects of these trends in farming practices are considered below.

Use of crops and grass by birds

In spring and summer much farmland carries low numbers of birds compared with many other habitats in the county. More breeding species are associated with the hedgerows and farmland copses than with the open fields themselves. Skylark stands alone as a ubiquitous field-nesting species. Lapwings, Corn Buntings and Yellow Wagtails are far more patchily distributed as the distribution maps later in the book show. Curlews and Meadow Pipits are even more local while Redshank and Snipe are nearly extinct as field-nesters in Buckinghamshire.

Far larger numbers of birds use the open fields for feeding, particularly in winter. Large flocks of Lapwings, Golden Plovers, Woodpigeons, Stock Doves, Redwings, Fieldfares, Starlings and Black-headed Gulls feed on grassland, especially permanent pastures, in winter. These species are supplemented by ducks, notably Teal and Wigeon, on the wettest riverside pastures. Along the Thame valley, for example, flooded grasslands regularly held flocks of ducks at Worminghall, Shabbington and

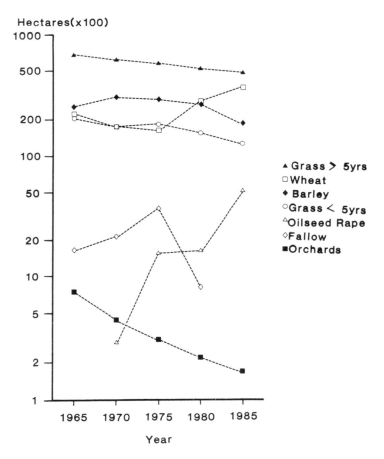

Figure 3. Total areas of selected crops and agricultural land-uses in Buckinghamshire. Statistics from Ministry of Agriculture, Fisheries and Food censuses are plotted at five-yearly intervals. Figures were unavailable for oilseed rape and fallow in 1965 and 1985 respectively. Note the logarithmic scale on the vertical axis.

Hulcott for short periods in most winters between the mid 1970s and mid 1980s. In general, arable crops seem to hold fewer wintering birds than grassland. Feeding Lapwings and Golden Plovers make heavy use of cereal fields in autumn and in mild winter periods, but finch and bunting flocks are now much scarcer on arable land than two decades ago.

Many of the birds that feed in fields are highly gregarious and, at any one time, use only a small number of the available fields. In part, this arises from birds concentrating at temporary food sources. Examples are wagtails and other insectivorous birds on freshly cut hay meadows; Rooks and ducks on recently harvested fields; Lapwings, gulls and Pied Wagtails on freshly ploughed fields; and gulls, plovers and ducks on flooded fields. However, the distribution of many bird flocks on farmland is less easily explained. The occurrence of wintering Lapwings and Golden Plovers on grassland, for example, is very patchy both in time and space (Fuller 1990, Fuller and Youngman 1979). Some grass fields are regularly used by spectacular assemblages while other, apparently identical, fields are consistently devoid of birds. These field preferences may reflect variations in the availability of food, resulting from differences in soil drainage and, perhaps, past management.

Changes in farming practice

Much farmland is an unpredictable environment for birds, with periodic changes in the types of crops grown and in the techniques of growing them. Some species are unable to adapt to changes in agriculture while others manage to adapt or even exploit new opportunities. There have been dramatic changes in farmland bird populations over the last two or three decades in response to rapid developments in agriculture (O'Connor and Shrubb 1986). These changes are summarised below. Now we are on the threshold of a new generation of changes in agricultural land-use stimulated by the need to reduce over-production. The Set-aside and Farm Woodland Schemes will certainly introduce greater variety onto some farms with the creation of various types of 'fallow' and new woodlands. At present it is too early to judge what effect these may have on numbers and distribution of birds.

In the mid 1970s there was a striking shift in the seasonal pattern of cultivation. Spring sowing of wheat was virtually abandoned in favour of autumn sowing. The area of traditional spring barley was also reduced and by the 1980s was less than that of winter barley. We know rather little about the use of different crops by birds in the county so it is difficult to assess the ornithological implications of these changes in arable farming. However, the loss of spring-sown crops has probably affected birds in several ways. First, there has been a loss of winter stubbles which once formed widespread feeding areas for huge flocks of finches, sparrows, buntings and corvids. Second, autumn-sown crops are not so attractive to nesting Lapwings as spring-sown crops. Third, spring ploughing may have provided a valuable source of food at the start of the breeding season for ground-feeding birds such as thrushes. Intensification of cereal agriculture during the 1970s was evident also in the breakdown of traditional rotations involving a fallow phase. The decline of fallow land (Figure 3) has been one further factor leading to a more uniform farmland landscape.

Since the mid 1960s the area of grassland has declined in Buckinghamshire as the area under cereals has risen (Figure 3). Undoubtedly, some of the grass fields lost to cereals provided important winter feeding for birds such as plovers and thrushes. Loss of grassland has probably been of less ornithological significance than the extensive changes in grassland management. Application of artificial fertilizer has risen hugely over the last 15 or so years, resulting in faster-growing, thicker swards. These grasslands are unattractive to some ground-nesting species such as Lapwings. To some extent, traditional hay meadows have also given way to silage crops which are relatively poor habitats for birds during the breeding season. Drainage improvements since the 1960s have been widespread and efficient throughout the county. These typically involve field under-drainage and regular dredging of streams and rivers. The net effect has been eradication of grassland that regularly remains wet into the spring and early summer. In the Vale of Aylesbury this has resulted in the loss of breeding Redshank from virtually all the traditional breeding sites. Winter flooding is also less widespread and prolonged along the Thame and Ray valleys than even ten years ago. Consequently wildfowl appear in smaller numbers and stay for shorter periods. Another effect of drainage is that large concentrations of wintering Snipe are becoming more local.

It is hard to avoid the conclusion that over the last 20 years the crops and grasslands of Buckinghamshire have become more uniform and less interesting habitats for birds. Perhaps the one positive change for birds has been the increasing area of oilseed rape. This crop appears attractive to many insects and it is used by several species of nesting and feeding birds. Reed Bunting and Sedge Warbler are amongst the more surprising species to be found holding territory in some rape fields.

Hedgerows and birds

The Enclosure Acts, which finally abolished the medieval open-field systems in the eighteenth and early nineteenth centuries, were responsible for producing many of the hedgerows that now exist in the county. 'Enclosure Act' hedges are generally straight, form a more or less regular network and contain few species of shrubs, typically being dominated by hawthorn. Such hedges are especially common north of the Chilterns. Not all our hedges are of such recent origin. Some fine ancient hedges do survive, often following parish boundaries or flanking green lanes. Generally richer in shrub and tree species than recent hedges (Pollard, Hooper and Moore 1974), and often following a sinuous path, these medieval survivors are irreplaceable features of our countryside. The greatest incidence of ancient hedges is probably found in the Chilterns where the broad pattern of the landscape familiar to us today was established long before the Enclosure Acts (Reed 1979). The Chilterns countryside is essentially ancient whereas that to the north is essentially planned (see Figure 1.3 in Rackham 1986). A detailed account of hedges in one part of the Chilterns is given by Casselden (1986).

Hedgerow destruction has received much publicity but its extent is hard to gauge in Buckinghamshire; at least we are fortunate that few parts of the county can be regarded as 'prairie farmland' devoid of hedges and trees. Since World War II Dutch elm disease has had a more profound effect on the clayland landscape of Buckinghamshire - and probably on birds - than has loss of hedges. Densities of breeding birds are greatest in hedges which have trees (O'Connor & Shrubb 1986) so presumably farmland was richer in hedgerow birds before Dutch elm disease.

Fortunately, hedges in many parts of Buckinghamshire are rich in trees other than elm. A remarkable abundance of black poplar occurs in the Vale of Aylesbury. Many of these trees are pollards offering nest sites for a range of hole-nesting birds which included Redstart until the mid 1970s. Further north, oaks and ash predominate. Unfortunately, we are now seeing serious ash dieback in many parts of the county.

Hedges vary greatly in their quality as habitats for breeding birds. In general, the greatest densities and numbers of bird species are found in overgrown hedges with outgrowths of thorn or bramble and with many mature trees. Hedges composed of many species of shrubs are likely to be attractive to a greater variety of birds than hedges with relatively few shrubs. Short, heavily-trimmed hedges support relatively few birds. Taller hedges which are gappy with little foliage close to the ground are also poor bird habitats. Although many species of birds will nest in hedges and their associated trees, few occur in all types of hedges. Judging from a small number of breeding bird censuses organised by the British Trust for Ornithology in Buckinghamshire in the 1980s the species most commonly encountered in hedges are Wren, Dunnock, Blackbird, Yellowhammer and Chaffinch. Other birds commonly breeding in Buckinghamshire hedges are Woodpigeon, Song Thrush, Robin, Whitethroat, Lesser Whitethroat, Blue Tit and Great Tit. In autumn and winter the fruit offered by overgrown hedges, especially hawthorn, is eaten by Redwings and Fieldfares. When the supply of berries is exhausted the birds resort to the open grass fields.

Hedge-trimming near West Wycombe. The chalk scrub on the slopes of West Wycombe, shown in the background, was the last breeding site of Cirl Bunting in the county.

Woodland

By the standards of the English Midlands Buckinghamshire is a relatively well-wooded county. Some 8% of the county is wooded but the woodland is extremely uneven in its distribution (Figures 4 and 5). On the Chilterns plateau barely a tetrad lacks woodland. North of the Chiltern escarpment, however, great tracts of country are devoid of woodland. There is scarcely a wood, apart from a small number of planted woods (often called 'Fox Covert'), in the Vale of Aylesbury and as far north as Winslow and Bletchley.

Ancient woodland

A high proportion of woodland in the county is ancient, ie on sites which have been continuously wooded since at least 1600. The distribution of ancient woods is very similar to the total distribution of woodland in the county, showing a very patchy

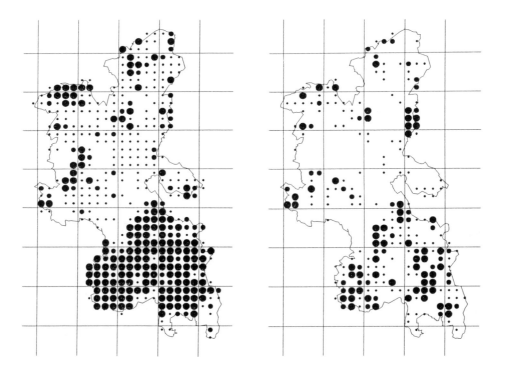

Figure 4. Distribution of broad-leaved woodland. Large dots represent > 20 ha, medium dots 10-20 ha, and small dots < 10ha.

Figure 5. Distribution of coniferous woodland. Large dots represent > 20 ha, medium dots 10-20 ha, and small dots < 10 ha.

distribution north of the Chilterns. Some 63% of all woodland in Buckinghamshire is thought to be ancient, of which 72% exists as semi-natural stands and 28% has been recently replanted with conifers (Spencer 1982). Replanting has been rather more extensive on the claylands where some 39% of ancient woodland present in 1925 had been replanted by 1983 compared with 20% in the Chilterns. Since 1925, approximately 3% of ancient woodland in the county has been grubbed out with most losses occurring in the clayland woods. The losses have been mainly to urbanisation and mineral extraction, such as Charndon Wood near Calvert which was finally destroyed in the early 1970s to feed clay to the Calvert brickworks. Relatively few ancient woods in Buckinghamshire have been converted to agriculture.

Ancient woods usually support semi-natural stands of native trees and shrubs and are often of considerable botanical and entomological importance. There is no evidence, however, that ancient woods are richer in birds than are more recent woods. Irrespective of the origin of the wood, the physical structure of woodland is an overriding influence on the nature of the bird community (Fuller 1982). As described below, the county's beechwoods give a clear illustration of the importance of woodland structure. Similarly, the changes in bird communities which accompany the growth of conifer plantations, also outlined below, are undoubtedly a response to the change in habitat structure. This is not to say that the botanical composition of a wood does not influence the nature of the bird-life found there. Different species of trees and shrubs vary themselves in structure, for instance in the density of their

A woodland glad in Ashridge Forest. This large National Trust estate straddles the Hertfordshire border near Tring. It embraces a variety of habitats including beech woods, birch woods, chalk scrub, and commonland. The bird life of Ashridge is among the richest of any comparable sized area of the Chilterns.

foliage and in the numbers of holes they offer, which means that each differs in the sort of nest sites it offers. The types and abundance of food (insects, seeds, fruit) offered will also vary. There is great scope for studying the use that birds make of different trees and shrubs.

The clay vale woods

Away from the Chilterns the larger woodlands occur in several quite discrete areas, in some cases forming the remnants of ancient Forests and Chases. The main concentrations of broad-leaved woodland outside the Chilterns are centred on Whaddon Chase, Whittlewood Forest, Yardley Chase, Salcey Forest and the country between Bernwood Forest and the Claydons (Figure 4). These clayland woods were once coppiced, probably hazel mixed perhaps with ash and field maple, under oak standards. Most of the broad-leaved stands fall into the following types (Peterken 1981): wet ash-maple (stand-type 2A), acid pedunculate oak-hazel-ash (stand-type 3A) and hazel-pedunculate oak (stand-type 6Dc). By the 1940s coppicing was virtually extinct as a method of managing woodland in Buckinghamshire. Some woods, such as Rushbeds Wood near Brill, still show in parts a neglected coppice structure but others were planted up with oak in the last century. Stands of ash and maple still survive in some of these oakwoods which are generally managed as high forest, usually by group-felling and replanting. The older stands of high forest can support high densities of hole and crevice-nesting birds including all three woodpecker

Rushbeds Wood near Brill. This BBONT reserve is an ancient wood with a long history of coppicing. The management policy is to restore working coppice over part of the wood but to leave a substantial block unmanaged, allowing it to gradually develop some of the attributes of natural woodland.

22

species, Nuthatch and Treecreeper. By comparison, old overstood coppice is generally a poor habitat for breeding birds (Fuller 1988); the bird communities of such woods tend to be dominated by Robins and tits. However, the edges of old coppiced woods, can be rich in warblers and some have Nightingales, particularly where there are stands of scrub, often of blackthorn (Fuller 1988). A small number of woods, for example Rushbeds Wood, are being returned to an active coppice regime and it will be interesting to follow the effects on the birds - one would anticipate an increase in numbers of warblers and perhaps Nightingales.

The Chilterns Woodlands

Much of the present distinctive character of the Chilterns is associated with its high forest beechwoods which vary considerably in structure. Beech hangers on the steeper slopes are usually almost devoid of any shrub layer and breeding birds are largely confined to hole-nesters and species which nest in the canopy. But on the deeper plateau soils the beech is sometimes mixed with oak and the field and shrub layers may be better developed; these woods can support moderate populations of Wrens, warblers and thrushes. The beechwoods in their present form are not natural (Roden 1968). They were created in the sixteenth and seventeenth centuries from more mixed broad-leaved woodland which was probably mainly coppiced. Those woods still supporting a mixture of trees such as cherry and hornbeam are of particular conservation value (Hornby 1987). Several systems of forestry are practised in the Chilterns. In some areas natural regeneration of beech is encouraged in small coupes but more commonly young beech is planted, sometimes together with oak and cherry, and often with a conifer nurse crop which is removed before the beech reaches maturity. Such coupes can do much to diversify the bird life of the Chiltern woods; they are often colonised by Tree Pipits soon after felling and support breeding summer visitors such as Willow Warblers, Chiffchaffs and Garden Warblers which are absent from the more uniform mature beech.

Some of the largest Chiltern woods have grown up, or perhaps even been planted, on former open commonland, for example Burnham Beeches, Penn Wood, Naphill Common and parts of Ashridge. In some of these woods the presence of massive beech pollards is evidence of former grazing. Those Chiltern woods now dominated by birch are likely to occupy former open commonland sites. Mature, fairly open, stands of birch, such as those on parts of Ivinghoe Common on Ashridge, can hold a rich assemblage of breeding birds including all three woodpeckers, Tree Pipit, Hawfinch, Redstart and Wood Warbler. The last two species have unfortunately declined recently in Ashridge.

Coniferous woods

Many of the clayland woods contain conifer plantations dating from the immediate post-war decades. To the east of Bletchley, along the Bedfordshire border, there are extensive conifer woodlands, which have been largely planted on former heathland. There are several large conifer plantations in the Chilterns too, for example at Wendover Woods and Homefield Wood. Most of the county's conifer woods are now at a late thicket or mature stage. Typical birds at these stages are Robin, Chaffinch,

Goldcrest and Coal Tit; but numbers of hole-nesters are generally low compared with much broad-leaved high forest. Of course, the bird communities of the early years of conifer growth were very different with many more warblers, Yellowhammers, Redpolls etc. The birds of the young plantations at Homefield Wood in the 1960s were described by Williamson (1974). With the welcome advent of the Forestry Commission's Broad-leaved Woodland Grant Scheme (now the Woodland Grant Scheme) in the 1980s it is unlikely that there will be much, if any, new planting of conifers in the county's deciduous woodlands for the foreseeable future.

Although the non-native conifers have been the target of much criticism, one cannot deny that they have made their mark on the Buckinghamshire avifauna. The most striking example must be the breeding of Firecrests in the Norway spruce plantations of Wendover Woods.

Scrub

No vegetation is more maligned than scrub and it is often under-rated as a bird habitat. Scrub arises almost anywhere that land has fallen into disuse and where there is no grazing to prevent its establishment. The essential features of scrub are that it is composed of woody shrubs or small trees and that it is a transitional stage between some form of open land and woodland. Only rarely in our region does scrub appear to form a relatively stable vegetation but an example would be the mature hawthorn thickets on some parts of the Chiltern escarpment. Hedgerows, young plantations and

Wendover Woods. This large tract of conifers, managed by Forest Enterprise, is a famous breeding habitat of Firecrest. Recently such habitats have been attracting increasing numbers of Crossbills. During the 1960s and 70s conifer plantations in the Chilterns were the main breeding refuge of the Sparrowhawk in Buckinghamshire at a time when numbers were depleted by organochlorine pesticides.

coppice regrowth in woodlands can all be regarded as special forms of scrub. In Buckinghamshire scrub is found on used and disused railway embankments, in old mineral workings, along canal banks and, occasionally, where buckthorn has suckered out into field corners or green lanes. Many of the Chiltern commons are now essentially mixtures of scrub and bracken. The most extensive areas of scrub, however, occur along the Chiltern escarpment on large areas of formerly open downland. Here an economic decline in sheep farming in the early twentieth century, and myxomatosis several decades later, initiated changes in the vegetation (Watt 1934, Smith 1980). The resulting secondary succession involved initial invasion by coarse grasses, such as *Bromus erectus* and *Arrhenatherum elatius*, and subsequently by shrubs.

Two types of scrub are typical of the Buckinghamshire escarpment. The first is a 'mixed scrub', commonly including privet, hawthorn, dogwood, roses, wayfaring tree, traveller's joy, and the now-scarce juniper. The second type of scrub is strongly dominated by hawthorn and is typical of the deeper soils with clay-with-flints and is also found on several of the plateau commons which have long since been ungrazed. On the most acidic Chiltern and Burnham Plateau commons a third type of scrub can be found which typically has substantial amounts of gorse. A very few of these commons carry relic heathland vegetation.

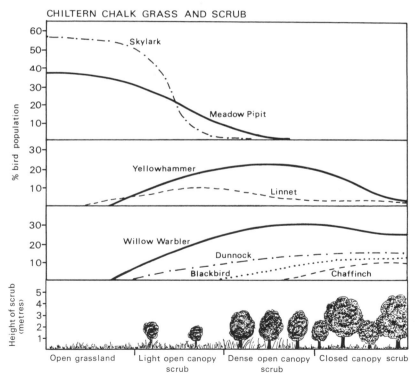

Figure 6   Changes in the composition of downland bird communities on the Chiltern escarpment as scrub invades the open grassland. From Fuller (1982).

Over large areas of the Chiltern escarpment the present vegetation is typified by small, superficially uniform patches, often less than two hectares in extent. This heterogeneity is largely a product of a varied history of land-use. Grazing pressure presumably did not relax evenly along the escarpment; some areas remained as grassland longer than others. Recent land-use has also contributed to the patchiness of the vegetation, especially at localities managed as nature conservation sites. Here, infrequent scrub removal, sometimes coupled with stock grazing, has been used in attempts to retain, or even to reinstate, the plants of open chalk downland.

Scrub is a rich habitat for birds. This can be illustrated for the Chilterns escarpment about which considerable information has been published (Williamson 1975, Fuller 1982, 1986). Scrub bird communities are highly dynamic, changing rapidly with the growth of the vegetation. Figure 6 shows how the composition of Chiltern chalk scrub breeding bird communities changes as scrub invades the grassland and gradually closes to form a closed canopy. Skylarks and Meadow Pipits are the dominant species on open grassland but Skylark quickly declines once scrub becomes established. In contrast, Meadow Pipit remains abundant in sparse scrub. Interestingly, this bird is only common along the escarpment east of the Tring Gap. Species particularly characteristic of open-canopy scrub are Tree Pipit, Whitethroat, Linnet, Yellowhammer and Reed Bunting. The latter expanded its range into dry habitats such as cereal farmland, young plantations and downland in the 1960s but in the 1980s underwent something of a reversal and is no longer so commonly encountered in dry

Steps Hill near Ivinghoe. The largest areas of scrub in the county are probably those at the eastern of the Chiltern escarpment. The scrub exists at various stages of growth and is especially notable for high densities of warblers and local concentrations of breeding Meadow Pipits

scrub. Species reaching peak numbers in closed-canopy scrub are Wren, Robin, Blackbird, Song Thrush, Chaffinch, Garden Warbler, Willow Warbler and Dunnock. The latter two species are also amongst the commonest birds in open-canopy scrub. The trends shown in Figure 6 are but crude reflections of the habitat requirements of some birds in chalk scrub. Each species prefers a certain structure of vegetation. For example, although Garden Warbler and Chaffinch both increase as the scrub thickens, the warbler only occurs where there is dense scrub reaching close to the ground while the finch will nest in mature hawthorn scrub lacking foliage within 2m of the ground.

No species occurs at all stages of scrub development. It follows, therefore, that areas of scrub supporting many different stages of the succession should be the richest in bird species. The total number of breeding species and the overall density of birds increases with scrub development. This does not necessarily mean that mature scrub is of greatest conservation value for birds because many of the more interesting scrub species such as the pipits and warblers avoid the most mature scrub.

Outside the breeding season the huge quantities of berries provided by scrub forms an important food resource for migrant warblers and for thrushes in autumn and winter respectively. Many areas of scrub are also used by roosting passerines.

Wetlands

Wetlands attract birdwatchers more than any other habitat. Consequently, many of the larger wetland sites are well known and relatively well documented (eg Swann 1971, Cooke 1982, Harding 1981). The great majority of wetlands in Buckinghamshire have been created by man; the only natural wetlands are rivers, and perhaps some ponds. The county has few fens or bogs and its wet meadows have been largely drained. The most interesting wetlands for birds in the county are now undoubtedly artificial lakes. The greatest number of these are gravel pits concentrated along the valleys of the Great Ouse, the Colne and the Thames. But there are also reservoirs at Weston Turville and Foxcote (Tring Reservoirs don't really count as only a very small part lies in Buckinghamshire), clay pits at Calvert and Bletchley, flooded chalk pits at Pitstone, a floodwater balancing lake at Willen and various ornamental lakes. The distribution of the main standing water bodies is shown in Figure 7.

In general, lakes are richer in breeding and wintering bird species than rivers and canals. In the breeding season only Mallard, Moorhen, Sedge Warbler, Reed Warbler and Reed Bunting are characteristic of both groups of water bodies (Fuller 1982). Outside the breeding season all the major concentrations of wildfowl are on lakes. At the turn of the century there must have been far fewer lakes than today. The large numbers of wildfowl, especially diving ducks, now wintering on the artificial lakes would presumably have been unknown at that time. On the other hand, the loss of flooded grassland may mean that dabbling ducks such as Teal and Wigeon are less widespread these days. Breeding birds must have benefitted too from the creation of wetlands. Great Crested Grebe increased its population in the county by 84% between 1965 and 1975, probably a response to an increase in habitat (Hughes et al 1979). Breeding species that have more recently colonised artificial waters are Common Tern and Ruddy Duck.

The largest lakes tend to support the most species of breeding birds and the largest flocks of wintering wildfowl. However, several features of lakes, other than simply their size, are important in determining the types of bird communities supported by Buckinghamshire lakes. Water depth strongly influences the abundance of submerged and emergent vegetation and this in turn affects the food supply of many waterbirds. To make a crude generalisation, dabbling ducks tend to feed where the water is shallow and rich in vegetation whereas many diving ducks make more use of open deeper areas. The physical structure and vegetation of the shoreline are important to several species. Scandinavian studies have shown that lakes with very complex shores, where the length of shore is high relative to the area of the lake, are particularly rich in breeding ducks. Vertical soft banks provide nest sites for Kingfishers and Sand

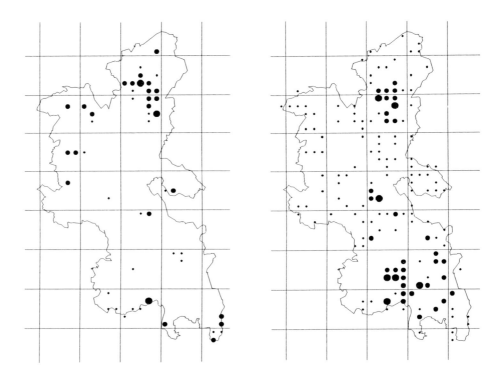

Figure 7. Distribution of standing water bodies (mainly gravel pits, reservoirs, brick pits). Large dots represent > 30 ha, medium dots 15-30 ha, and small dots < 15 ha.

Figure 8. Distribution of urban areas. Large dots represent > 267 ha, medium dots 133-267 ha, and small dots < 133 ha.

Martins while emergent vegetation is the main nest site for grebes, Coots, Moorhens and certain 'marshland passerines', most notably Reed Warbler. Islands are specially important to breeding wildfowl because they offer a refuge from predators and humans. A study on lakes in the north of Buckinghamshire showed that Mallards and Tufted Ducks nesting on islands had the greatest success (Hill 1984). In winter, too, freedom from disturbance by boats and shooters is a major factor determining the usage made of lakes by wildfowl.

Of all the artificial lakes, the physical structure of gravel pits is often the most conducive to supporting rich communities of breeding wetland birds. They often have some vertical banks, complex shorelines and islands. Occasionally, gravel pits are assigned as nature reserves before they have been worked-out. In such cases the operators may be prepared to co-operate with conservation bodies to create special features such as spits, islands or submerged bars to enhance the eventual conservation value of the reserve. I return to the subject of creating new wildlife habitats at the end of the chapter.

Artificial Habitats

The entire landscape of Buckinghamshire is a product of man's actions over many centuries. We have no truly natural habitats in our county. It may seem strange, therefore, to include a section on artificial habitats. But, with the exception of farmland, much of what we have considered so far has at least been semi-natural or offers an illusion of naturalness. Here we look at sites which make no such pretence: the urban and industrial areas.

Gardens typically offer nest sites for a rather limited range of species but outside the breeding season huge numbers of birds feed in gardens. Indeed an increasing number of private gardens are being designed specifically with birds and other wildlife in mind. It would be surprising if gardens in Buckinghamshire were any different to those in other parts of southern Britain and for an excellent account of garden birds the reader is referred to Glue (1982).

The expansion of Milton Keynes offers a fascinating example of how birds will exploit newly created urban habitats. Huge numbers of trees and shrubs have been planted in the new city. Despite their urban, and often roadside, location these amenity plantations have been colonised by many commoner breeding woodland birds. It would be interesting to know how the present and future bird populations of the new city compared with those present when the area was rural.

The urban habitat that has held the attention of ornithologists more than any other must surely be the sewage works and its much-lamented forerunner, the sewage farm. The old farms with their irrigation areas and shallow lagoons were justifiably famous as haunts of migrating waders but they could also hold spectacular numbers of wetland birds in winter (Fuller and Glue 1980). The best known sewage farms in Buckinghamshire were in the south notably at Slough. The area was transferred to Berkshire in 1974. Some modern sewage works still hold interesting bird communities as David Glue and Dennis Bodenham (1985) have shown with their study at Aylesbury. This works has a tertiary treatment system involving broad irrigation of about 5 hectares of land which has created an artificial marsh carrying a wide range of wetland birds at all times of year. Sewage works with the familiar rotating percolating filters often attract huge numbers of feeding wagtails and Starlings. A study at Aston Clinton sewage works (Fuller and Glue 1978) before it became disused, found that the filters consistently attracted more birds than any other part of the works. Another product of man's waste - rubbish tips - can also be used by huge numbers of birds, particularly Starlings, gulls and corvids.

Creative Conservation

It is appropriate to finish this chapter on a very positive note by considering opportunities for creative conservation provided by old mineral workings. Excavation of clay, chalk and gravel will long continue in various parts of Buckinghamshire. In some cases the original land-use may be restored but this is frequently uneconomical, thus opening the door to other land-uses. The creation of nature reserves and environmental education areas are amongst several amenity options which are increasingly considered. Here I can only sketch out some of the potential principles and problems of creating new ecosystems. For detailed information and further references see Bradshaw and Chadwick (1980) and Bradshaw (1983).

First, some examples of what can be achieved. Several BBONT wetland nature reserves have been established in such sites including the Calvert Jubilee reserve (a brick pit), Pitstone Fen (a chalk quarry), College Lake (a chalk quarry) and the Stony Stratford reserve (a gravel pit). The last two reserves provide remarkable examples of what can be achieved by taking nature conservation into account *before* the mineral extraction was finished; the credit belonging to Castle Cement and to the Milton Keynes Development Corporation respectively. Many old mineral workings are used as landfill and these sites are, obviously, not candidates for creating lakes. An interesting example of the restoration of such a site is provided by a small gravel pit some 2 km west of Heathrow Airport (Worthington and Helliwell 1987). The pit was filled with waste clay and other inert material. Subsequently 350 square metres of dry grassland, 2,500 square metres of moist grassland and 1,500 square metres of marshland were transferred to this site from a nearby location which itself had been scheduled for gravel excavation. The topsoil, subsoil and overburden were moved as separate layers. The result appears to have been a success in that plant growth was rapid and the appearance and diversity of the vegetation was similar before and after the transference.

Old mineral workings, if left to themselves, will eventually develop vegetation which often proves to be of special floristic interest. But this is an extremely slow process because the conditions for plant growth are frequently poor. It is, therefore, usually desirable to improve these conditions to speed up the colonisation process. The development of a rich bird community on an abandoned mineral working depends to a large extent on creating vigorous vegetation which will provide food and cover. In many cases the original soil will have been lost, although often efforts are made to store and replace this. Absence of soil means that many of the nutrients vital to plant growth are lacking. This can be rectified through fertilizer application but, unless one is prepared to repeat this regularly, nitrogen levels will not be sustained because this nutrient is stored only in organic matter. The logical solution is to plant nitrogen-fixing species. Alder is particularly useful in this context because not only does it fix nitrogen but it is a native tree of considerable conservation value in its own right. Attaining adequate nutrient levels is usually of overriding importance but old mineral workings often suffer from physical problems such as soil compaction, excessive wetness and surface instability. Refuse landfill also has the problem that methane is liberated which kills vegetation. Techniques are available, however, for overcoming all these difficulties to ensure satisfactory plant growth.

Presented with the opportunities for creative conservation, and because wetlands are such threatened and locally distributed habitats, there is a case for favouring these wherever possible. It should be possible to shape the drainage characteristics of many landfill sites to create shallow wetlands carrying fen or marshland vegetation. If this approach proved attractive to breeding wetland birds such as Redshank it could be viewed as partial compensation for the widespread losses of wet grasslands in recent decades. It may even prove possible to create alder carr which is a scarce habitat in the county. On drier ground there would be much advantage in creating scrub habitats. Large areas of scrub are rarely met with in Buckinghamshire yet, as shown above, they can be extremely rich in birds at all times of the year. There would need to be a long-term programme of rotational cutting to ensure that different ages of scrub persisted.

Buckinghamshire now lies in the most congested part of England where all derelict land is at a premium. The choices on offer are many, but the case for creating new habitats and landscapes to go some way towards offsetting the losses elsewhere is a strong one.

Weston Turville Reservoir. One of the most important wetlands for birds in the county, the reservoir and its marginal vegetation supports rich bird life at all times of the year.

BIRD MIGRATION IN BUCKINGHAMSHIRE

David Ferguson

Approximately one quarter of the birds breeding in Britain winter outside the national boundaries. Many other species pass through the country on their way between northern Europe and the Mediterranean and Africa, and while most of these birds move along the coasts, a significant number pass through Britain on a broad front which must include Buckinghamshire.

Much of this migration is invisible to human eyes. The birds either fly at night, or very high, or both, or trickle unobtrusively through the trees and bushes. It may be that the only sign to an urban birdwatcher of a large-scale movement of birds is the appearance of a Willow Warbler in the garden.

The accounts of the rarer birds later in the book can only be the tip of the iceberg of what actually comes into the county. While a fairly high proportion of some species are likely to be recorded - such as the waders, which are only found in specific localities where they are easily seen - many birds must remain unrecorded. For instance, the two records for Aquatic Warbler can only represent a small fraction of the Aquatic Warblers which have visited the county.

There are many gaps in our knowledge, though some are beginning to be filled. Ringing at a constant effort site on the Chilterns escarpment just over the border in Oxfordshire has shown that the escarpment may be an important staging post for *Sylvia* warblers which feed on the berries of elders, wayfaring trees, and brambles to gain body weight before flying on. On three days between 29 Aug and 10 Sep 1992 412 Blackcaps were ringed. It is estimated that this represented about one-third of the total birds at the site. At the same place 43 Garden Warblers were ringed on three days between 15 Aug and 21 Aug 1992. 15 Aug 1992 was a remarkable day: 160 birds of 7 warbler species were ringed, including - in a completely dry area - a Sedge Warbler and 7 Reed Warblers.

It is likely that the escarpment is an important flyway. It is planned to ring simultaneously at several sites along the ridge to determine to what extent birds move along this conspicuous topographical feature.

On 8 Sep 1991 the same ringing group played House Martin calls to an empty sky and almost immediately became surrounded by the birds. During the course of the day it was estimated that 20,000 birds passed through. Presumably these were birds flying over the escarpment on a broad front and were only a small fraction of the total on the move that day. A week later 3000 House Martins and 500 Swallows were watched flying low through the valley to the north of Bledlow Ridge towards High Wycombe. A tape lure at Little Marlow STW produced 900 House Martins on 8 Sep 1991 and 800 on 6 Sep 1992. On 27 Sep 1992 the same technique at the same site produced an unprecedented 3000 Meadow Pipits.

Some birds are, however, large enough and fly low enough to be seen migrating without the use of such aids. Lesser Black-backed Gulls flying south in July and August are a familiar sight to Buckinghamshire birdwatchers. The brief, dramatic passage of Arctic Terns in late April is a feature of birdwatching around the lakes in the northern part of the county, although until 1977 identification difficulties seem to have prevented birdwatchers from being aware of it. Rarer are the Whimbrels which are again seen - or more often heard - in late summer, often near the Chilterns escarpment. Migrating waders are a feature of all lakes in spring and autumn if the water levels are low enough for mud to be exposed. When water levels are high the passage of waders is rarely observed.

Where are the best places to watch migration? The Chilterns escarpment has already been mentioned. Many birds are known to follow such landmarks and the escarpment has long been known as a stopping off place for Ring Ouzels in late April and again in October. The grassy slopes around Ivinghoe Beacon and Steps Hill are the most likely localities. The radio masts at nearby Dagnall must be a good spot for chats, although it is badly underwatched. Also in the Chilterns, Booker Airfield has turned up wheatears but is again underwatched. It appears that the Chess Valley is good for observing migration, while the Misbourne Valley is not. The reasons for this are not obvious. In the Milton Keynes area Campbell Park, the highest point, has recorded Pied Flycatchers and Whinchats.

But finding rather scarce migrating passerines in Buckinghamshire is problematical. While some places are better than others, the birds can turn up almost anywhere. Recent records include a Black-eared Wheatear in a field near Chearsley, which is hardly a migration hot-spot, and an Aquatic Warbler at a pond in Botolph Claydon, which is a tribute to the alertness of the observer. Some indication of what could be missed can be gleaned from the numbers of Sedge Warblers ringed at Little Marlow STW - up to 33 in a day - which are presumably migrating down the Thames Valley.

The spring migration of passerines rarely matches the numbers in autumn but there was a fall of Lesser Whitethroats and Garden Warblers at Little Marlow STW on 25 Apr 1992 after a clear night which gave way to rain.

Most local birdwatchers tend to favour the county's lakes during the migration periods. The special birds - waders and terns - are seen with relative ease, although passerines can also been found. Late March at Willen Lake often produces flocks of migrating Reed Buntings, for instance, while the rough grassland around Caldecotte Lake has produced Whinchats in August and September. Swallows, martins, and Swifts can be seen in great numbers at all the lakes during the migration periods, and Yellow Wagtails frequent the margins. Of the larger birds, Ospreys are now annual although they rarely stay for long, while the Hobbies that may be seen at any of the waters in spring and early autumn may be local birds or passage migrants.

This is a very brief account of the migration that has been observed in Buckinghamshire, because very little is known. As has been indicated, this situation is beginning to change and it is likely that any successor to this book will include a comprehensive discussion on migration within the county.

THE COUNTY BREEDING SURVEY

When the first national Breeding Atlas (Sharrock 1976) was published, several counties were considering producing maps which would be more meaningful on a local basis. The 10-km squares used by the national survey were at too coarse a scale to show much of interest at the local level although within the county the Sparrowhawk and Hawfinch, for example, were clearly only in the southern half, in the woods of the Chilterns (see Fraser and Youngman 1976).

Starting with Hertfordshire, who did their fieldwork largely coincident with the national atlas 1968-1973, several counties started surveying their counties by tetrads and using the same field methods as the national survey. Buckinghamshire too was considering doing this and fieldwork started in 1980 largely at the instigation of Ron Youngman. Responsibility for the organisation quickly devolved to the Buckinghamshire Bird Club, with Trevor Brooks acting as co-ordinator. Fieldwork continued on a wide scale until the summer of 1985, although there was a limited amount of 'gap-filling' during 1986.

Methods Used

The units of distribution were the tetrads (2-km squares) of the National Grid. Observers were asked to record the species they saw or heard in one of three categories of breeding - possible, probable or confirmed. This followed exactly the pattern established by the National Breeding Atlas ten years earlier.

The criteria for the birds to be recorded in each category have been more or less agreed by the European Ornithological Atlas Committee. Possible breeding means simply that the species was seen in possible breeding habitat during the season. Probable breeding means that breeding was deemed likely, for example the species was holding territory, or a pair of birds were seen courting. Confirmed breeding means that a nest was found with eggs or young, parent birds were seen carrying food for their young, etc. As has become the standard practice these records are represented on the maps in this book by three sizes of dot in the relevant tetrads. A small dot means possible breeding, a medium sized one means probable breeding and a large dot confirmed breeding.

Coverage Achieved

The objective at the start of the survey was to find all the species breeding in each tetrad in the county and to confirm breeding there. It is unlikely that this was fully achieved. Indeed there were some tetrads, especially in the northwest of the county, which received only a very scanty coverage. There is a gradient of an increasing number of species recorded from north to south. This is partly the result of less coverage in parts of the north but it is likely that it is also partly due to the range of habitats present in tetrads in many parts of the south being considerably greater than farther north. Nevertheless there is no doubt that the maps for several, even some very common species, are less complete than we would have hoped, and where it is thought that reduced coverage is the cause of an apparent gap in the distribution of a species, this is mentioned in the accompanying text.

34

THE SPECIES ACCOUNTS

Scope

This book contains accounts for all bird species that are believed to have occurred in Buckinghamshire. There are four lists:

a) The main group contains those species on the British list which have been confirmed as having occurred in Buckinghamshire. There are currently 270 species in this category.

b) The second list contains species that are known to have been introduced or to have escaped from captivity. The species range from Wood Duck, which may be a contender for inclusion into the main list in due course, to such unlikely species as Rufous Tinamou, which apparently bred in a neighbouring county for a brief period. The list includes a number of species which are on the British list, but which were seen in circumstances which suggested they were deliberate releases or escapes from captivity. Exotic species records have not always been considered by the county records committee so there is the occasional possibility of misidentification.

c) The third list contains those species which have been mentioned in older works on the birds of Buckinghamshire but which are considered to be unsafe by the current records committee. They have been included in order to provide continuity with the older works.

d) The fourth list contains species which have been recorded within the vice-county of Buckinghamshire but outside the present county boundary. There are five species in this category. The discrepancies between the present county boundary and that of the Watsonian vice-county are discussed in the next section.

The county boundary

In 1974 the county boundary was altered. The main change was the transfer of Slough from Buckinghamshire to Berkshire which meant that the ornithologically important sites of Slough and Langley Sewage Farms were lost to the county. Only records occurring within the present county boundary are included in this present book. This led to the loss of one species from the county list: Marsh Sandpiper at Slough SF in May 1940. Other rarity records for this area were Pectoral Sandpiper at Slough SF on 1 Aug 1944, Lesser Yellowlegs at Langley SF on 21 Nov 1953, and Aquatic Warblers at Slough SF in Sep 1942 and 9 Aug 1944.

The loss of the Slough area has occasionally made the compilation of the species accounts difficult. For instance, the first record in Buckinghamshire for Little Ringed Plover is quoted in the contemporary accounts as Slough SF. Subsequent records which are within the present county boundary are not mentioned, so it has been very difficult to discover where the first record was. The occasional references to sites in the Slough area are an attempt to circumnavigate the problem.

Another problem exists in the Tring Reservoirs area. Parts of Startopsend and Marsworth Reservoirs are in Buckinghamshire, but it has been assumed, unless known otherwise, that records for these sites occurred in Hertfordshire.

Biological recorders use vice-counties, rather than the present counties. The Buckinghamshire vice-county has slightly different boundaries to those currently marked on the maps. The most important changes are both losses: the Slough area has already been mentioned, but New Wavendon Heath, which is part of Brickhill Woods, has interesting birds. It is now part of Bedfordshire. Birds which have been recorded in the Buckinghamshire vice-county, but not within the present county are listed separately.

Taxonomy and names

The species accounts are in Voous order, and this has been used for scientific names except for the Rock and Water Pipits which are now considered separate species, and American Golden Plover, which is no longer considered a subspecies of Lesser Golden Plover. The common names are those that are in current use. Consideration was given to the order proposed by Sibley and Monroe (1990) which is based on DNA-DNA hybridisation techniques. While there may be some merit in this classification, it is too early to be sure that it will be accepted. Similarly, the names proposed by the British Ornithologists' Union and *British Birds* go a long way towards producing a desired aim of one English name for each species, but many of the names are controversial, and any general agreement is at least some years away.

Time period

The species accounts begin with the earliest available records. Occasionally these are from the invaluable 18th century records of Dinton Hall, but more often it is Clark Kennedy's book of 1865 that provides the first comments. It must be stated, though, that this remarkable book contains some unsubstantiated and doubtful records. It also includes many Berkshire records which have been incorporated into global statements for both counties.

At the other extreme, important individual records may be as late as October 1992, but more generalised comments consider records up to the end of 1991.

Rarities

No records of national rarities after 1958 have been included without acceptance by the British Birds Rarities Committee. Before 1958, when the BBRC did not exist, it is assumed that the records were subjected to some kind of local vetting process.

Extreme rarities have their records listed in full. Those species which are still sufficiently rare to have their records listed individually in the annual report of the Buckinghamshire Bird Club usually have their records since 1972 shown by two histograms. The numbers of records and individual birds are then given. Dividing the second figure by the first gives the average flock size. This has been done to compensate for the fact that the histograms do not take into account flock size. The records are then divided into three regions: north, middle, and south. The county is 80 km from north to south but on average only 30 km wide. If there are any differences in the distribution of a species within the county they are likely to be on a north south axis. Finally, details of the largest flocks and of any significant ringing recoveries are given.

The histograms

The histograms for scarce species are usually in pairs. One shows the number of birds recorded each year, while the other shows the number of birds recorded each week. No differentiation is made between a flock of x birds and x individual birds arriving on the same day. The date of the record is taken as the date the bird was first recorded, and no account is taken of duration of stay or of changes in location. This accords with the methodology of the histograms in *Rare Birds in Britain and Ireland* (Dymond et al 1989).

The histograms showing wildfowl count data are also in pairs. The first shows the average total numbers for each month of the survey period (September to March) while the second shows the average total numbers for each of the 20 years between the winters of 1972/73 and 1991/92. For a few species counting did not begin until 1982. In these cases the period shown is from this date.

It should be emphasised that the graphs display *average* counts and that numbers can vary considerably from year to year. No account is taken of missed counts, though this is believed to be insignificant.

A number of commoner species also have histograms. These are shown to display some particular feature of interest, such as the increase in the number of wintering Cormorants. They are explained in the accompanying text.

The maps

Tetrad distribution maps for most of the of breeding species in the county are shown. All the records are inside the Buckinghamshire county boundary. This means that the survey area within the edge tetrads varies and may be very small. Thus these tetrads tend to have fewer records than those in the interior of the county. Because of this, the coverage is not comparable with that of the neighbouring counties of Hertfordshire and Oxfordshire, which surveyed complete tetrads, even if this meant conducting surveys within adjoining counties.

Consideration was given to updating these maps using data from *The New Atlas of Breeding Birds in Britain and Ireland: 1988-1991* (Gibbons et al 1993), and incorporating more recent records from local observers. It was, however, decided to leave the maps as they are for the following reasons:

1. The time-span of the survey would remain clear.

2. The more recent national atlas uses a different methodology which makes it difficult for its data to be incorporated into the maps.

3. In order to maintain the purity of the original data the more recent records would have to be displayed in a different way, for instance by using open circles instead of solid dots. This could give the impression of a range expansion, when, in fact, earlier under-recording was being shown.

4. Less than a dozen species are thought to have undergone a significant change in distribution since the end of the survey period. These changes are fully discussed in the species accounts. A number of maps have been omitted. Most are of very local species, whose distribution can be covered adequately in the text. For

security reasons the map of Hobby is also omitted. This species is still subject to persecution and egg-collectors locally so it was decided that it would be in the best interests of the bird not to publish the map. It is also likely that the map, as it is known to the organisers, is rather incomplete. It is known that there were, and still are, observers who do not tell anyone about this species even if they know it is present.

The population estimates

Under each map is an estimate of the breeding population. Occasionally, when it is believed that the population has significantly changed since the end of the mapping period in 1986, a population estimate for 1991 is given. The method used to calculate the populations is described on page 315.

The Garden Bird Survey

The Buckinghamshire Bird Club began its Garden Bird Survey in the autumn of 1986. The data it provides has been used in the accounts of many of the commoner species. More details about the survey are provided on page 316.

Abbreviations

The following abbreviations are used:

BBC	Buckinghmashire Bird Club
BBRC	British Birds Rarities Committee
Breeding Atlas	Sharrock, J.T.R. 1976. The Atlas of Breeding Birds in Britain and Ireland. Poyser, Berkhamsted.
BTO	British Trust for Ornithology
BWP	Cramp, S. and K.E.L. Simmons 197?-1992. The Birds of the Western Palaearctic, vols 1-7. University Press, Oxford.
CBC	Common Birds Census (of the BTO)
F & Y	Fraser A.C. and R.E.Youngman. 1976. The Birds of Buckinghamshire and East Berkshire. Middle Thames Natural History Society, Slough.
GP	Gravel Pit
Handbook	Witherby H.F, F.C.R.Jourdain, N.F.Ticehurst, and B.W.Tucker. 1938-1941. The Handbook of Britsh Birds, vols 1-5. Witherby, London.
H & J	Hartert E., and F.C.R.Jourdain. 1920. The BIrds of Buckinghamshire and the Tring Reservoirs. ??? Zool. ???
H & R	Hartert E., and W.Rothschild. 1905. Birds pp 128-152 in A History of Buckingham (ed W.Page). Constable & Co., London.
MTNHS	Middle Thames Natural History Society
NBBR	North Bucks Bird Report
NR	Nature Reserve
OOS	Oxford Ornithological Society
Res	Reservoir

SF	Sewage Farm
STW	Sewage Treatment Works
WAGBI	Wildfowlers Association of Great Britain and Ireland (now British Association for Shooting and Conservation)
Winter Atlas	Lack P.C. 1986. The Atlas of Wintering BIrds in Britain and Ireland. Poyser, Calton.

Red-throated Diver
Gavia stellata

Rare vagrant. All records are given.

There is an undated record from Burnham in Clark Kennedy.

A few years before 1910: shot near Aylesbury Station and presented to the Buckinghamshire County Museum.

1952: adult from 27 Oct-7 Nov, Little Marlow GPs.
1970: 1 from 11-31 Mar, on River Thames at Hurley.
1976: 1 from 13-16 Feb and 22 Feb, Calvert.
1978: 1 from 5-12 Mar, Wotton Lakes.
1979: 1 on 14 Mar, Willen.
1980: 1 from 7-10 Oct, Willen.
1986: 1 on 7 Feb, Willen.
1987: slightly oiled adult from 8-10 Dec, Weston Turville Res, was taken into care where it later died.
1989: 14 on 2 Apr, Willen. 6 were present just after dawn on 3rd and 2 remained until 0900.
1990: juvenile from 16 Dec-12 Jan 1991, Little Marlow GPs.

The extraordinary 1989 record may have been prompted by sudden snowfalls on the east coast.

Black-throated Diver
Gavia arctica

Rare vagrant. All records are given.

1954: 1 on 25 Dec, Hartigan's GP, Broughton.
1955: 1 on 9 Jan, Marlow.
1966: 1 on 5 Nov, Old Slade.
1972: 1 early Mar, Willen where it was picked up dead after an overnight storm.
1976: 1 at Tring reservoirs from 12-13 Mar, flew W into Bucks on 13th.
1979: 1 on 18 Feb, Little Marlow GPs.
1983: 1 on 13 Nov, was found in a field near Waddesdon and taken into care where it later died of aspergillosis.
1985: 1 first-winter from 31 Oct-17 Nov, Caldecotte.

It is surprising that there should be almost as many records of Black-throateds as Red-throateds in the county, because on the east coast (the most obvious source of our divers) Red-throateds outnumber Black-throateds by 100:1. It is possible that the present species is more likely to visit inland sites, either deliberately for food or because some birds regularly migrate over land. A similar pattern is also shown in neighbouring counties.

Great Northern Diver
Gavia immer

Rare vagrant. All records are given.

1774: 1 on 3 Dec, Ford area.
1850: a 'young bird' on 9 May, was captured alive in a ditch at Chequers Court.
1859: 1 Nov or Dec, Chesham.
1865: 1 killed Nov or Dec on River Thames at Marlow.
1865: 1 killed at Temple Island near Henley.
1944: 1 immature shot on 11 Nov, Calvert.
1964: 1 found on 4 Nov in field by Foxcote Res. It was released later on the reservoir but was found dead 2 days later.
1965: 1 on 17 Jan, Iver GPs.
1972: 1 on 12 Nov, Linford GPs.
1986: 1 from 12 Dec-11 Jan 1987, Taplow GP.

Diver species
Gavia sp

1971: 1 from 25 Feb-8 Mar, Stanton Low GP was considered to be a Red-throated.
1978: 1 on 19 Feb, River Thames below Hurley was considered to be a Red-throated.
1988: 1 on 17 Nov, Calvert was considered to be a Red-throated.

Little Grebe
Tachybaptus ruficollis

Resident, winter visitor and passage migrant, breeding on suitable waters throughout the county.

Though widespread in Buckinghamshire, the Little Grebe is often overlooked because of its shy nature; in fact it is more often heard than seen. Clark Kennedy classed it as 'common on our ponds, streams and lakes, and on the river Thames'. H & J reported that it 'breeds in considerable numbers on the reservoirs ... and on the Thames from Boveney to Hambleden'. However, F & Y commented that it was 'Not

41

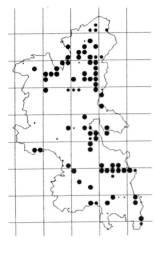

300 pairs

uncommon on the Thames and other waters but numbers appear to be decreasing', a point echoed in the 1981 BBC report where it was suggested that numbers were declining owing to loss of habitat.

As a breeding bird in the county, the Little Grebe is found on lakes, large ponds, rivers and canals wherever there is sufficient marginal vegetation and little disturbance. The map is dominated by the Ouse and Thames valleys with their associated gravel pits and tributaries. The Aylesbury and Wendover arms of the Grand Union Canal are also prominent. Other dots may indicate one pair or several, depending on the extent of the water.

In the autumn there is some aggregation, with Latimer Park, Wycombe Rye and Abbey Lakes often holding up to 30 birds. 22 were recorded on the River Ouzel at Willen on 6 Sep 1980. There is some evidence that these birds could include passage migrants. During the winter months flocks concentrate more on the larger waters, their numbers probably augmented by birds from colder parts of the country and migrants from NW Europe. Even the smaller waters can hold good numbers: eg there were 45 birds on Wycombe Rye and Abbey Lakes on 31 Dec 1981 and 33 at Latimer Park in December 1983. In hard weather, birds are forced to move temporarily to more open waters on rivers and estuaries.

NHFS

Great Crested Grebe
Podiceps cristatus

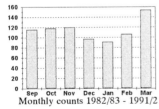

Monthly counts 1982/83 - 1991/2

Resident and winter visitor, breeding locally.

The earliest record of a Great Crested Grebe in Buckinghamshire is that of a bird shot at Dinton Hall in 1774, but otherwise it is unrecorded in the county before 1901, when a pair bred at Stowe. H & R stated that 'the bird is occasionally obtained in the county and breeds in some numbers at Weston Turville Reservoir'. Throughout this century, however, the increasing availability of suitable breeding waters, mainly as a result of mineral extraction, has produced a steady and continuing increase in the population.

The Great Crested Grebe has a preference for waters at least 2 ha in area, with a depth of 0.5-5m. For breeding, a shallow, shelving shore with a flat or sloping edge is essential, together with some emergent vegetation. Fish must be present, for the bird feeds only in its breeding waters. The main breeding

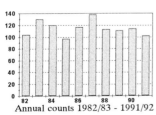

Annual counts 1982/83 - 1991/92

200 pairs

season in southern England is March to June and it is preceded by a period of display from January to March. The distribution of breeding records largely follows the deposits of river gravels in the valleys of the Thames and Ouse; some ornamental lakes and reservoirs, such as those at Stowe, Wotton Underwood, Weston Turville, and Willen are also used.

The Great Crested Grebe is still increasing as a breeding species in Buckinghamshire, not only as further gravel extraction takes place, but also along the Rivers Thame, Colne, and Ouse (F & Y). The increase in the number of breeding sites as recorded by the BTO surveys demonstrates the scale of the colonisation: in 1931 Great Crested Grebes were recorded at just 6 sites; by 1965, 3 of those sites (Black Pit at Lillingstone Dayrell, Latimer House, and Shardeloes) had disappeared or become unsuitable, and a fourth held no birds, but the number of breeding sites had increased to 17, including 11 that had not existed in 1931. In the 1975 breeding survey there were 32 sites. The accompanying table shows the increase in the number of breeding *birds*.

R.E. Megeary found the first pair breeding on the Ouse in Buckinghamshire in 1970; the first record of breeding on the Thames in the county dates from 1971 (Youngman 1977). In recent years non-breeding birds have summered on some waters; at Willen during the breeding season up to 37 adult birds have been recorded (2 Jun 1984), though the breeding population is thought to be only two pairs.

Autumn sees gatherings of resident birds and winter visitors from northern Britain and Europe, including Denmark. There has been no study of marked birds in the county and it is not known what proportion of the Buckinghamshire breeding

Year	Breeding birds
1931	26
1946	63
1947	52
1948	71
1949	60
1950	93
1951	73
1952	66
1953	116
1954	97
1955	68
1965	132
1975	216

43

population winters here. BWP states that 'it is unlikely that any western Palaearctic population is truly sedentary, thoughsome individuals may be'. The number of birds wintering in the county between October and February has remained fairly constant since 1970, usually with 110-130 birds recorded on all waters. The maximum count was of 164 in December 1983, the minimum was 11 in January 1982. In extreme weather none of the Buckinghamshire waters remains free of ice, and Great Crested Grebes then move out to larger, deeper lakes in adjoining counties (Grafham Water and Stewartby Lake to the north and east, Wraysbury and the London reservoirs to the south) and also possibly to the coast. March usually sees the highest county numbers (about 180), with some breeding birds already displaying and nest building alongside part of the wintering population.

JK

Red-necked Grebe
Podiceps grisegena

Scarce migrant.

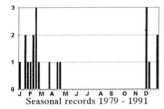
Seasonal records 1979 - 1991

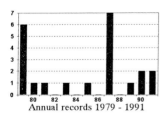
Annual records 1979 - 1991

Prior to 1979 there are 2 records:

1848: 1 shot 10 Oct, Saunderton.
1974: 1 from 9-26 Nov, Weston Turville Res.

Since 1979 there have been 21 records of 22 birds. 15 were in the north of the county, one in the middle, and 6 in the south. They are shown on the histograms.

There is an interesting contrast with Slavonian Grebe in the seasonal distribution. Red-neckeds tend be recorded in January and February, while Slavonians are found in November and December.

In February 1979 there was a major influx of Red-necked Grebes throughout inland England, the harbingers being two birds at Willen on the 14th. A total of 481 birds were recorded, of which four were in the county (Chandler 1981). A number of other species were involved, in particular Red-breasted Merganser. The reason for the influx appears to have been severe conditions on the Baltic and Continental North Sea coasts.

Another influx of Red-necked Grebes took place in January 1987 when five birds were found in the county.

Slavonian Grebe
Podiceps auritus

Scarce migrant.

Prior to 1973 there are 8 records:

1860s: 1 shot at Great Marlow.
Between 1874 and 1880: 2 shot Weston Turville Res.
1924: 1 from 29 Jan-10 Feb, Weston Turville Res.
1937: 1 from 6 Feb-6 Mar, Weston Turville Res.
1937: 1 on 14 Feb on pond at Bletchley Station.
1964: 1 on 29 Nov, Foxcote.
1969: 1 from 31 Aug-1 Sep, Foxcote.
1972: 1 (in full summer plumage) from 18-21 May, Weston Turville Res.

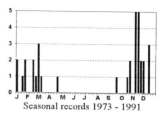
Seasonal records 1973 - 1991

Since 1973 there have been 27 records of 34 birds. 30 were in the north of the county, and 4 in the middle. They are shown on the histograms. Most were single birds, but 4 birds were seen on 13 Nov 1984 at Caldecotte. Exceptionally, a bird stayed at Caldecotte Lake from 15 Dec 1988 to 3 Mar 1989, and a bird was there again from 29 Nov 1989 to 29 Mar 1990. It is likely that the same individual was involved in both these records.

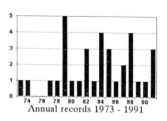
Annual records 1973 - 1991

Black-necked Grebe
Podiceps nigricollis

Scarce migrant.

Prior to 1973 there are 6 records:

1776: 1 shot 20 Nov, Dinton Hall.
1925: 2 on 9 May, 1 on 16 May, Weston Turville Res.
1953: 1 on 7 Sep then for several days, Marlow.
1957: 4 from 9-10 Jun, Foxcote Res.
1961: 1 on 21 Oct, Foxcote Res.
1968: 1 from 26 May-7 Jun, Shardeloes.

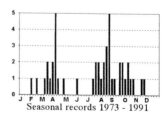
Seasonal records 1973 - 1991

Since 1973 there have been 29 records of 45 birds. 35 were in the north of the county, 4 in the middle and 6 in the south. They are shown on the histograms. The records are scattered between February and November with distinct peaks in early April and late August.

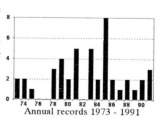
Annual records 1973 - 1991

45

Fulmar
Fulmarus glacialis

Very rare vagrant. All records are given.

1989: 1 on 4 Sep, Cliveden.
1989: 1 on 11 Sep, Caldecotte. What was presumed to be the same bird was found dead on 16 Sep.
1989: 1 on 10 Nov, Marlow.
1990: 1 on 30 Mar, Willen. Most of the country was cloaked in dense fog that day.

Manx Shearwater
Puffinus puffinus

Rare vagrant. All records are given.

1927: 1 caught 17 Sep, Bradenham House.
1967: 1 found dead 9 Sep, Marlow Common.
1970: 1 flying over 1 Jul, Old Slade.
1970: 1 found Sep, Chesham. It was released at Beachy Head.
1970: 1 found Sep, High Wycombe. It was released at Beachy Head.
1972: 1 found 6 Sep, Mentmore Towers.
1980: 1 recently dead 17 Sep, Lillingstone Dayrell.
1982: 1 found 7 Sep, Pitstone. It was released off the Devon coast.
1983: 1 on 7 Jun, Tilehouse North GP.
1983: 1 found alive 7 Sep, Quainton. It was released at the coast.
1983: 1 on 16 Sep, Calvert.
1984: 1 found 1 Sep, Aylesbury.
1984: 1 found 3 Sep, Calvert.
1984: 1 found 21 Sep, Buckingham.
1988: 1 found 8 Sep, Weston Turville Res.
1988: 1 found 14 Sep, Penn Street.

All five 1984 and 1988 records were of birds found alive and taken to Aylesbury Wildlife Hospital.

The small number of records in the county is in contrast to Oxfordshire where there is an average of two records per year (Brucker et al 1992). The counties to the east have a similar number of records to Buckinghamshire, which suggests that the birds arrive direct from their western breeding sites.

Storm Petrel
Hydrobates pelagicus

Rare vagrant. All records are given.

There is one undated record from Buckingham in H & J.

Other records are:

1859: 1 found dead Oct, Burnham Priory.
1865: 1 shot near Burnham.
1868: 1 on 21 Jan, near Wycombe.
1880: 1 picked up Nov, near Wendover.
1928: 1 found dead 28 Nov, Whaddon.
1929: 1 found alive 8 Dec, Grendon Underwood. It later died.

It is puzzling that there are no recent records.

Leach's Petrel
Oceanodroma leucorhoa

Rare vagrant. All records are given.

There is one undated record at Woughton in H & J.

Other records are:

1859: 1 found 1 Nov, Latimer Park.
1881: 1 on 14 Oct, Bierton.
1910: 1 in Nov, Westcott.
1929: 1 found dead 14 Dec, Lenborough.
1948: 1 found dead 24 Dec, Chalfont Park Lake.
1952: 1 found dead 26 Oct, Great Brickhill, was presumably this species.
1952: 1 found dead on 31 Oct, Penn.
1952: 1 found dead 7 Nov, Penn.
1976: 1 found injured from 24-26 Nov, Drayton Parslow. Died 28 Nov.
1983: 1 on 3 Sep, Willen.
1987: 1 on 16 Sep, Willen.
1989: 1 found 21 Sep, Fishermead, Milton Keynes. It was taken into care where it died.
1989: 1 on 29 Oct, Marlow.

The frequency of records compared to the more widespread Storm Petrel is interesting. Neighbouring counties show a similar pattern.

Petrel species

1877: 1 mid October, High Wycombe was thought to be a Storm Petrel.

Gannet
Morus bassanus

Rare vagrant. All records are given.

1847: 1 caught Nov, Sherington near Newport Pagnell.
1886: 1 killed on canal near Wendover. The specimen is in Tring Museum.
1910: 1 found alive 9 Dec, Hambleden.
1978: 1 found dead 9 Oct, Heavens Lea, near Skirmett.
1981: 1 from 16-26 Apr, Old Slade. The bird was finally found dead.
1981: 1 from 27-28 Apr, Willen, was plunge diving.
1981: 1 on 27 Apr, Walton, Milton Keynes.
1981: 1 picked up exhausted 27 Apr, Woughton, Milton Keynes.
1990: 1 adult picked up partially oiled 25 Jan, Chalfont St Peter. It was later released.
1990: 1 adult 28 Oct flew south-west into Buckingamshire from Wilstone Res.

The 1981 records followed gales.

Cormorant
Phalacrocorax carbo

Regular winter visitor with a few birds summering.

Until recently Cormorants were an unusual sight in the county. Clark Kennedy, referring to one shot near Marlow Railway Bridge about 1857, wrote that it was an 'extremely rare visitor so far inland'. He also mentions one shot at Weston Turville in 1858. H & J give no certain records for the county, but Price (1947) wrote that it was an occasional visitor recorded six times since 1920, three times in August, once in October, and once in November, while one was seen on the Thames near Bourne End at intervals from the end of February to the beginning of August 1943. It is interesting to compare this with the contemporaneous records for Tring Reservoirs, where, out of 40 recorded occurrences, 10 were recorded in April and May, 22 from August to November, and only one each for December, February, and March.

Maximum numbers 1980 - 1991

Cormorants remained scarce visitors to Buckinghamshire until the mid 1970s, although they began to winter at Wraysbury GPs (now in Berkshire) in 1968. Numbers began to increase through the 1980s. Medmenham recorded c30 in February 1985 and 50-60 in February 1986, while in the same year Little Marlow recorded 11 birds. In 1987 up to 15 were recorded at Linford GPs and 10 at Willen Lake. By 1991 up to 43 were roosting at Newport Pagnell GPs and up to 103 at Little Marlow.

Numbers begin to build up in October and peak in December. By the end of April most birds have departed, but a few birds summer in the county.

The birds prefer to roost on an island in trees overhanging water, but during periods of strong winds the birds may move to less exposed positions, such as the main island at Little Marlow. During the day they tend to range through a fairly extensive area. The birds roosting at Newport Pagnell move between Linford GPs, Willen Lake, and Caldecotte Lake, while those at Little Marlow feed at the other gravel pits in the area or on the River Thames.

Birds carrying nesting material have been observed, and display has taken place since 1990 but no attempt at breeding has yet taken place.

The increase is part of a general increase in the numbers of birds wintering at inland sites in the British Isles. The origin

Roosting Cormorants at Little Marlow

of these birds remains somewhat of a mystery. One bird colour-ringed as a nestling on St. Margaret's Is., near Tenby, Dyfed in June 1987 has spent every winter since at Little Marlow, while another bird from St Margaret's appeared at Little Marlow on 11 Apr 1992, but it is unlikely that the British breeding population alone would account for the increase in wintering numbers. The presence of adults showing the characteristics of the Continental subspecies *P.c.sinensis* may not indicate that birds from Europe make up part of the population as some British birds show similar characteristics, but it is likely that birds from Europe are involved. There has been a dramatic increase in the North Sea and Baltic populations, so these areas may be a source of some birds. The population in the Netherlands drops in the winter (SOVON 1988). It is possible that some of these birds winter in inland Britain.

NHFS

Shag
Phalacrocorax aristotelis

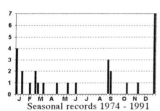

Seasonal records 1974 - 1991

Annual records 1974 - 1991

Scarce but increasing migrant.

Prior to 1974 there were 10 records of 11 birds:

1909: 1 at Oving.

1954: 1 found 6 Feb, High Wycombe was ringed as a pullus 10 Jul 1953 on the Isle of May.

1956: 1 found 23 Sep in a wood near Marlow was released at Staines where it was later found dead.

1958: 1 probable on 26 Jan, Weedon.

1958: 1 picked up 27 Jan on road at Wendover. It was released the next day.

1958: 1 on 27 Jan, flying over Aylesbury.

1958: 2 on 1 Feb on canal, Marsworth. 1 was still present a few days later.

1962: 1 immature mid Mar to late Apr, River Wye, High Wycombe. It was hand tame and fed daily until it was captured and released at Cookham Weir.

1970: 1 from 11 Apr-31 Dec, Marlow Weir.

1971: 1 undated on River Thames at Bisham.

Since 1974 there have been 27 records of 28 birds. They are shown on the histograms. The dramatic increase in the number of records is paralleled by a similar though much larger increase in the numbers of Cormorants wintering in the

50

county. These figures do not include a record of 14 in the Buckinghamshire section of Marsworth Res on 17 Jan 1974. Remarkably, a bird remained at Caldecotte Lake from 19 Jan 1990 to 5 May 1991.

Bittern
Botaurus stellaris

Regular winter visitor in very small numbers.

Clark Kennedy records that a bird was shot at Medmenham in 1851, another at Fawley Court in January 1864, and several near Chesham. The next to be recorded (and shot) was on 12 Dec 1892 at Cholesbury Common. Between 1920 and 1947, 8 birds were recorded, the longest staying being one at Weston Turville Res from December 1927 to early May 1928. From mid March it was heard booming.

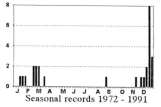

Seasonal records 1972 - 1991

Between 1947 and 1971 there were 17 records of 19 birds, including a bird booming at Wotton Lake on 12 Mar 1961. Since 1972 there have been 23 records of 27 birds. They are shown on the histograms. Though the latter period shows a slight increase in the number of birds recorded each year, it is likely that, when the increase in observers is allowed for, a considerable decrease has taken place. Since the mid 1950s the British breeding population has been in decline, and it is possible that there has been a similar decrease in NW Europe, from where it is believed the birds wintering in the county originate.

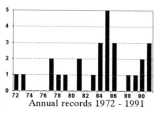

Annual records 1972 - 1991

Favoured sites are Old Slade, Weston Turville, Wotton Lakes, and more recently, Linford GPs, but individuals can appear at almost any lake, river, or canal, particularly when they are forced to move by freezing conditions.

NHFS

Little Bittern
Ixobrychus minutus

Rare vagrant. All records are given.

There is an undated record from Uxbridge in H & R.

The dated records are:

1827: 1 noted in Buckinghamshire.
1866: 1 in High Wycombe.
1911: male shot in summer, near Olney.
1921/22: 1 shot during winter, Shardeloes.

Night Heron
Nycticorax nycticorax

Very rare vagrant. All records are given.

1797: 1 immature shot, Cliveden.
1899: 1 in Aug, Taplow; may have been an escape.
1967: immature on 3 Aug, Newport Pagnell GP.
1987: juvenile on 26 Oct, Willen.

Little Egret
Egretta garzetta

Very rare vagrant. All records are given.

1989: 2 on 20 Sep flew into Buckinghamshire from Wilstone Res.
1991: 1 on 26 Mar, Marlow.

The appearance of Little Egrets in the county in the last few years is part of a large national increase in the number of records which, in turn, is caused by the species' northward spread in Europe.

Egret species
Egretta sp

1987: 1 on 15 Nov near Foxcote.

Grey Heron
Ardea cinerea

Local resident and winter visitor.

The status of the Grey Heron has probably changed little this century though the breeding sites may well have. H & J recorded it as breeding in 2 or 3 localities. The oldest was probably one at Harleyford Manor, near Marlow. In 1866 there were 40 nests, but by 1902 this had reduced to only a few nests in tall fir trees. The colony no longer exists. In 1919 a heronry at Fawley Court held 44 nests, but this too has gone. There were also temporary heronries at Dinton and near Gayhurst.

The Buckinghamshire population is now centred on 4 heronries where the birds breed every year. The sites - at Hambleden, Taplow Court, Eythrope, and Tyringham - are in the grounds of large houses with nearby water which give the

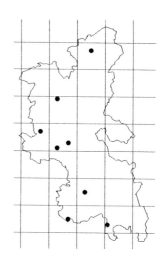

birds comparative seclusion. In addition there are other smaller sites where Herons breed less regularly. These are Boarstall, Wotton Lakes, Adstock, Hartwell, Wooburn Common, and near Buckingham. Most of these sites are also in the grounds of large houses.

The Heronries Survey is the longest running in Britain, having started in 1928. The major Buckinghamshire heronries have been surveyed most years, but the coverage of the smaller sites has been more patchy. It is thus rather difficult to establish population trends, but it is possible there has been a decrease since the late 1970s. For example, Tyringham has decreased from a high of 41 occupied nests in 1979 to only 17 nests in 1990, while Hambleden has decreased from a high of 17 occupied nests in 1978 to only 2 in 1989. In contrast, the heronry at Taplow Court has fluctuated between 8 and 15 occupied nests since 1973.

Populations are subject to decreases in severe winters. The mortality rate of first-winter birds can be very high during prolonged cold weather. After the severe winter of 1985, all 5 heronries counted that year showed their lowest numbers of the decade.

Outside the breeding season birds tend to disperse to suitable waters within the county, and occasionally large groups can occur. The largest recorded is one of 50 birds at Old Slade on 15 Feb 1981, while double-figure counts are regular at Willen, Caldecotte, and Linford.

Ringing records show that most birds keep within a 100 km

radius. There is some indication that birds from E England winter in the county. There have been recoveries of birds ringed in Kent, Norfolk, and Lincolnshire, and there has been one continental recovery. A bird ringed at Taplow on 24 Apr 1928 was found at Cuidad Real, Spain on 16 Nov 1933.

NHFS

Purple Heron
Ardea purpurea

Very rare vagrant. All records are given.

1978: immature on 28 May, Newport Pagnell.
1980: 1 adult on 13 Apr, Hyde Lane.

These are typical dates for this species whose nearest breeding area is the Netherlands.

White Stork
Ciconia ciconia

1846: 1 shot in September, a few miles from Buckingham.

The record was published as a White Stork *Ciconia ciconia*, (Morris 1870), and there seems no reason why this record should not be accepted.

Glossy Ibis
Plegadis falcinellus

Very rare vagrant. There has been one certain record.

1886: 1 shot in October, by the canal at Halton.

After review by the BBRC the record of a bird at Willen on 29 May 1987, which was previously accepted, has been rejected on the grounds that the long-staying escaped Puna Ibis *Plegadis ridgwayi* normally to be found at Whitwell, Herts, was not eliminated from the descriptions and thus could have been the Willen bird.

Spoonbill
Platalea leucorodia

Very rare vagrant. All records are given.

1947: 1 on 9 May, Wilstone Res flew into the county.
1969: 1 on 11 May, Marlow.
1976: adult on 28 Jun, Willen.
1977: 1 on 27 Apr, Willen.

Mute Swan
Cygnus olor

Local resident.

The early accounts suggest that Mute Swans were regarded not as a wild species, but as royal birds. Clark Kennedy mentions that Eton College had long held the right to keep swans on the River Thames, and quotes Yarrell regarding the College 'Swan mark' which represented 'the armed point and the feathered head of an arrow'.

Mute Swans are indigenous to E England. They were semi-domesticated in mediaeval times for their culinary worth and were kept on many rivers and lakes. Later, when they faded from the gastronomic scene, they reverted to the nominal wild state they occupy today.

There is some evidence of an increase this century with a decline during the Second World War. After the war the population increased although hard winters affected numbers (Campbell 1960, Ogilvie 1967). The increase in the county has been assisted by the increase in waters available through gravel extraction (Morgan 1980, Knight and Stone 1986). Numbers on the River Thames were affected by lead poisoning, but this has not affected the Vale of Aylesbury and the Ouse Valley areas as lead weights and shot tend to settle and sink in the mud rather than mix with the gravel as elsewhere (Brown and Stone 1990). Lead fishing weights were banned from 1 Jan 1987.

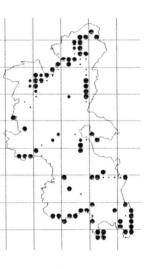

40 pairs

The rapid increase in numbers of Canada and Greylag Geese in Buckinghamshire is beginning to affect swan breeding. Although Mute Swans are dominant, the sheer pressure of numbers of geese on some of the breeding sites, and the shorter breeding cycle of the geese, which means that fledged goslings are augmenting goose numbers when the cygnets are still in down, can cause nesting failures.

Non-breeding birds herd together on open waters in summer and also form flocks in the winter. The largest recorded flock

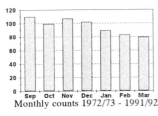

Monthly counts 1972/73 - 1991/92

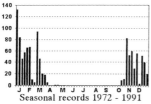

Annual counts 1972/3 - 1991/92

is one of 197 birds at Willen Lake in November 1987.

There are two ringing records of interest. A bird ringed at Spade Oak on 1 Sep 1986 was recovered on 18 Jul 1987 at Whitcombe Reservoir, Gloucestershire, while a breeding bird ringed at Linford on 20 May 1973 was found dead at the same locality on 15 May 1991, 18 years later.

Mute Swans have been the subject of regular censuses. The results for Buckinghamshire are:

Year	1955	1961	1978	1983	1990
Coverage	incomplete	poor	96%	70%	99%
Adults breeding	84	42	82	59	79
Non-breeding	90	200	187	183	317
Total birds	174	242	269	242	396

NHFS

Bewick's Swan
Cygnus columbianus

Regular winter visitor and migrant.

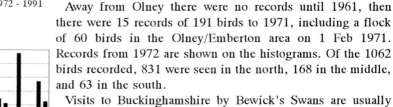

Early records of this species cannot always be relied on because of confusion with the Whooper Swan. The first certain record is of 3 or 4 at Olney in March 1942, but it was very rare until 1955. In that year a flock of 10 birds appeared at the same site on 10 March. The numbers built to a maximum of 17 birds on 15 Mar. This site - meadows by the River Ouse - was used in the early part of the year until 1957. There was a maximum of 40 birds on 10 Mar 1956. Birds reappeared at this site in 1964 and 1965.

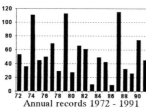

Seasonal records 1972 - 1991

Away from Olney there were no records until 1961, then there were 15 records of 191 birds to 1971, including a flock of 60 birds in the Olney/Emberton area on 1 Feb 1971. Records from 1972 are shown on the histograms. Of the 1062 birds recorded, 831 were seen in the north, 168 in the middle, and 63 in the south.

Annual records 1972 - 1991

Visits to Buckinghamshire by Bewick's Swans are usually short stops on passage or the result of bad weather movements, the birds usually occurring on lakes in the north of the county. As with Whooper Swans, longer stops are dependent on suitable grazing near water.

Whereas Whoopers tend to move as family parties, Bewick's are more often encountered in small flocks. The largest group reported is of 46 seen together at Willen on 30 Oct 1974. They can be expected from early October onwards, having left their Siberian breeding quarters and migrated through N Europe, but they are more often recorded from January to March than in the autumn. Some birds show signs of shot sustained during their long passage over land.

NHFS

Whooper Swan
Cygnus cygnus

Regular winter visitor and migrant.

As it was not until 1830 that the distinction between Whooper and Bewick's Swans was made. All early records refer simply to 'wild swans'. They should therefore be used with extreme caution unless the actual specimen was obtained and can be verified. Clark Kennedy noted several occurrences, but as he made no mention of Bewick's, these could refer to either species or both. Mistaken identification, even by generally competent observers, can still not be discounted entirely.

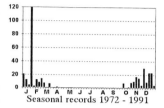
Seasonal records 1972 - 1991

Clark Kennedy provided a cautionary anecdote, albeit from outside the county: 'I received the following letter from a Windsor lad of 1831: " - I remember about twenty-five years back a Mr. Hughes, connected with the Royal household, and well-known in Windsor as 'old Buffy Hughes', shooting in the neighbourhood of Clewer Point, Windsor, a couple of Whoopers or Wild Swans; and I well remember that one was converted into soup, and most of the people who partook of it were very much disturbed in their internal economy".'

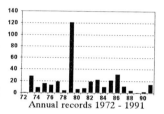
Annual records 1972 - 1991

There were no post-war records until 1959 when 23 flew over Dorney. This was followed by 6 records of 13 birds between 1960 and 1971. The records from 1972 are shown on the histograms. During this period about 358 birds were recorded. 274 were seen in the north, 16 in the middle, and 90 in the south. The last figure represents one record. On 28 Dec 1979, 90-100 birds were seen flying in formation SW over West Wycombe, the largest flock recorded in the county.

From 1971 to 1988 a small family group wintered regularly along the River Ouse between Deanshanger and Buckingham. The birds usually arrived about mid November and departed during March. They often associated, but did not mix with, a herd of Mute Swans on the meadows. Rust stains on the head feathers seemed to indicate that the Whooper Swans were part of the Icelandic population.

The Whooper Swan spends more time grazing than our other

swans, returning to water to drink and bathe as well as for protection. All the wild swans depend on sufficient grazing near water, and recent ploughing of this family's favourite meadows along the Ouse has meant that the visits have now ceased.

NHFS

Bean Goose
Anser fabalis

Very rare vagrant. All records are given.

Clark Kennedy gives undated records for Slapton and Chesham, and both Clark Kennedy and H & R mention records from the River Thames.

1947: 1 in Jan, Calvert, perhaps same bird later recorded as Pink-footed Goose on 2 Feb at Waddesdon
1982: 1 from 1-11 May, Stony Stratford NR, joined by a second bird on 6 May. In view of the date, the birds were almost certainly feral.
1985: 1 on 9 Feb by Wilstone Res. The bird was present in Herts from 9 Feb-23 Mar.
1989: 1 on 30 Apr, Willen was also reported at Linford.

It is likely that all the records refer to feral birds.

Pink-footed Goose
Anser brachyrhynchus

Scarce migrant.

Prior to 1982 there were 9 records:

1947: 1 on 2 Feb, Waddesdon (see above under Bean Goose).
1963: 1 from 13 Feb-10 Mar on River Thames between Marlow and Bourne End.
1965: 6 on 30 Jan, Iver GPs.
1966: 60-70 on 6 Mar, Mentmore flying in moonlight.
1968: 30 flying north-west on 31 Dec, High Wycombe.
1970: 1 on 24 Jan, Old Slade.
1977: 1 on 12 Feb-June, Tilehurst GP. This was an escape.
1977: 1 on 2 Apr, Marsworth Res.
1978: 1 from 12 Feb-13 May, Linford.
1979: 70 on 28 Jan flying W over Concord, The Lee.

Since 1982 there have been records of one or two birds almost every year.

It is likely that the above records referring to single birds are all feral birds. The preponderance of records in the early part of the year is strange, however.

White-fronted Goose
Anser albifrons

Scarce migrant.

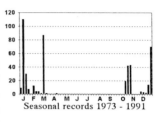

Seasonal records 1973 - 1991

There are about 27 records prior to 1973. The first is an undated record from Olney in H & R. Between 1920 and 1939 there were about 6 records, with the largest flock one of 24 birds on 7 Jan 1938 near Olney. Between 1940 and 1959 there were 5 records, with the largest flock 89 birds on the River Thames at Boveney on 18 Feb 1940. After 1960 there was a considerable increase in the number of records. Between 1960 and 1972 there were 16 records with c200 birds seen on 25 Jan 1970 at Boarstall.

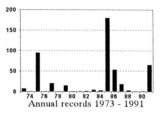

Annual records 1973 - 1991

The records since 1973 are shown on the histograms. The largest flock during this period was one of 86 birds flying north over Grendon Underwood on 9 Mar 1975, and 110 birds in 3 skeins were seen on 12 Jan 1985 flying east over Willen.

Greylag Goose
Anser anser

A resident feral population, possibly augmented in winter.

The early history of the Greylag Goose in Buckinghamshire is very shadowy. Clark Kennedy mentions that flocks sometimes landed in winter on flooded meadows near Hulcott and Aston Clinton. H & R report that, according to Mr Wigglesworth, they were sometimes seen near Castlethorpe on the River Ouse. An individual shot in September 1886, singles seen on 18 Mar 1927 and 13 Oct 1942 at Tring Reservoirs (Hayward 1947), and a pair at Weston Turville Res in July 1938, are all suspected of being 'escapes'. Free-flying birds from Whipsnade also visited the Tring Reservoirs after the Second World War. In 1959 WAGBI (as it was then) turned its attention to the Greylag in a translocation scheme that aimed 'to try to re-establish the Grey Lag as a wild nesting bird in England' - something that had been lost to England

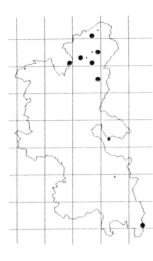

50 pairs

since the draining of the Fens in the 17th and 18th centuries. 16 birds were released at Linford in 1972, the year which saw the beginning of the Canada Goose influx at that site. From this small group the Greylag population increased, slowly at first. Now flocks of up to 500 can be seen. Major breeding concentrations are found today both at Linford and Claydon, with several smaller groups elsewhere.

Greylag in Buckinghamshire associate with Canada Geese, grazing on arable farmland and improved pasture. In the north of the county, where such pasture is limited, the birds will graze on autumn-sown cereals and other crops. This has not endeared them to farmers, and a certain amount of persecution has ensued. Yet, despite fluctuations, the overall increase in numbers has not been affected.

There is competition with Canada Geese and Mute Swans for breeding sites, especially on islands. Greylag often nest farther away from water, but whether this makes it harder for predators to find the nests is difficult to establish (Wright & Giles 1988). Competition between the three species may eventually lead to stabilisation of numbers.

The Greylag's normal breeding range in Eurasia extends from the low tundra to the temperate zone, and unlike its relatives it often remains in its breeding area throughout the year. Thus, once established in an area, feral populations tend to spread outwards from the centre as densities increase. The normal wintering range for W European birds is the Mediterranean area including N Africa, but it seems very unlikely that the birds in Buckinghamshire will ever develop a migratory pattern. One ringed at Slimbridge on about 15 Jul 1956 was, however, shot at Ickford on about 1 Feb 1960.

NHFS

Canada Goose
Branta canadensis

Feral species that is increasing and spreading rapidly.

The Canada Goose was probably ignored by commentators in the nineteenth and early twentieth century as an ornamental fowl on private waters and an 'escape' on others. In the 1950s and 1960s, and in Buckinghamshire as late as the early 1970s (Giles & Wright 1986), populations were being established in suitable habitat throughout the country. Some populations were the result of introductions to provide shooting, others were the result of expansion from established colonies. It is likely that

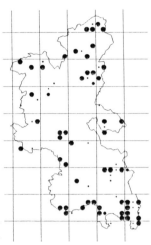

200 pairs

deliberate introductions were a mistaken policy, as the Canada Goose has responded with an unprecedented population explosion and has become a nuisance in many areas. In Buckinghamshire it is causing concern among farmers in the north of the county.

Canada Geese began to colonise the Linford Pits in 1972, at the time that gravel extraction was nearing completion. An examination of the Wildfowl Count returns shows a moderate increase in the early years, accelerating to rapid growth in the 1970s. Richardson (1982) gives an account of the Canada Goose in Northamptonshire, particularly its establishment and spread. It is logical to surmise that an overflow from the Nene Valley gravel pits population provided the nucleus for the present stock in N Buckinghamshire, although Ogilvie (1977) suggests a link from the west in Oxfordshire. In late 1988 the population stood at about 1,000. The birds move from water to water in groups of up to 50, often combining on the grazing and resting areas to produce numbers in excess of 500. On taking flight they will frequently revert to smaller groups. Other flocks of Canada Geese in the county were probably established earlier and from a different source, most probably one based in the Thames Valley. Small parties were appearing on ornamental waters in the 1950s. Wotton Underwood seemed to be very attractive to these birds, 180 being present in November and December 1982.

The geese are variable in size. Most come within the measurements of the nominate race *canadensis*, which was the race most commonly introduced from the seventeenth century to grace the grounds and waters of the landed gentry. Others

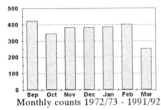

Monthly counts 1972/73 - 1991/92

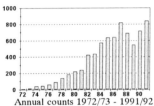

Annual counts 1972/73 - 1991/92

are nearer the Giant Canada Goose *maxima* in size, yet some are so small as to resemble the Cackling Goose *minima*. These variations are puzzling. It would have been expected that by now the gene pool would have been thoroughly mixed and that there would be little or no size variation, but this is not so. Perhaps there is still an influx from private collections. Occasionally wild Canada Geese arrive with flocks of Greenland White-fronted or Barnacle Geese on the north-west coast of Scotland (Owen et al 1986), but these resemble the smaller, tundra races *hutchinsii* and *parvipes*.

The Canada Goose feeds mostly by grazing and can therefore come into direct competition with grazing livestock, particularly sheep. There is also the possibility of competition with Wigeon, the numbers of which do appear to have dropped in Buckinghamshire concurrently with the increase in Canada Goose numbers. The geese also eat roots and tubers and could be in competition with grey geese. In mitigation, their digestive system is so inefficient that they return nearly as much to the land in droppings as they crop.

Their nesting preference is for quiet waters with plenty of marginal growth. The site itself is by choice an island, as in their original habitat, though the birds have fewer predators to cope with here. In their study, Giles & Wright (1988) found that although nesting success was high for both Canada and Greylag, gosling mortality was higher in the former. The earlier nesting of Canada was suggested as a reason. There is competition for nesting sites with Mute Swans, the swans usually establishing a territory after some show of force. Occasional hybridisation of Canadas with Greylags occurs.

At present there is no sign in Buckinghamshire of an established moulting migration as has happened in the West Midlands. Small parties tend to remain around favoured waters from midsummer onwards for their moult. Should a moult migration develop, it is possible that Buckinghamshire birds will fly north-east to the Lincolnshire shores of the Wash.

NHFS

Barnacle Goose
Branta leucopsis

Feral birds resident.

The first record was:

1959: 1 on 15 Nov, Weston Turville Res. It is not known if
it was a genuinely wild bird.

The next record was not until December 1970 when a bird
was seen with Canada Geese at Little Marlow GPs. It may
well have been an escape. Since then small numbers of clearly
feral birds have been regularly seen, although up to 47 birds
have been recorded in the resident feral flock at Emberton.

On 27 Dec 1991 about 50 flew over Drayton Parslow on a
day when many geese were on the move. Even so, with the
large feral flock frequenting the Emberton area, the birds
cannot definitely be considered as wild.

There is no evidence of nesting in the county.

Brent Goose
Branta bernicla

Rare vagrant.

The first record within the present county boundary was:

1965: 1 dark-bellied on 4 Oct, Foxcote.

There were no more records until 1981. Since then there
have been 20 or more records of 60 birds. They are shown on
a seasonal histogram. Most of the records were at Willen,
Linford, and Marlow, although the largest flock recorded is
one of 20 birds flying west over the Thames Valley at Little
Marlow on 17 Nov 1991. Four of the records were definitely
of the dark-bellied race *B. b. bernicla* and only one bird, at
Willen from 29-30 Mar 1982, showed the characters of the
light-bellied *B. b. hrota*.

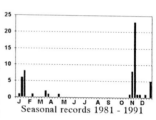

Seasonal records 1981 - 1991

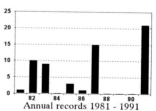

Annual records 1981 - 1991

Shelduck
Tadorna tadorna

Annual visitor in small numbers and occasional breeder.

The Shelduck was first noted in Buckinghamshire in March 1780 when a male was shot in the Tring neighbourhood (illustration in Dinton Hall MS). Price noted that 'since 1920 it has been recorded many times at the Slough Sewage Farm, several times near Olney and occasionally elsewhere, in every month but July, though most frequently in April, May, August, and September. The largest number seen together was seven near Olney in March 1942.' Hayward (1947) attributed many of the early records to escapes but noted 'a party of eleven which visited Wilstone for about twenty minutes before flying off to the west, on August 30, 1925.'

Since the Second World War numbers and visits have increased and breeding has been recorded on a number of occasions. Breeding first took place in the county at Linford in 1975. Birds occur regularly at the other large lakes in the north of the county, but they have not yet bred.

The spread of the Shelduck inland seems to have coincided with the range expansion of the small snail *Potamopyrgus jenkinsii* from brackish to fresh water since the end of the nineteenth century. This snail is parthenogenetic, in fact no male has ever been found; also it does not appear to suffer from any flat-worm endoparasites and is altogether one of those intriguing mysteries of evolution. This snail, together with its saltwater counterpart *Hydrobia ulvae*, constitutes a considerable part of the Shelduck's diet, being sifted out of the soft mud. Its presence or non-presence may therefore be a deciding factor in the Shelduck's inland distribution. The small but increasing number of breeding Shelduck in the county provides some evidence for this. If the water is shallow enough and with soft mud, and if *Potamopyrgus jenkinsii* is present, then eventually Shelduck will occur.

Shelduck were - and still are where possible - burrow nesters, favouring rabbit warrens. However, the spread of myxomatosis, plus the post-myxomatosis habit of some does to give birth above ground rather than in special breeding stops, has forced Shelducks themselves to breed more often above ground as they most likely did before the rabbit was introduced to Britain. This change of habit may be a factor in the spread of the Shelduck away from sandy coastal dunes.

It has long been known that non-breeding Shelduck migrate to certain areas where they congregate for the annual moult. It was thought that they all used the Waddensee area of the

German coast, but it is now known that several smaller areas are also used for this purpose. The nearest to Buckinghamshire is on the Wash and may be the one used by such birds as occur in the county. However, the number which actually breed is insufficient for a creche system to develop as happens on the coast, and the Buckinghamshire breeding birds probably therefore moult on the breeding site.

NHFS

Mandarin
Aix galericulata

Very local but increasing resident.

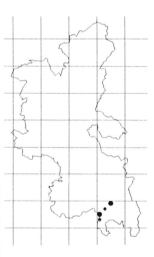

1986: 1 pair
1991: 17 pairs

Mandarins have long been a component of wildfowl collections in Great Britain. They seem to have been imported into this country in the 18th century, but only in small numbers as the Chinese were reluctant to allow their export. By the 19th century, however, they were being frequently imported and no major collection was without some specimens.

Our local birds probably originated from two sources. In 1928 Mr Alfred Ezra added six pairs of Mandarins to his wildfowl collection at Foxwarren Park in Surrey. These birds found the conditions so congenial that within four years the species had escaped and was breeding in Windsor Great Park and Virginia Water. They have been spreading from this source ever since until there are now over 500 pairs breeding in Surrey and E Berkshire.

The second source is the origin of so many of Britain's exotic fauna. The 11th Duke of Bedford had some Mandarins in his great collection of wildfowl at Woburn, where they soon began to breed around the estate, favouring the rhododendron thickets around the lakes. Birds have spread outwards from the estate in small numbers.

The first record within the present county boundary was of a pair seen at Littleworth Common from 6-11 Apr 1955. On 15 Jun 1955 a female with young was seen at nearby Dropmore. It is not known if the same birds were involved. The next record was in the north of the county. A female was seen on the River Ouzel near Linslade at the end of June or early July 1964. After this, there were one or two records per year until 1978 when birds were recorded at five sites. A pair bred at Stoke Hammond in 1982, at Cliveden in 1984, and at Wooburn Common in 1985.

There was a considerable increase in the number of records in 1987. Single pairs bred at Three Locks, Cliveden, and Boveney, while two pairs bred in specially designed nestboxes at Taplow Court. 20 birds were seen at this site in October, while 30 were seen at Hedsor in the same month. The birds have continued to increase until by 1990 Taplow Court had 14 breeding pairs, a pair bred in a nestbox at Wooburn Common, and two broods were seen near Three Locks. On 7 Oct 1990, 44 birds were seen at Taplow Court.

During 1992 a radio-tracking and colour ringing project was started at Taplow Court, a site now under threat by the Thames flood relief scheme. The indications so far suggest that there are at least 100 birds in the area, a figure much higher than was previously thought.

The increase in numbers within Buckinghamshire is part of a general increase in the British population, but is also helped by the nestbox scheme in the south of the county. The British population in 1990 was around 7,000 individuals, and is significant on a world scale, where Mandarin numbers in China, Japan, and Russia are about 6,000 pairs. In this context, even the peripheral local population has some significance.

There is one ringing recovery. An adult female ringed at Taplow on 3 Jun 1989 was recovered at Southgate, Greater London on 16 Feb 1991.

NHFS

66

Wigeon
Anas penelope

Regular winter visitor, mostly to the north of the county.

Historically, the Wigeon appears to have been a bird of coastal marshes and saltings, but more recently it has increasingly moved inland. A major reason for this was probably the virtual disappearance, through disease, of eel-grass from the coastal shallows in the 1930s. Another factor was the increase of lowland water through gravel and other extraction, particularly where suitable grazing and loafing areas were available close to the water. This would seem to be the case in Buckinghamshire, with Weston Turville Res attracting large numbers of birds in the nineteenth century.

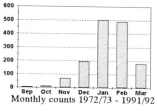

Monthly counts 1972/73 - 1991/92

In recent years Foxcote, Linford and Willen have also attracted large numbers of birds, though at Willen human disturbance is reducing feeding time and causing numbers to decline. Competition for grazing by geese, especially Canada Geese, is a further limiting factor both at Willen and Caldecotte. To compensate for this, the new reserve at College Lake is attracting flocks of up to 180 birds.

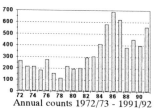

Annual counts 1972/73 - 1991/92

Wigeon graze in compact flocks, feeding on fine grasses, roots and stolons. Some seeds are also taken. They will associate with Mallard on autumn stubble, but nowadays this is often ploughed in before it can be utilised. The birds compensate for this by feeding on newly-sprouted winter cereals. There is some competition with sheep, as both prefer the finer grasses. Wigeon feed by day and night, but where there is disturbance their feeding is restricted to night-time.

Single birds and the odd pair are reported occasionally during the summer months in Buckinghamshire. Though well outside the normal breeding range, sporadic nesting does occur in SE England and may yet be seen in the county.

A few birds appear as early as August, but these may be birds dispersing from breeding grounds elsewhere in Britain. Most start to arrive from October onwards, some from Iceland but the majority from Scandinavia and the USSR, fleeing severe weather on the continent. Numbers peak in January, the highest count being about 1,000 at Linford on 17 Jan 1987.

NHFS

Gadwall

Anas strepera

Regular winter visitor and now possibly a regular breeder.

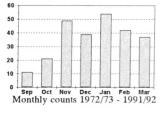

Monthly counts 1972/73 - 1991/92

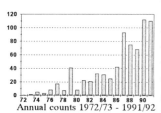

Annual counts 1972/73 - 1991/92

The Gadwall, on the extreme edge of its range in Britain, owes its position as a breeding bird in Britain to the release of two pinioned birds at Narford in Norfolk in 1850, these birds having previously been caught at Dersingham Decoy. Prior to this it had not been known to breed, although it was a regular winter visitor in small numbers. Clark Kennedy says that it was 'uncommon' and only included it 'on the authority of the Rev. H. Harpur Crewe of Drayton Beauchamp', who reported that birds of this species had occasionally been killed on the reservoirs at Marsworth and Wilstone. H & J reported that they had no definite record for Buckinghamshire apart from the above. Price reported one killed at Boarstall Decoy about the beginning of February 1932, described as a new record for the county. Hayward (1947), however, reports an adult male shot at Wilstone on 19 Aug 1925 as the first. Sporadic occurrences were considered noteworthy until the 1950s, when numbers started to increase. Birds first bred in the county at Willen in 1985. A female with 2 young were seen in the county on the River Colne at Denham, but they may have bred in Hertfordshire. A nest was found at Drayton Beauchamp in 1989, and a pair bred at College Lake in 1990.

A predominantly freshwater species, the Gadwall is found on the county's shallow waters, though it is not so dependent on gravel pits as some other ducks. It has a mainly vegetarian diet, feeding mostly on floating and submerged plants. Feeding is generally from the surface of the water, with a small amount of dabbling; diving is rare. The Gadwall is also a kleptoparasite, mainly on Coot, but other ducks that bring vegetation to the surface are also parasitised. Nesting is in rank vegetation close to water, though tending to be in rather drier areas than Mallard.

It would appear that general colonisation of Buckinghamshire did not take place until the late 1970s. The Wildfowl Counts from 1961-83 showed only odd birds in the early years, scattered over a number of sites, but by 1978 double figures began to appear, and some sites seemed to be more favoured than others. 26 at Old Slade on 15 Jan 1978 and 84 at the same site on 17 Feb 1980 were noteworthy. Other good numbers were 22 at Linford on 12 Feb 1978 and 16 at Willen on 17 Dec 1982. However, a count of 154 at Willen in January 1988 shows how rapidly the position is changing. From an examination of both the Breeding Atlas and the

68

Winter Atlas it would seem that the colonisation of the county has two separate sources: that in the south being from the London area, and that in the north being from the East Midlands. Birds raised in Britain are mostly sedentary, though a few ringed in East Anglia have been recovered abroad, mainly in locations to the south-west. This could be a case of abmigration, as wintering and passage birds come from NE Europe.

The main breeding range of the Gadwall in Europe is east of 20 degree longitude, with scattered populations to the west. Climatic changes may be responsible for the expansion of its range westward from a continental climate to a more maritime one (mirrored by an eastward spread in N America), but there can be little doubt that the establishment of feral populations in W Europe including the British Isles has accelerated the process.

NHFS

Teal
Anas crecca

Winter visitor and occasional breeder.

With the increase in the water area in Buckinghamshire over the last few years, notably in the north of the county, growing numbers of Teal are present in winter. Against this, increased drainage has reduced suitable breeding sites, and the presence of Teal (particularly single males) in summer should not be taken as an indication of breeding. Non-breeding birds often spend the summer, and the males later disperse for moulting.

Clark Kennedy mentions that 'in the summer of 1861 two nests ... were discovered among some moss and rank herbage growing by the side of a pond near Burnham: it is probable that the birds had bred there previously'. He also states that 'the Rev. H. Harpur Crewe had taken the nest of this bird by the banks of the Wilstone and Marsworth reservoirs, where this species breeds in limited numbers every season.' According to H & J, they continued to do so until 1887. No further breeding was noted until 1918 when a brood was hatched at Marsworth Reservoir. H & J also reported that the late Lionel Wigglesworth had found the species breeding in small numbers near Castlethorpe. Teal continued to breed regularly on Marsworth and Wilstone Reservoirs until 1934. Mallard were artificially reared on these reservoirs from about 1890 to 1914 and again from 1933 to 1939, and this may have

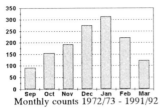

Monthly counts 1972/73 - 1991/92

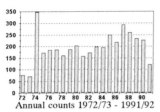

Annual counts 1972/73 - 1991/92

had some influence on Teal breeding. Since then it has only bred rather sporadically. The habitat requirements of the species rather limit its distribution in Buckinghamshire. Teal come midway between Mallard and Shoveler in feeding specialisation. They prefer shallow water, not more that 25 cm in depth, over a muddy bottom. They feed by walking, slowly filtering mud through their bills, occasionally up-ending and very rarely diving. Though they are omnivorous, in autumn and winter their diet consists mainly of seeds, and they occasionally join Mallard on stubble grain. They feed both by day and night. For nesting they require thick marginal vegetation or cover such as an overhanging willow or bank. Breeding can be difficult to establish as the female and young tend to keep to cover rather than swim in open water. During the period of the breeding survey, confirmed breeding was obtained only on the River Chess, while breeding was probable at Little Marlow. Linford, Stony Stratford NR, and College Lake may also prove to be suitable breeding sites.

Teal start to appear in moderate numbers in autumn. An exceptionally high number was 211 at Willen on 12 Sep 1976. Winter peaks have been 550 at Aylesbury STW in January 1987, 385 at Boarstall Decoy on 17 Nov 1971, 300 at Willen on 16 Jan 1977, and 250 at Linford on 13 Oct 1971. The birds seen in winter in Buckinghamshire are probably all immigrants from NW Europe. Being small they are susceptible to bad weather, and in sustained cold spells the majority may move south-west as far as S France and the Iberian peninsula.

NHFS

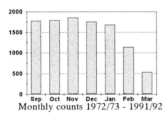

Monthly counts 1972/73 - 1991/92

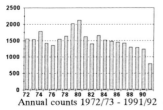

Annual counts 1972/73 - 1991/92

Mallard
Anas platyrhynchos

Common resident and winter visitor.

The Mallard is by far the commonest duck in the county, and has been since records began. It breeds throughout the county, except for parts of the Chilterns which are without surface water. It is likely that the gaps in the north-west are due to under-recording.

Mallards are likely to breed anywhere that has water, from pollarded willows by a ditch and small tree-fringed field ponds, to large lakes and rivers. Estimating the local breeding population is even more difficult than usual for the Common Birds Census only covers farmland and woodland, which are not the major habitats for the species. There are also wide regional variations in population densities. A further complication arises from the large-scale releases at nearby Tring Reservoirs, whose birds may spill over into the county. The National Common Birds Census population density for farmland, 4 pairs per 100 ha, gives a population of 5,000 pairs. This is probably too high and the true figure for the county is more likely to be about half this figure.

The wildfowl counts show that numbers rise to a peak in December, when the average for the years 1980-91 is 1600 birds. The largest monthly count is one of 2816 birds in November 1980 while the largest count at a single site is 840 birds at Linford GPs in December 1980. The large flocks are dispersed by March.

More than 90% of recoveries of birds ringed in the county have been made in S England, half of which have been within 100 km. The longest distance travelled involved a bird ringed in the county on 3 Jul 1965 which was recovered in Cornwall on 9 Dec 1967. There has been one foreign ringing recovery. A bird ringed at Boarstall Duck Decoy on 6 Nov 1985 was recovered near Calais on 12 Oct 1986.

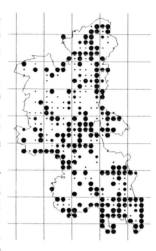

5,000 pairs

NHFS

Pintail
Anas acuta

Scarce migrant and winter visitor.

The earliest record is that noted by Clark Kennedy of one 'shot on a sheet of ice in Stoke Parke by a man named Gregory in the winter of 1863'. H & J, writing in 1920, did not record any within the county, though in 1947 Price stated that the species was 'an uncommon winter visitor'.

Between 1946 and 1959 21 birds were recorded, but between 1960 and 1969 this had increased to 222 birds. In the early 1970s a number of wing-tagged birds were released at Linford GPs by the Game Conservancy, but although some were present for several years they did not become established. They did, however, succeed in confusing the status of the species in the county.

Birds have been recorded annually since 1954, except for 1962. Flocks have usually been in single figures, but large gatherings are occasionally seen. The largest flock is 57 birds seen flying south-west into Buckinghamshire from Wilstone Res on 31 Jan 1985. The next largest flock is one of 40 birds seen at Foxcote Res on 1 Mar 1964. On 16 Jan 1972, 26 were seen on Foxcote Res at the same time that 10 flew over.

Birds have been seen at all the major waters in the county, with the largest numbers at Foxcote. Numbers tend to be small in the south of the county, with the birds usually only making brief stays. The earliest birds are occasionally found in October, but numbers do not peak until the early months of the year. By the end of March most birds are gone, but a male was seen at Willen on 9 May 1976

NHFS

Garganey
Anas querquedula

Scarce migrant and summer visitor.

Seasonal records 1972 - 1991

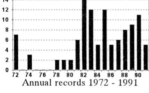
Annual records 1972 - 1991

The first record of Garganey within the present county boundary was not until 1937 when birds were recorded at Olney from 11-20 May 1937. Since then it has become a rare but annual passage migrant and summer visitor. It is our only summer visitor among the ducks, usually first appearing in April and leaving in October.

Between 1946 and 1971 there were 19 records of 41 birds, while between 1972 and 1991 there were 66 records of 105 birds. 61 birds were found in the north of the county, 27 in the middle, and 17 in the south. These later records are shown on the histograms. It is likely that the increase is due to increasing observer awareness of the difficulties in identifying the birds in their long-lasting eclipse plumage as well as the larger number of observers in more recent years.

Although pairs of Garganeys have frequently been seen in suitable breeding habitat in the spring the species has never been proven to have bred in Buckinghamshire. It is opportunist in its summer quarters, preferring ditches and other drainage channels, small pools, or larger waters well broken up with plenty of cover. It is very elusive at this time, and proof of breeding is difficult to obtain. During the period of the breeding atlas survey, birds were recorded in two tetrads - SP84Q and SP80U. Both records were of probable breeding.

The graphs show that the spring migration peaks at the end of April, while the smaller autumn migration peaks in mid August. The earliest record is of a pair on 9 Mar 1969 on the Wendover Canal, although there is a record of a female which wintered at Willen, not leaving until 15 Apr 1984.

NHFS

Shoveler
Anas clypeata

Resident in small numbers, and a winter and passage visitor.

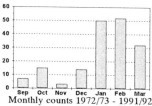

Monthly counts 1972/73 - 1991/92

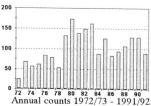

Annual counts 1972/73 - 1991/92

The Shoveler, a duck of southerly distribution, has shown a huge population increase in Great Britain and W Europe over the last hundred years (Alexander and Lack 1944, Parslow 1973), though the latter suggests that the increase may have slowed down since the 1950s. This expansion may be related to an improvement of the climate following the 'little ice age' from the seventeenth century to the first half of the nineteenth.

The Shoveler makes very poor eating, its flesh being rank. It is therefore not a target for fowlers. There is, however, a record of one shot near Dinton Hall on 10 Sep 1774 and another of four present on 29 Aug 1800, of which one was shot. Clark Kennedy indicated that it was a winter visitor to Buckinghamshire, but not a common one. H & J noted that in June 1918 Hartert came across a female leading 8 ducklings along a ditch leading to Wilstone Reservoir; they also reported that Shoveler had been breeding there from at least 1905. Hayward (1947), however, states that they were breeding regularly by 1887 but declined after that. Breeding occurred again from 1914 to 1934, after which the next record was in 1943. These gaps in breeding coincide with the artificial breeding of Mallard on the reservoirs, which obviously limited breeding sites. Shoveler were first noted breeding at Willen in 1980 and now breed there regularly.

In Buckinghamshire it is difficult to get an accurate picture of the growth in the numbers of Shoveler over the past few years. Although there has been an increase in water area in the county, not much of it is suitable for this species. One of the reasons why Willen is so attractive is the large area of shallow, mud-based water as at Weston Turville Res, and this is no doubt why the two places are the only ones so far to attract breeding birds.

Wintering Shoveler start to arrive in late autumn after the moult, and numbers peak about November. The largest flock recorded is one of 225 birds at Willen on 29 Aug 1988. In Buckinghamshire numbers rarely reach three figures on any water. It would appear that summering birds in Britain move out in the autumn to S France and Spain, to be replaced by other birds from Europe which in turn move down to winter quarters in the south. Up to the 1950s and early 1960s there was also a peak in February and early March, presumably a stop-off on the return migration. Since then the pattern seems to have altered, and birds by-pass Britain on the return. This may again be due to climatic change, allowing a single movement from winter to summer quarters. It is interesting to speculate whether, if conditions changed again, Shoveler would revert to their earlier migration pattern, and if so how often this may have happened in the past.

NHFS

Red-crested Pochard
Netta rufina

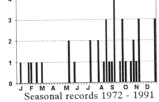
Seasonal records 1972 - 1991

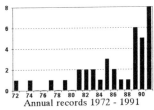
Annual records 1972 - 1991

Rare vagrant, most of which are probably feral.

1918: 1 at Weston Turville Res, perhaps escaped from Woburn.

1920: 1 at Weston Turville Res, perhaps escaped from Woburn.

1961: female on 6 Apr, Marlow GPs.

1971: female on 10 and 17 Oct, Marlow GPs. Exceptional numbers occurred in SE England at this time, and this may well have been a wild bird.

Since 1972 there have been 32 records of 37 birds. They are shown on the histograms. 13 birds were recorded in the north of the county, 10 in the middle, and 14 in the south. There is some evidence of a small autumn passage, particularly at Linford, which may indicate that some of the birds are wild, although it is possible that they are feral birds engaged in post-breeding dispersal.

Pochard

Aythya ferina

Uncommon breeding species, but common winter visitor and passage migrant.

The first record of Pochard in Buckinghamshire is of one shot at Dinton Hall on 16 Jun 1825. According to Clark Kennedy, the Rev. Harpur Crewe stated that this duck was 'a common winter visitor to the reservoirs near Drayton Beauchamp', but that it was 'rare on the rivers'. He also noted that it had bred on two occasions at Marsworth and Wilstone reservoirs in the 1850s. It would appear to have increased in the county during the latter part of the nineteenth century, as H & J reported that it 'breeds numerously at the Halton and Tring Reservoirs'. Two pairs nested on a pond at Burnham Beeches in 1916 (H & J), while Höhn (1943) said that the bird had bred annually on a pond in Buckinghamshire since the beginning of the century.

The Pochard has a more southerly distribution than the Tufted Duck. In common with most of Europe, the British population has increased markedly during the present century, probably for the same reasons that apply to the Tufted Duck (qv). There has, however, been some decline since the early 1970s when there were very high numbers in Britain. This is particularly marked in SE England, where most of the country's Pochard breed. In Buckinghamshire this decline is offset (or masked) by the availability of additional waters favourable to the species. Poor breeding success or climatic change may account for what is probably a temporary dip in numbers.

In Buckinghamshire the Pochard is still an uncommon breeding bird; birds seen in summer are usually non-breeders. The bird prefers shallower water than the Tufted Duck. Its dives are only up to 3 m and are of shorter duration. Occasionally it feeds by up-ending. Though it feeds by day as well as at night, it is most often seen in daytime sleeping on the water. The preferred food is vegetable matter, but some animal material is taken. For breeding, the female prefers undisturbed waters with plenty of marginal vegetation. The nest is constructed close to the water's edge. The only regular breeding site in the county is Weston Turville Res where up to 5 pairs have bred. Birds have also bred at Tilehouse GP, Shardeloes, and Linford. It may be that the species is under-recorded as a breeding bird in the county, especially in the north where there are a number of apparently suitable sites.

The build-up of numbers starts about the middle of August

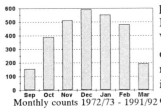

Monthly counts 1972/73 - 1991/92

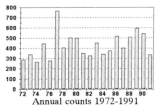

Annual counts 1972-1991

when post-moult birds arrive to join those which have summered, and by the middle of winter large numbers can be present on some waters. In the winter of 1977-78 Shardeloes Lake held over 300, Great Linford 497 on 13 Nov 1977, and Willen 655 a few weeks later on 18 Dec. There is some evidence that females travel further south than males, which may account for the high proportion of males in winter flocks in Britain. The larger male may be more adapted to withstand cold, and the separation of the sexes in winter could have survival benefits. Ringing recoveries in Buckinghamshire appear to indicate east to west movements in winter. A bird ringed on 13 Jun 1933 in Helsinki, Finland was recovered in the county on 22 Dec 1937 (the first record of a Pochard ringed abroad and recovered in the UK); one ringed at Lake Engare, Latvia on 6 Jun 1964 was shot at Iver on 12 Dec 1966; and one ringed in Czechoslovakia on 12 Dec 1966 was recovered at Latimer on 30 Dec 1967. There is also a record of a bird ringed on the North Slob, Co. Wexford on 18 Jan 1979 being shot at Stone almost exactly eight years later on 14 Jan 1987.

NHFS

Ring-necked Duck
Aythya collaris

Very rare vagrant. All records are given.

1971: male from 14 Feb-10 Apr, returning from 14 Nov-30 Mar 1972, 17 Dec 1972-15 Jul 1973, and 16 Dec 1973-17 Apr 1974, Marlow GPs.
1979: male from 7-16 Mar, Willen.
1989: female from 14 Jan-2 May, Yiewsley GP, Iver.
1991: male on 12 May, Willen.

Long-staying individuals are a feature of this species, though the Marlow bird, which appeared in four successive winters, was exceptional.

Ferruginous Duck
Aythya nyroca

Very rare vagrant. All records are given.

1974: male from 24 Feb-12 Apr then throughout Oct, Newton
      Longville.
1976: male on 15 Feb, Eythrope.
1979: male on 2 Feb, River Colne at Iver.
1989: female from 3-4 Dec, Marlow GPs.

In addition one reported as this species on 7 Oct 1978 at
Calvert may have been 'Paget's Pochard' (hybrid Ferruginous
Duck x Pochard).

The status of all these birds is problematical. It is possible
they were all feral, although the dates are consistent with them
being wild birds.

Tufted Duck
Aythya fuligula

Common resident, passage migrant and winter visitor.

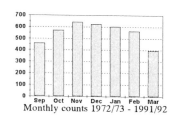

Monthly counts 1972/73 - 1991/92

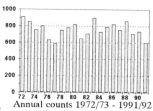

Annual counts 1972/73 - 1991/92

A bird of more northerly distribution than the Pochard, the
Tufted Duck has shown a dramatic increase in both its range
and numbers in W Europe since the end of the last century.
This has been linked to climatic changes, particularly to the
drier conditions in SW Asia which have resulted in losses of
breeding habitat there. It is now the most familiar diving duck
in Buckinghamshire, found on most waters with a depth of
more than one metre. Undoubtedly the increased availability
of suitable sites this century, due in large measure to gravel

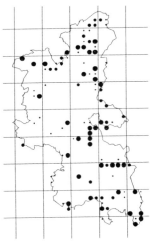

150 pairs

and mineral extraction, has contributed significantly to this spread.

Clark Kennedy described the Tufted Duck as a common winter visitor to the Marsworth and Wilstone reservoirs, but noted that it did not often occur on the rivers. By 1920 it was already nesting on the Tring and Weston Turville reservoirs (H & J). Since then it has continued to increase in numbers, particularly in winter, wherever there are suitable waters. In recent years the creation of flood balancing lakes as part of the development of Milton Keynes has augmented the number of favourable sites.

The diet of the Tufted Duck consists of about 80% animal material, with molluscs predominating, and the rest insects. Vegetable food is usually in the form of seeds. This food is normally obtained by diving, but upending is sometimes resorted to in shallow water. Dives can be up to 5 m but are generally about half that and average 15-20 seconds in duration. Males tend to dive to greater depths than females, and this probably accounts for some separation out of the breeding season. The males start to flock and begin their moult while the females are still on the nest. Later, the males congregate on the slightly deeper waters, leaving the shallower waters for the females. This may have some survival value, but there may be other factors involved (see Pochard).

This is one of the last duck species to nest, often as late as June or July. The nest is usually close to the water, well concealed in tussock or rushes. In Buckinghamshire, breeding is restricted to waters of moderate size. The birds prefer to use small islands, though these are not always a safeguard from predators; foxes have been known to swim out and search them for sitting birds. The recorded sites follow the line of the river valleys where gravel is worked. Both Willen and Great Linford regularly report over 100 ducklings, but nesting is probably under-reported in the county.

The wintering population builds up from October onwards. Post-moulting flocks are swelled by birds from more northerly parts of Britain as well as from NW Europe and Iceland. It may be that the majority that arrive in Buckinghamshire are from Europe, crossing the North Sea and spreading inland from the Wash. The largest flocks recorded are 558 at Little Marlow GPs in December 1990, 502 at Old Slade on 17 Dec 1972, and 478 at Great Linford on 12 Dec 1976. Wintering flocks start to disperse about the middle of March. In very bad weather, when the waters are completely frozen over, the birds may desert the county for larger waters elsewhere, such as Stewartby (Bedfordshire) or Grafham (Cambridgeshire), or even the coast, only returning as conditions improve.

Ringing recoveries mainly involve birds ringed in eastern counties of England in autumn or spring being found in Buckinghamshire during the winter.

NHFS

Scaup
Aythya marila

Rare vagrant and winter visitor.

There are 8 records prior to 1973:

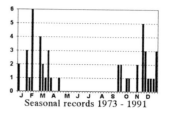

Seasonal records 1973 - 1991

1855: 1 female on 26 Jan, on River Chess, Latimer.
1923: 1 on 4 Nov, Weston Turville Res.
1928: 1 on 28 Oct, Weston Turville Res.
1950: 2 females or immatures 29 Oct, Weston Turville Res.
1958: male on 16 Mar, Foxcote.
1958: male from 30 Mar-13 Apr, Hartigan's GP.
1960: female from 30 Nov-16 Dec, near Foxcote.
1970: male on 21 Feb, Old Slade.

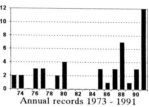

Annual records 1973 - 1991

There are 35 records of 46 birds since 1973. They are shown on the histograms. 23 birds were seen in the north of the county, 8 in the middle, and 15 in the south. The largest flock was one of 6 birds from 10-11 Feb 1991 at Boveney Lock.

Eider
Somateria mollissima

Very rare vagrant. There is one record.

1988: 2 females on 5 Apr, Weston Turville Res.

An earlier record of a male at Foxcote on 11 Feb 1961 was unreported at the time and cannot now be substantiated.

Long-tailed Duck
Clangula hyemalis

Rare vagrant and winter visitor. All records are given.

1957: 1 from 18-19 Nov, Weston Turville Res.
1959: male from 17-19 Nov, Foxcote.
1966: male and 2 females on 11 Apr, Marlow GP.
1969: female/immature on 15 Feb, Shardeloes, during severe weather.
1970: immature from 29 Oct-13 Jan 1971, Calvert.
1973: male from 18 Feb-18 Mar, Calvert.
1979: female from 17 Nov-18 Dec, Willen.
1979: immature from 31 Dec 1979-19 Jan 1980, Startopsend Res., typically along Buckinghamshire edge.
1981: female on 9 Dec, Willen.
1982: female/immature from 19 Nov-26 Dec, Stony Stratford.
1983: immature female on 4 Mar, Blue Lagoon, Milton Keynes.
1988: 1 from 23 Oct-4 Jun 1989, Startopsend Res, Herts, was often seen in the Buckinghamshire section.
1990: immature male and female from 16 Dec-13 Jan 1991, Weston Turville Res.
1991: 2 from 2 Nov-10 Dec, Willen.

Common Scoter
Melanitta nigra

Scarce migrant.

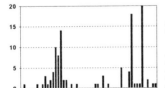
Seasonal records 1974 - 1991

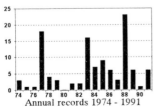
Annual records 1974 - 1991

There were 8 records prior to 1974:

1893: young male on 18 Dec was shot at Deadmere, Great Marlow.
1910: 11 on 10 Apr, Weston Turville Res.
1913: 1 on 19 Jul, Weston Turville Res.
1957: pair on 4 Apr, Weston Turville Res.
1957: pair and a female on 15 Apr, Weston Turville Res.
1958: male on 31 Mar, Weston Turville Res.
1958: female from 18-20 Oct, Shardeloes, after severe gales.
1960: 2 females on 25 Oct, Foxcote.

Since 1974 then there have been 46 records of 111 birds. They are shown on the histograms. 104 birds were seen in the north of the county, and 7 in the middle. The largest flocks recorded are of 18 birds on 27 Oct 1977 at Foxcote, and 20 birds on 20 Nov 1988 at Willen. Neither contained any adult males.

There is a distinct peak in the first half of April.

Velvet Scoter
Melanitta fusca

Very rare vagrant. All records are given.

1890: 1 killed on 27 Oct, Linford.
1948: male from 12-13 Dec, near Iver.
1982: 11 on 9 Jan, Willen.

Bufflehead
Bucephala albeola

Very rare vagrant. There has been one record.

1961: male from 28 Feb-9 Mar, Foxcote Res.

This was the sixth British record of this North American bird.

Goldeneye
Bucephala clangula

Regular winter visitor.

Clark Kennedy refers to this duck as being 'A winter visitant, but never appearing in great numbers'. H & R, however, talk of 'an irregular winter visitor, often appearing in great numbers on the Tring Reservoirs in very cold weather'. H & J only speak of 'small flocks'. In 1849 the Rev

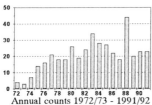

Monthly counts 1972/73 - 1991/92

Annual counts 1972/73 - 1991/92

J Williams stated in 1849 that 'small flocks visited the Tring Reservoirs annually, arriving at the end of October and staying until driven away by frost,' and that 'nearly all were females or birds of the year'.

Mainly a sea duck, the Goldeneye prefers large open waters such as estuaries. Inland it will frequent larger waters of reasonable depth. Dives are up to 7 metres, the food being mainly of an animal nature. The increase in the number of suitable waters in Buckinghamshire, particularly in the north, plus the increased number of observers, has meant that more are reported; but it is still possible to overlook 'redheads' among other diving ducks.

Goldeneye tend to arrive in October and begin to disperse in late March. As many as 40 birds are occasionally seen on some waters. Willen can regularly be relied upon to produce double figures in suitable weather in winter. The earliest record for the county, 12 Aug 1987, was of a 'redhead' (possibly a juvenile) at Caldecotte Lake. Another early record was of a bird at Foxcote on 14 Sep 1986. The latest record was of a female at Willen on 4 May 1984. There is a tendency for more 'redheads' to be seen on Buckinghamshire waters in winter. This has more to do with females moving further south than males, rather than segregation of the sexes as such, and, of course, the dispersal of juveniles.

NHFS

Smew
Mergus albellus

Seasonal records 1978 - 1991

Annual records 1978 - 1991

Scarce winter visitor.

The first county record is of a female shot at Dinton Hall on 23 Nov 1774.

There were 7 records between 1920 and 1947, mostly at Weston Turville Res. Between 1947 and 1968 birds failed to be recorded in only 4 years, but there followed 9 blank years until birds began to be recorded regularly from 1978.

The main wintering area in Britain is SE England and E Anglia. This is reflected in the local records, which indicate that Tilehouse GPs are the most regular site in the county, where small numbers of Smew are recorded almost every year. Birds have been recorded at all the major waters in the county, usually in January and February.

Before 1978 there was one major influx. In February 1963, during severe weather conditions when most waters were frozen, birds appeared on the River Thames. A flock of 19 birds was seen at Cliveden Reach on the 4th, and a flock of 15 birds at Medmenham on the 7th, but the largest recorded flock is one of 26 birds which was seen flying round Marlow GPs on 26 Jan 1992 at a time when many waters were frozen.

The graph indicates the large numbers seen in the county between 1985 and 1987. It is possible that the figures are exaggerated due to flocks moving between different waters and being recorded more than once.

The earliest date is of a redhead at Weston Turville Res on 28 Sep 1951. This is so early that some doubt must be cast on the record, especially as it is not commented on in the MTNHS report. The next earliest date is of two redheads at Calvert on 18 Nov 1989. The latest date was of a male which stayed at Willen until 28 Mar 1985.

NHFS

Red-breasted Merganser
Mergus serrator

Rare vagrant and winter visitor.

Clark Kennedy stated that 'individuals were occasionally shot on the Thames', but the only dated record prior to 1973 is:

1970: 2 females from 31 Jan-1 Feb, Old Slade.

Since 1973 there have been 25 records of 37 birds. They are shown on the histograms. 20 of the birds were seen in the north of the county, 8 in the middle, and 9 in the south.

The February peak may be the result of cold weather movements. In February 1979, when 12 birds were seen in the county, 420 birds were reported in inland Britain, an event that was due to severe weather conditions on the Baltic and North Sea coasts (Chandler 1981).

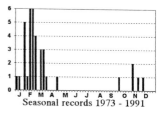
Seasonal records 1973 - 1991

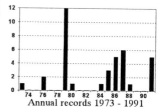
Annual records 1973 - 1991

Goosander
Mergus merganser

Regular winter visitor.

    Unlike the Red-breasted Merganser, the Goosander is mainly a bird of inland waters in winter. The earliest extant record for Buckinghamshire is of a female shot at Dinton Hall on 26 Nov 1774. It has increased its range considerably in recent years. Today it is recorded in all months from November to March, and occasionally birds stay later. Unlike the Red-breasted Merganser, the Goosander will remain on suitable waters for a considerable time. Slightly different feeding techniques may give it an advantage; it has a deeper bill with a more pronounced hook at the tip, which may assist it when searching among stones on the bottom. In common with the other sawbills, adult males arrive later than the 'redheads'. It is also possible that 'redheads' winter further south than the adult males. There are three regular wintering sites in the county: Foxcote, Caldecotte Lake, and Linford. The largest flocks recorded are 49 at Linford in December 1986, 40 at Foxcote on 23 Mar 1979, and 38 at Caldecotte in February 1987. The other large waters record the bird irregularly, usually in single figures.

NHFS

Ruddy Duck
Oxyura jamaicensis

Very local resident and scarce migrant.

Prior to 1980 there were just 7 records:

1960: female from 1 Jan-23 Apr, then 7 Sep-12 Nov, Foxcote Res.
1974: female from 29 Dec-3 Jan 1975, Foxcote Res.
1975: male from 28 Aug-25 Oct, Weston Turville Res.
1976: male on 7 Jun, Wotton Lake.
1976: female from 23-31 Oct, Weston Turville Res.
1977: male from 23-29 Aug, Weston Turville Res.
1979: male on 25 Feb, Willen.

In 1980 two pairs bred successfully at Weston Turville Res, and at least six other birds were seen in the county. Subsequently the species has attempted to breed every year at Weston Turville, and raised 5 broods in 1982 and 1984. Display took place at Wotton Lake in 1982 although breeding was not proved. In 1987 there were two pairs at Shardeloes, one pair in 1988, and two broods were raised in 1990. The drastic reduction in the mean flow rate of the River Misbourne since this date has made this site unsuitable for water birds. In 1989 they were reported to have bred at Linford.

Ruddy Ducks can be rather secretive during the breeding season as they tend to stay in the reed beds that they require and may be overlooked. They are best located when they give their spectacular and noisy display, which often takes place at night.

Birds are now regularly seen throughout the year at most of the major waters in the county, though usually only in very small numbers. The largest flock recorded is one of 15 birds in April 1984 at Weston Turville Res.

Ruddy Ducks are a North American species where they breed in the marginal vegetation of small reed-fringed ponds and lakes. At least 70 juveniles escaped from the wildfowl collection at Slimbridge between 1952 and 1973 and were first recorded breeding in the wild in the West Midlands in 1961. The population remained fairly constant for a few years then rapidly expanded, breeding as far away as Scotland and Northern Ireland. Ruddy Ducks were first recorded at Tring Reservoirs in 1960 and first bred there in 1965 (Gladwin & Sage 1986). The small county population presumably originates from there.

There are few places in Buckinghamshire that meet the requirements of Ruddy Ducks. It is likely that they have now all been colonised and that the local population has reached a stable maximum.

DMF

Honey Buzzard
Pernis apivorus

Very rare vagrant. May have bred in 19th century.

All records are given:

1837: reported by John Gould to have nested in Burnham Beeches.
1842: 1 captured, Chesham/Missenden.
1882: 2 killed about 23 Sep, Shabbington Woods.
1969: 1 on 2 Aug, Newport Pagnell.
1986: 1 on 12 Jun, Rushbeds Wood.
1988: 1 on 29 May, Philipshill Wood.
1991: 1 on 14 Jul, Windsor Hill NR.

Red Kite
Milvus milvus

Scarce vagrant.

It is likely that Red Kites formerly bred in most of the larger woods of the county, but by the mid 19th century it had become 'very rare' (Clark Kennedy). H & J give undated reports of nesting near Quainton.

Since the middle of the 19th Century there were only 3 records prior to 1967: in the 1880s, in 1913, and in 1914. These records were followed by a long gap until one was seen in 1967. Two more were recorded in the 1960s and two in the 1970s.

The 1980s saw a marked increase, which may be explained by the improvement in the species' fortunes in Wales. Seven birds were seen between 1981 and 1988. Two birds were seen in each of January, March, and August, four were seen in April, and one in December. All were seen in the southern half of the county with six over or near the Chiltern escarpment. All were seen briefly except for one bird which remained at Littleworth Common from 28-30 Apr 1988.

Since 1989 the situation has become blurred owing to the RSPB/English Nature release scheme. Birds from Spain have been introduced at a site in southern England in an attempt to re-establish the species. They apparently wander widely, and a number of tagged birds have been seen in the county, which makes the acceptance of any truly wild birds almost impossible.

White-tailed Eagle
Haliaeetus albicilla

Very rare vagrant and winter visitor. All records are given.

1846: 1 trapped Chequers Court.
1857: 1 shot Hambleden.
1894/5: 1 Fawley.
1983: 1 3rd/4th year, from 22 Nov-18 Feb 1984, in the area of Longwick, Brill, Chilton, and Oakley.

The last record, of arguably the most spectacular bird ever seen in the county, was of an unringed bird, and was thus not a bird from the release scheme in the Hebrides. It probably originated from East Europe or the Baltic whose birds are increasing as winter visitors on the British east coast and in northern France. During its time in the county it was seen to feed on rabbits and, once, a muntjac.

Marsh Harrier
Circus aeruginosus

Scarce migrant.

Clark Kennedy made the remarkable statement: 'resident throughout year, nowhere numerous. Distributed sparingly.' He gave Chesham and Risborough as sites. H & J showed some scepticism towards these remarks and only gave one record: of a male shot at Spade Oak Ferry on 19 Jan 1881.

There were no more records until 1955, when there was one at Shardeloes on 28 Aug.

Since 1976 there have been 16 records all of single birds with a maximum annual total of 3 birds. They are shown on a seasonal histogram. Recent sites have included Weston Turville Res, Willen, and Linford.

The histogram shows that all the records were in late April, May and August, except for the 1881 record.

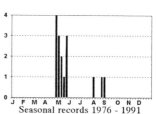

Seasonal records 1976 - 1991

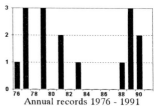

Annual records 1976 - 1991

87

Hen Harrier
Circus cyaneus

Rare migrant.

There are undated records for Chesham and Langley Park in Clark Kennedy.

There were 5 records to 1961:

1921: 1 shot in December, Olney.
1924: ringtail on 9 Mar, Pitstone Hill.
1939: 1 shot in January, St Leonard's.
1951: male on 24 Mar, Iver.
1952: ringtail on 9 Nov, over Chiltern above Halton golf course.

During the 1960s there were four records, in the 1970s there were 12, while between 1980 and 1991 there were four. The birds have been found throughout the county. All records were between September and April.

Adding the records for Harrier sp, the figures become 8 in the 1960s, 10 in the 1970s, and 7 in the 1980s and 1990s.

Even if the records of harriers which have not been specifically identified are included, it is obvious there has been a sharp decline in the number of records since 1980, particularly when the increase in the number of observers is considered. This is in marked contrast to the situation in neighbouring counties, where birds are annual in Oxfordshire, Bedfordshire, and Hertfordshire.

Montagu's Harrier
Circus pygargus

Very rare vagrant. All records are given.

1929: 1 late April or early May, trapped by gamekeeper, Black Park.
1968: adult female on 24 Jun, Frieth.
1977: female on 26 May, Marsworth.

Harrier species
Circus sp

All records are given.

1956: ringtail on 17 Jan, Weedon.
1959: ringtail on 28 Jun, Oakley Wood.
1961: 1 on 23 Nov, Oakley Green.
1974: ringtail on 23 May, Weston Turville.
1974: ringtail on 22 Aug, Chenies.
1983: male on 19 May, Lodge Hill.
1983: ringtail on 27 Oct, North Marston.
1983: ringtail on 16 Nov, Aston Abbots.
1985: 1 on 19 Nov, Oakley, thought to be Hen Harrier.
1989: ringtail flying north on 14 Apr, Iver Heath.
1991: ringtail on 1 Oct, Hughenden Valley.

Goshawk
Accipiter gentilis

Rare visitor but reported with increasing frequency; potentially a breeding species.

The history of the Goshawk in Britain is well summarised in the Breeding Atlas. It appears to have ceased nesting in England well over a century ago and to have become re-established in recent decades, probably due to the release of birds by falconers or to escapes. Two 16th century breeding records are quoted by F & Y. First, in a wood near Amersham 'there hath bene this twentie or thirtie yeres an Ayerye of goosse hawks contynually there bredyng'; and second, Thomas Hawtrey was summoned to appear before the Court of the Star Chamber for taking the young from a nest near Ellesborough (see p.5). A male shot on 10 Sep 1789 near Dinton Hall by the Rev. W. Goodall figured in the Dinton Hall MS. The first 20th century sighting was one near Denham Green in March 1955 (F & Y). Most recently, the 1984 BBC reportcommented that sightings in three separate areas may all have indicated the presence of breeding pairs.

Extensive woodland is the Goshawk's chief requirement for nesting, and widespread planting of conifers in post-war years provided this to some extent. However, beech is much favoured on the Continent and the Chiltern woodlands of Buckinghamshire must include many suitable localities. No large wood can be discounted as long as it is reasonably undisturbed. Prey supplies are unlikely to be a problem. An experimental study with released birds in Oxfordshire found the chief prey to be Woodpigeon, rabbit and Moorhen (Kenward 1979).

Locating the bird is never easy, since it has the stealthy ways of the Sparrowhawk and actually spends more time in woodland. Breeding sites several kilometres apart may be used in alternate years, adding further to the difficulties. Soaring display flights in spring offer the best chance of discovering a breeding pair. The nest itself may be hard to find, situated as it is in a high tree fork. This is to the bird's advantage, for although it receives special protection under Schedule 1 of the Wildlife and Countryside Act of 1981, it is still subjected to the depredations of egg-collectors and falconers.

PJKB

Sparrowhawk
Accipiter nisus

Resident, breeding throughout the county.

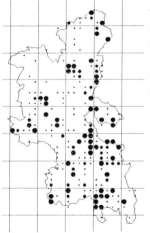

150 pairs

The history of the Sparrowhawk in Buckinghamshire has been one of fluctuating fortunes. Earlier this century, it was regularly persecuted by keepers (H & R, H & J), though common enough where unmolested. Recent decades have seen a change in attitudes, and while direct persecution does still occur, it is a much smaller problem than formerly. A more serious threat, due to the effects of organochlorine pesticide residues on breeding success, became evident during the 1960s, and the population dropped severely, both in the county and nationwide. Stricter controls on the use of certain pesticides since then have permitted a gradual recovery, as noted in MTNHS reports since the early 1970s, and the species is now arguably at least as abundant in the county as at any time this century.

The Sparrowhawk is primarily a woodland bird, especially during the breeding season, and the distribution shown on the map closely matches the extent of tree cover. Highest densities in the county are reached in well-wooded areas of the Chilterns, where Fuller et al (1985) record a mean nearest-neighbour distance of 0.94 km, with a range from 0.5 to 1.5 km. North of the Chilterns, the more scattered woodlands of the Vale of Aylesbury, Woburn Sands and near the Northamptonshire border provide the main breeding habitat. However, a few pairs nest in small spinneys or hedgerows in otherwise open farmland. Parkland around stately homes, with

mature trees such as cedars, is also used despite the higher
levels of human disturbance. In the Chilterns study area
conifer plantations were found to be a favoured habitat; 73%
of the nests recorded were in larch, 22% in other conifers,
and only 5% in broad-leaved trees. Elsewhere in the Chilterns,
especially where there are extensive pure beechwoods, broad-
leaved trees are presumably used more frequently. In the Vale
of Aylesbury, nests in hedgerow hawthorns and willows have
been recorded.

Sparrowhawks commence breeding from mid to late May,
and most young fledge in late July or early August. A period
of 2 to 3 weeks is then spent in the vicinity of the nest, with
the young attended by the parents. The birds may be
conspicuously noisy at this time. From early autumn onwards,
young birds disperse away from the breeding areas, and
mortality at this time is high. Of 44 recoveries of Chiltern
Sparrowhawks analysed by Burton (1986), 11 occurred within
100 days of the ringing date, with a peak in September. On
the national scale, this dispersal appears random in direction
(Newton 1986), but the Chiltern-ringed birds showed a strong
bias towards moving along the scarp, especially north-east or
southwards. Only 8 had moved out into the Vale of
Aylesbury, and 7 of these were females, confirming the trend
noted by Newton (1986) for females to venture more readily
into open country. Most birds do not move very far, over half
of all recoveries being under 10 km. The longest recorded is
one of 63 km, from a site near Hastoe to Basingstoke,
Hampshire. This is typical of Sparrowhawks in S England,

although those from the north and Scotland often travel considerably farther. Sparrowhawks breeding in the Vale of Aylesbury have been less intensively ringed than those in the Chilterns, and the few birds recovered have stayed within the low ground to the north and west of the Chilterns. To what extent Vale-bred birds may move into the Chilterns remains unknown.

During the winter, a proportion of Sparrowhawks move out of woodland to hunt in open country, or even in suburban gardens, where concentrations of small birds at feeders and bird tables can prove an attraction. Winter roosts of thrushes or Starlings may also have their attendant Sparrowhawks. At the Calvert roost, for example, up to 5 have been seen in the air together on an evening when Redwings were abundant. These birds are usually females, as are the majority of Sparrowhawks recovered around human dwellings. Such recoveries commonly occur through collisions with windows or greenhouses while in pursuit of prey.

From late winter onwards, Sparrowhawks may be seen soaring in display flights near the breeding areas, and nest building often commences many weeks before egg laying. A new nest is usually built each year, and other half-completed structures may also be seen in nearby trees. Whether egg laying will follow, and how successful it will be, depends on conditions in early spring. Harsh winters and late springs may reduce breeding success considerably among early-nesting passerines, whose fledglings form an important food source later, when Sparrowhawks have their own young to feed. Consequently, hard weather early in the year is often followed by a poor year for Sparrowhawks, as happened in 1979, 1982 and, less severely, in 1986. Poor productivity is caused both by the failure of nesting attempts, and by failure to breed at all. In the latter case, birds may remain in regular attendance at a nest, without ever laying in it.

PJKB

92

Buzzard
Buteo buteo

Uncommon migrant which occasionally breeds.

Changes in the distribution of Buzzards in England are well documented. Persecution of Buzzards by man is said to have started as early as the beginning of the 17th century (BWP) although at the beginning of the 19th century the range of breeding Buzzards still extended right across England and Wales (the Breeding Atlas). By 1865 the main breeding range had significantly contracted with the low point being around 1915 when they were virtually confined to Cornwall, Devon, Wales, the Lake District and West Scotland. It seems very unlikely that any Buzzards would have been seen in Buckinghamshire at this time, even as vagrants, as they do not normally wander far from their breeding site (Brown 1976). By 1954 the breeding range had extended eastward to as far as Buckinghamshire (the Breeding Atlas) although there is evidence that Buzzards were regularly summering in the west of the county for some years before that. The introduction of myxomatosis in 1955-56, along with organochlorine poisoning, caused some retraction in the range in central and southern England (BWP) and may explain the lack of Buzzard breeding records from Buckinghamshire for the period between 1954 and 1967. The Breeding Atlas only has Buzzards recorded in three 10-km squares (two confirmed and one possible breeding), these being from tetrads which are partly shared with other counties. The BTO Buzzard survey (Taylor, et al 1986) concluded that 'the population has not extended significantly since 1972'. Since the late 1970s there have been records of possible breeding activity in most years. However confirmation is rarely obtained. This usually involves just one locality in the county but records have been received from up to three separate territories in some years.

The current status of Buzzards in the county is not very different to that in the last 20 to 30 years. It seems that usually one, but up to three pairs, breed, attempt to breed, or simply hold territory. Uncertainties in the status of this species are partly due to:-

1. Doubts as to the exact location of the breeding sites as a number of the potential breeding areas are on the boundaries with other counties and a different nest is likely to be used from year to year.

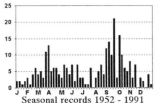

Seasonal records 1952 - 1991

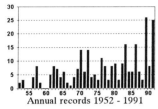

Annual records 1952 - 1991

2. Many sightings of Buzzards are not accompanied by field notes and are therefore recorded as 'Buzzard sp.', even though the two possible confusion species (Honey Buzzard and Rough-Legged Buzzard) are extremely rare in the county.

3. There is a reluctance by some observers to supply records of breeding birds.

Buzzards may be seen at any time of the year in the county. Adults usually remain on their territories throughout the year (the Winter Atlas), with the bulk of the sightings in late summer (see histogram). It seems likely that many of these are recently fledged birds forming part of a general post-breeding dispersal. They are usually seen in and around wooded areas or open country with scattered trees. Approximately two thirds of the sightings are south of the Chiltern escarpment. Within the county, Buzzards tend to be less vocal and display less than in areas where they are common. This is due to the 'triggering' effect that displaying birds have on birds in neighbouring territories (BWP). So, despite their size, breeding Buzzards can be secretive and are less likely to be located within the county than in SW England and Wales.

Vagrant and temporarily resident individuals are perhaps increasing slightly in numbers (see histogram). There are no ringing recoveries of Buzzards within the county but recoveries elsewhere have indicated that '74% of ringing recoveries are within 50 km of the nest and with movements over 100 km rare' (BWP). It seems likely that wandering Buzzards seen in the county have in fact been raised in the county or are from nearby counties.

Why Buzzards have not recolonised the county more widely is probably a combination of continued persecution, general disturbance, and loss of habitat, as well as a lack of areas with good numbers of their preferred food, the rabbit. As recently as 1980 the BBC Annual Report stated that 'There is evidence which suggests the use of poisons' in an area where Buzzards have been known to have bred in previous years. There was no breeding reported that year. Loss of habitat is perhaps not so great a threat but the general urbanisation of parts of the south of the county cannot have helped and will certainly have increased disturbance.

JER

Rough-legged Buzzard
Buteo lagopus

Rare vagrant and winter visitor. All records are given.

1839: pair shot in November, Bledlow Woods.
1880: 1 trapped on 6 Dec, near Wycombe.
1890 or 1891: 3 trapped in late autumn, Halton. 2 of these
    birds are now in the Tring Museum.
1912: 1 Aston Clinton.
1966: 1 from mid Dec-28 Jan 1967, Chiltern escarpment.
1971: 1 on 17 Apr, Dorney Common.

There is some evidence that the bird is under-recorded in the
county as there are more records in neighbouring counties,
including Oxfordshire, where one would expect this Fenno-
Scandian vagrant to be rarer (Brucker et al 1992).

Osprey
Pandion haliaetus

Rare but increasing migrant.

Prior to 1968 there were 10 records of 11 birds.

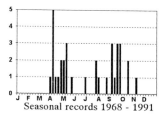
Seasonal records 1968 - 1991

1845: 1 killed in February, Chequers.
1854: 1 shot, canal at Halton.
1858: 1 seen in winter, Fawley Woods.
1862: 1 killed on 9 Sep, Ditton Park.
1863: 1 shot on 26 Sep, Ditton Park.
1864: 2 in September, Weston Turville Res/Wendover Canal.
    The female was shot on 30th.
1901: 1 shot on 11 Oct, Aston Hall, Halton.
1938: 1 on 14 Sep, on Buckinghamshire bank of River
    Thames 3 km west of Maidenhead.
1952: 1 found injured, Latimer. The bird was released after
    treatment.
1958: 1 on 6 or 16 Sep, Shardeloes.

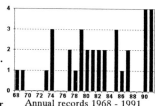
Annual records 1968 - 1991

Since 1968 there have been 34 records of single birds with
a maximum annual total of 4 birds. They are shown on a
seasonal histogram. The increase in the number of records is
paralleled by the increase in the Scottish breeding population.
The birds have all been found at the well-watched lakes, or
flying over. Their visits are normally brief, but one bird was
present in the Willen-Linford area from 7 Sep-13 Oct 1991.

Kestrel
Falco tinnunculus

Breeds throughout the county, resident and partial migrant.

In the early part of the century the Kestrel suffered persecution by keepers, but shooting and nest robbing no longer pose a major threat. In fact, the bird is popular with farmers and landowners, and many now actively encourage it. Kestrels were affected by the pesticide problems of the 1960s, but much less severely than the Sparrowhawk, presumably because their more varied diet did not concentrate the organochlorine residues so intensely.

The Kestrel is essentially a raptor of open ground, which in Buckinghamshire means mainly farmland. Valuable habitat is also provided by road verges, gravel pit surrounds, marginal areas of rough grass, and woodland edges adjoining farmland such as abound in the Chilterns.

Most prey is taken from the ground. Rodent numbers have a significant effect on breeding success, though much less so here than, for example, in the Scottish Borders. Moderating the effect of rodent fluctuations is the more dependable food source provided by newly fledged Starlings and House Sparrows. Pellets and kill-remains at nests show these to be the principal food source for Kestrel nestlings at most sites in the county.

Another vital habitat feature is the availability of nest sites. Like all falcons, Kestrels make no nest but use various natural sites, tree cavities being the predominant choice in the county. Old crows' nests, bale ricks and farm buildings are also used, but less frequently than in some parts of England. Where elms were dominant, extensive felling following Dutch elm disease has probably reduced breeding density. In one such area in the county a network of Kestrel nest boxes has proved highly successful, providing sites for the majority of breeding pairs over some 200 sq km. Fieldwork in the Vale of Aylesbury from 1981 to 1986 indicated a density of 9-10 breeding pairs per 100 sq km, perhaps 11-12 in a good year. Figures for the Chilterns are harder to establish, due to the difficulty of locating all pairs in this habitat, but data so far suggest perhaps 12-15 per 100 sq km in an average year. Both figures are far below the densities suggested in the Breeding Atlas, which appear to be a considerable overestimate for most parts of Britain (Village 1990).

The start of breeding is spread over 5-6 weeks, with extreme first-egg dates ranging from 12 April (1985, near Amersham) to 2 June (1986, near Winslow). Early clutches are larger on

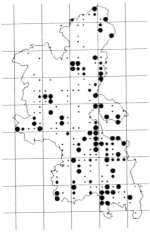

1,000 pairs

average than late ones. Intensive monitoring since 1981 (Burton 1993) has shown that Kestrels breeding in the Chilterns consistently start earlier and produce larger average clutches and broods than those in the Vale. In most years the former generally start before the end of April and Vale birds from early May onwards. This presumably reflects a difference in habitat quality, perhaps related to the greater extent of woodland edge in the Chilterns. Fledging is correspondingly spread out, from early June to the end of July. In two years, 1984 and 1985, cold wet weather in late May and early June severely reduced breeding success. Newly fledged young generally spend some time in the nesting locality, attended by their parents, but a few long distance recoveries occur within 4-5 weeks of fledging. Possibly these are birds which become separated too early from the family group and keep on moving in deteriorating condition.

Mortality in the first autumn appears even higher than in the Sparrowhawk; of 77 recoveries of local Kestrels since 1978, 37 have occurred within 100 days of ringing. Preliminary analysis of recoveries of Kestrels ringed in the county reveals an interesting pattern. There are many recoveries under 50 km and over 100 km, but surprisingly few between 50 and 100 km. Intriguingly, those under 50 km show a north-east bias, while those over 100 km show a south-west bias. Possibly land immediately to the north-east provides better winter habitat than that in other directions. Certainly, E England is an important wintering area, as shown by the Winter Atlas. Recovery distances in other directions can be considerable. Recoveries over 200 km away include 12 in Spain (Bilbao and Zaragoza), five in France, several in Wales, and two in N England. By winter, many locally-bred young Kestrels have moved out of the county, while others have moved in. Older birds mostly remain near their breeding places, and some nest sites serve as roosts throughout the year. Precise hunting areas alter in line with the changing pattern of farm work through the winter (Shrubb 1980). Recoveries in autumn and winter are mainly of birds found dead in poor condition, with relatively fewer accidental deaths than in the Sparrowhawk. Accidents that do occur commonly involve drowning in farm water troughs, and collisions with cars or trains. One unfortunate local bird ended up on the track in Euston station, presumably having been carried there by the train which killed it.

Diving and grappling courtship displays can be observed as early as January, reaching a peak in March and early April. For some established pairs with a well situated traditional site, nest selection is a foregone conclusion; one such site in the Vale has been used successfully for at least eight consecutive years. Others find their site, if at all, only just before breeding (Village 1990). The number of these marginal pairs (often first-year birds) varies from year to year, as does the average starting date, which may differ between seasons by as much as ten days. In most years, a few pairs occupy sites without actually nesting in them. More detailed discussion of the factors involved is to be found in Cavé (1968), Snow (1968), and Village (1990).

PJKB

Red-footed Falcon
Falco vespertinus

Very rare vagrant. Only one reliable record.

1983: 1 male on 27 Jul, Woughton, Milton Keynes.

A record of one shot in January 1858 at Steeple Claydon has a remarkable date which must cast considerable doubt on its authenticity. The more recent record has a more typical date for this East European species.

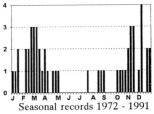

Seasonal records 1972 - 1991

Annual records 1972 - 1991

Merlin
Falco columbarius

Rare winter visitor and passage migrant in small numbers.

The status of Merlins has probably remained unchanged this century. Since 1972 there have been 51 records, all of single birds. There is a small passage in March and again in September and October, but most birds have been seen in winter. They have been recorded throughout the county.

Many sightings are very brief and this has resulted in a high proportion of reports being rejected. Some of these are quite clearly not Merlins, but probably male Sparrowhawks, but equally it is known that there are other reports of probable Merlins not in the county records at all.

Hobby
Falco subbuteo

Uncommon breeding summer visitor. As this species is known to suffer from the activities of egg collectors locally a map is not included.

Historical records indicate that the Hobby has long been a breeding bird in Buckinghamshire and adjacent counties, and also that it was often persecuted in the past. Clark Kennedy notes that a pair nested in a wood near Datchet in 1861 and that the young birds were shot almost as soon as they had learnt to fly, and H & R state that an adult pair was shot in August 1894 near Long Marston, Hertfordshire, close to the Buckinghamshire border. F & Y describe the species as a very scarce breeder, though this assessment was made before any thorough fieldwork had been done.

Recent fieldwork has revealed that breeding Hobbies are widely distributed within the county with no particular concentrations. Pairs were found breeding both on farmland and in woodland. Many pairs have been found in 10-km squares of the national grid where they were not found during the survey for the Breeding Atlas, but this is more likely to be an indication of better coverage than an actual increase in numbers. Hobbies can be very elusive during the breeding season and birds may be seen only rarely, even in areas where they are known to be breeding. They appear to spend the day perched unobtrusively in trees or hunting at high altitude. Taking this into account it is almost certain that many breeding pairs remained undetected, even in tetrads which received a comparatively thorough coverage. Breeding was proved in 4% of Buckinghamshire's tetrads with probable or possible breeding in a further 10%. A conservative estimate of 2.5 pairs per 100 sq km suggests a county population of some 48 pairs.

The first spring migrants generally arrive in the county during the first week of May although they are occasionally recorded in April, usually near reservoirs or other large water bodies. Pairs are usually on breeding territories by the second week of May and it is at this time that they are fairly vocal and perform spectacular aerial displays.

The Hobby lays its eggs in the disused nests of other species, especially those of the Carrion Crow. In Buckinghamshire it does not appear to have any preference for particular tree species, with the proportion of crow nests used in each of them being directly proportional to the availability of nests in that species (Fuller et al 1985). Several sites in the county were used in successive years during the survey period, and one was used for at least four consecutive years. Fuller et al (1985) refer to a breeding pair which used the same site in 1982 as was used by Hobbies in the late nineteenth century.

Young Hobbies usually fledge about mid August. Fledged young are often very noisy, particularly when following an adult with food. Family groups are sometimes active after sunset but it can be very difficult to observe what prey, if any, is being pursued then. They have been recorded taking bats (MTNHS 1965), and young birds have been observed to spend long periods on the ground attempting to catch insects (P J Stevens and G J F Marsh). Feathers collected from plucking points at four nest sites in the south of the county indicated that Swifts were the main prey species there. In the autumn, Hobbies are frequently seen at Swallow roosts bordering the county. Tring Reservoirs and Slough SF, for example, have been regular haunts, with several occasionally recorded on the same evening. Hobbies are known to travel up to 10 km in search of food (R J Fuller and R A Morgan), so it is possible that Swallow roosts attract birds from a wide area.

Family groups do not generally begin to disperse until mid September and most birds have departed by the end of the month, although birds are occasionally reported near nest sites in early October. There is one very late record of a bird near Old Slade NR on 10 Nov 1979. A nestling ringed in the south of the county on 1 Aug 1984 was found dead at Beckingham, Lincolnshire on 10 Oct 1984, while another nestling ringed in the county was trapped in Kreiss Beeskow, Germany on 6 Aug 1985. The latter is the most easterly record for a British-bred Hobby.

PJS

Peregrine
Falco peregrinus

Scarce migrant.

Between 1848 and 1919 there were 10 records, then there were at least 13 until 1957. Between 1957 and 1991 there were 17 records, mostly during the winter. The Vale of Aylesbury seems to be the favoured area. Recent sites have included Eythrope, Hartwell, and Drayton Parslow. The increasing regularity of the records corresponds with the increase in the British breeding population.

Red-legged Partridge
Alectoris rufa

Fairly common introduced resident.

The first recorded introduction of this bird from south-west Europe was in 1673 when birds were released in Windsor Great Park. After 1830 a large number of releases were made. By 1835 they were established at Stokenchurch and by 1920 they had increased sufficiently for H & J to describe them as 'locally common'.

The map shows a widespread though discontinuous distribution in the Vale of Aylesbury and the north-east of the county with very few in the Chilterns. In contrast to the Grey Partridge, whose map shows a widespread distribution in the south, Red-legged Partridges are rather uncommon in this area. Red-legged Partridges prefer drier habitats and this may be reflected in their distribution.

During the 1950s the population declined but this has been masked by birds bred in game farms being released. The decline can be attributed in part to the reduction in the amount of cover required for nesting. Red-legged Partridges leave their eggs uncovered during laying, so they need to build their

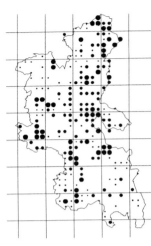

1,500 pairs

nests in cover if they are not to be predated. The amount of suitable cover has been reduced because of hedge removal and changes in cropping patterns. Another factor in the decline in numbers is the increased use of insecticides and herbicides which has reduced the numbers of insects available for the young, although this is less of a requirement than it is with Grey Partridges. The recent method of leaving wide unploughed, unsprayed field boundaries is beneficial to the species.

Unusual nest sites have included a 6 m high straw stack at Loughton in 1899, and one next to a Barn Owl's nest at Beaconsfield in the 1960s. Roosting under house eaves has been recorded at Mentmore (A G Knox), and Buckland Common (Dowson, pers comm), while males calling from the tops of barns is not uncommon, for instance at The Lee, as is calling in the night in the breeding season. A strange record is of a bird which frequented the compound of Aylesbury Prison in 1986. Broods of downy young were recorded at Hughenden in September 1989. The largest recorded coveys have been of 30 birds at Pitstone on 1 Dec 1984 and Dorney Common on 3 Nov 1985. Large coveys have also been recorded at Oakley.

The birds are considered to give poor sport compared to Grey Partridges. They tend to run rather than fly, and to explode, unlike Grey Partridges, whose coveys pack together.

Red-legged Partridges hybridise with the introduced Chukar. This is discussed under the latter species (p.298).

SC

Grey Partridge
Perdix perdix

Fairly common but decreasing resident.

It is evident from the numbers recorded in the game books of country estates that Grey Partridges were much commoner in the 19th century and the early years of this century than they are now. The game book of the Dashwood Estate, West Wycombe records that 192 Grey Partridges were shot between 14 and 23 Sep 1872. On The Lee Estate, an area of c700 hectares near Great Missenden, 355 Grey Partridges were shot between 1925 and 1933. They were much more numerous than Common Pheasants and were known as 'the poor man's pheasant'. Indeed they were common enough to be the subject of some advanced gastronomy. Partridge Salmi combined

102

goose liver, truffles, chopped lemon, and Madeira, and was served in a silver casserole! Since the Second World War there has been a considerable decline in numbers. For instance none has been seen at The Lee since the 1970s, although 1970 and 1976 were considered comparatively good years in the south of the county. The map shows a discontinuous distribution with most birds in the south and the Vale of Aylesbury. Grey Partridges are birds of arable fields with hedgerows, but they do occasionally occur in woods with clearings and rides, such as Little Hampden and Homefield Wood.

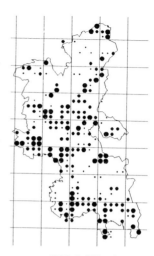

1986: 2,000 pairs
1991: 500 pairs

The decline has a number of causes. The break up of country estates and lack of keepering has increased the amount of nest predation, while the removal of hedgerows and bramble clearance has reduced the nesting area so that the nests are closer together and thus easier for predators to find. These factors account for about half the post-1940 decrease. The other half is due to the use of herbicides and insecticides which has decimated the population of insects upon which the chicks feed in June. The disappearance of winter stubbles and old stack yards which were frequented in hard weather must also be a factor. Modern farming practice, whereby silage replaces hay, is another cause. Silage has a dense, lush grass and is frequently cut, and is thus a difficult feeding ground (O'Connor and Shrubb 1986).

The mapping and the national Common Birds Census data give a population in the county of 2,000 pairs in 1986. The population in 1990 may be no more than 500 pairs.

The large area of set-aside in the county since the late 1980s is not thought to be useful for breeding gamebirds. The vegetation structure is such that young chicks become readily soaked and these open areas allow easy viewing for aerial predators. Partridge parents are more likely to take their chicks into a cereal crop, even if the insect supply there is lower (Game Conservancy Trust, pers comm). The Trust considers that the Conservation Headland scheme, whereby edges of arable fields have restricted spraying of pesticides is of much greater benefit to the birds. This enterprise may well result in a recovery of the species.

SC

Quail

Coturnix coturnix

Rare summer visitor which occasionally breeds.

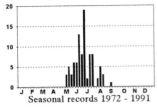

Seasonal records 1972 - 1991

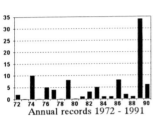

Annual records 1972 - 1991

There appears to have been a decline in the Quail's fortunes towards the end of the 19th century. Clark Kennedy wrote 'a visitor in spring and autumn...the majority are shot in either May or September... a few are killed near Drayton Beauchamp almost every September.' The mention of this village refers to the presence there of Clark Kennedy's correspondent, the Rev. Harpur Crewe, and not for any particular liking of the birds for this locality. The impression given is that Quails were regular passage migrants through the county in small numbers.

In 1920 H & J stated 'now very rare summer resident', a comment that still holds true. A few are heard almost every year and occasionally larger numbers are recorded. In 1970 about 20 were heard calling in fields around Wolverton, while a few other birds were scattered around the county. The next large invasion took place in 1989 when about 34 birds were recorded at 20 sites.

The seasonal histogram clearly shows that birds begin to appear in early May, peak in June, and are gone by September, or have stopped calling. There is no evidence of the passage hinted at by Clark Kennedy. Birds can turn up in arable land almost anywhere in the county, but there may be a preference for certain areas. A bird was recorded at Dorney in five years between 1952 and 1966, while the Pitstone/ Ivinghoe Beacon area has recorded birds since Clark Kennedy's time. The Milton Keynes area has also had a number of records. There appears to be an association with fields of barley.

Breeding does not seem to have been proven in Buckinghamshire, but was possible at Coleshill in 1950, Monks Risborough in 1965, and Sherington in 1982. A covey at Monks Risborough on 23 Oct 1965 is the latest record.

Almost all of the records refer to calling birds. Quails are very secretive and are rarely seen. It is possible that most are single males and not breeding birds. They are known to travel considerable distances and may therefore cause duplication of records.

DMF

Pheasant
Phasianus colchicus

Common introduced resident.

The subspecies *P.c.colchicus* from the Caucasus was probably introduced to Britain in the late 11th century as a cagebird, although introduction may have been as late as the 14th century. By the 16th century it had become fairly well established. In the 18th century *P.c.torquatus*, which has a white neck-ring, was introduced from China. The Dowager Duchess of Portland brought some to Bulstrode Park, near Gerrards Cross, at this time, and in 1900 Lord Rothschild introduced birds into the county. H & J mention other subspecies being introduced and also *P. versicolor*, the Japanese Pheasant. It can be safely assumed that all these variations are now hybridised.

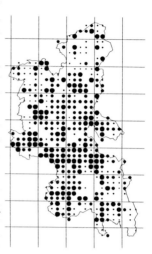

5,000 pairs

Artificial rearing of Pheasants is widely practised in Buckinghamshire. Pheasant pens and feeders are a common sight in the Chilterns and in the woods in the Vale of Aylesbury, and these undoubtedly keep the population at an artificially high level. Many Pheasants are reared on country estates and farms holding syndicated shoots, where keepers remove the eggs and hatch them in incubators. In addition, poults are bought from game farms and reared in pens, and fed with corn after they are released, mainly to keep them from straying onto neighbours' land. In the early years of this century, pheasant farming was a rural industry. Those who tended them lived in shepherd's huts in the rearing field which had wire netting enclosures for the birds known as keep pens. This artificial rearing was carried out at The Lee and Prestwood among other places.

The map shows gaps in the Chilterns and in the north of the county, but these are certainly due to under-recording. It is likely that every wood in the county holds the species. In areas where artificial rearing is practised the population density can be up to eight times that of areas where there is no artificial rearing. This makes estimating populations particularly difficult. Mapping and the national Common Birds Census data gives a population of 5,000 pairs.

Food consists of a wide variety of fruits and berries, and it is said that they are the only birds to eat Deadly Nightshade, though Dr David Snow reports that despite hours of watching in the hills above Kimble, he did not see any berries taken.

SC

Golden Pheasant
Chrysolophus pictus

Introduced or escaped in very small numbers. Recent releases may have led to feral breeding.

The spectacular coloration of the male makes the Golden Pheasant a popular bird in collections. It is likely that all the records up to 1987 refer to birds that have escaped from collections rather than truly feral birds. All the records up to 1987 are listed.

1976: 1 on 2 May, Bow Brickhill.
1977: 3 heard on 8 May, Burnham Beeches.
1977: 1 male on 24 Jul, Brickhills.
1979: 1 male on 11 Apr, Burnham.
1979: 1 male on 9 Jul, Homefield Wood.
1982: 1 on 25 Apr, Rush Green, near Iver.
1987: 1 male on 25 Mar, Downley Common.

The preponderance of records in spring may be due to the fact that these secretive birds are more obvious at this time of the year.

Birds were released at Taplow Court around 1987 and it is possible that they are now breeding ferally at this locality. Smaller numbers of birds were also released at Winchbottom in late 1990 or early 1991.

DMF

Lady Amherst's Pheasant
Chrysolophus amherstiae

Very local introduced resident.

Although Lady Amherst's Pheasants were brought to England in 1828 it was not until around 1900 that they were released at Woburn. The birds gradually spread from the estate until the western edge of their range became the Brickhill Woods. Birds were released at Mentmore in 1930 and maintained a small population until the late 1960s. In the 1930s birds were released at Whipsnade and these spread to the nearby Ashridge Estate. The species was admitted to the British list in 1971.

The birds inhabit young conifer woods which have reached the stage where the undergrowth has thinned following canopy closure. Rhododendron thickets are also favoured.

Lady Amherst's Pheasants are exceptionally wary and are

usually located by the call of the male, which is heard in the morning and evening. When disturbed, they prefer to run and hide rather than fly. Their value as sporting birds is nil.

Very little is known of their breeding biology. Indeed there is no record of a nest ever having being found in the county. Proof of breeding is confined to sightings of broods of young birds.

The population is very small and appears to be decreasing. There are no records for Ashridge since 1985, or Mentmore since the 1960s. The population in the Buckinghamshire Brickhills may not amount to more than a dozen pairs, but the difficulties of locating the birds make this no more than a guess. The largest number recorded was 20 calling males on 2 May 1976. Single birds have also been recorded at Hambleden and Winchbottom; these were presumably escapes from collections or deliberate releases.

The decline in Buckinghamshire is paralleled by a similar decline in neighbouring Bedfordshire, which holds the main population. The reasons appear to be habitat changes, cold winters, and wet springs (Bedfordshire Nat 42, 1988).

Lady Amherst's Pheasants, like Mandarin Ducks, have suffered a considerable decline in their native China. The small British population of around 150 pairs is thus assuming some importance. It is, however, under threat, although this is probably not the case locally. Golden Pheasants freely hybridise with Lady Amherst's Pheasants and any of the latter released into an area already containing Golden Pheasants soon disappear as the latter seem to be genetically dominant. No large-scale introduction has taken place in Buckinghamshire of Golden Pheasants so that the local population of Lady Amherst's Pheasants has survived in a relatively pure state.

10 pairs

DMF

107

Water Rail
Rallus aquaticus

Very local resident and winter visitor in small numbers.

The specialised habitat requirements of Water Rails have meant that the species has probably always been a very local breeder in Buckinghamshire. Clark Kennedy described Water Rails as 'not very plentiful, but specimens have been killed at all times of the year'. He mentioned Chesham, Drayton Beauchamp, and Aylesbury as sites. H & J commented 'not uncommon winter visitor; resident in very small numbers.' No nests had been found in Buckinghamshire, though two nests had been discovered near Wraysbury (then in the county) in 1896.

The only locality where the species is known to breed regularly is Weston Turville Reservoir where the extensive reed beds provide an ideal habitat. There are usually 2 or 3 pairs present, although in 1965 6 to 10 pairs were thought to have bred. The only other site where breeding has been proven since 1947 is Old Slade where breeding took place in 1970. The species is not difficult to locate in the spring when its loud nocturnal calls reveal its presence, but breeding may be difficult to prove. The most productive method is to watch at dusk when the adults may be seen with young birds at the water's edge. The county breeding survey revealed only one tetrad where breeding was proven, although there were another 9 tetrads where birds were present. It is possible that breeding may have taken place at some of these sites.

The tiny local population is probably secure. Weston Turville Reservoir and Old Slade are nature reserves, but Shardeloes and Chesham Waterside, which are important sites for wintering birds, and may hold breeding birds, are fed by the Rivers Misbourne and Chess respectively. These two rivers are subject to excessive extraction by the water utilities, and the sites are liable to dry up.

During the winter, birds are more widespread. Overgrown canals, ditches, and even gardens may be utilised as well as larger wetland sites such as Shardeloes, Calvert, and Caldecotte. The largest number recorded at one site during the winter is 11 at Shardeloes in February 1969, while Waterside, Chesham has held up to 10 birds. National ringing data suggest that many of these birds originate from continental Europe, although there have been no ringing recoveries involving Buckinghamshire birds.

DMF

Spotted Crake
Porzana porzana

Very rare vagrant. All records are given.

There is an undated record from High Wycombe in Clark Kennedy, and both he and H & R note several records by the River Thames. They are however with no date or localities and are probably in Berkshire.

1897: 1 Olney.
1925: 1 on 7 Feb, Westhorpe, Little Marlow.
1980: 1 on 19 Aug, Old Slade.

Corncrake
Crex crex

Very rare migrant. Formerly a breeding summer visitor.

The decline of the Corncrake in Buckinghamshire began in the second half of the 19th century. Clark Kennedy described its status as 'very numerous', but H & J wrote 'not now common. Only a few pairs in the Thames Valley.' By 1947 Price was writing 'summer visitor in decreasing numbers.'

Since then the records are:

1948: 1 heard several times in the breeding season, Hambleden.
1949: 1 calling all summer, Fulmer.
1952: 1 on 29 Aug, Ivinghoe.
1957: 1 calling 26 Jun, near Ickford.
1959: adult with 8 chicks 16 Aug, Haversham. Last seen 4 Oct.
1959: 1 from 25-27 Aug, Hyde Heath/Great Pednor.
1960: 1 on 17 Apr, Newport Pagnell GPs.
1960: 1 on 4 Jun, Great Linford GPs.
1960: 1 on 2 Aug, Haversham.
1961: 1 in Jul-Aug, Great Pednor.
1961: 1 from 15 May-10 Jun, Haversham. 2 were present on the last date.
1974: 2 heard on 14 Sep, Newton Longville.
1985: 1 calling from 25-30 Jun, Shipton Lee.

The decline of Corncrakes in the county parallels its decline in the country as a whole. The process began in the south-east of England in the second half of the 19th century and is still continuing in its last breeding areas, Ireland and the Western Isles.

The cause of the decline has been well studied. The primary habitat of Corncrakes is hay fields which need to remain uncut until the young are fledged. Mechanisation of hay cutting has had two effects: first, the machines do not allow the birds to escape so easily as hand-cutting did, and second, mechanisation, together with increased fertiliser input, enables cutting to take place earlier in the year. This means nests have a greater chance of being destroyed. Improved grasslands, which have largely replaced traditional hay fields, have a limited insect population, and are thus unattractive to Corncrakes, while it has recently become clear that the birds require tall, rank vegetation when they first arrive, a habitat that has all but disappeared with modern agricultural practices (Cadbury 1980).

With a British population of under 600 birds, 90% of which are in the Hebrides, it is unlikely that Corncrakes will ever be other than a very rare migrant in the county.

DMF

Moorhen
Gallinula chloropus

Common resident and winter visitor.

The Moorhen is found everywhere near water as long as some cover is available. Their status appears not to have changed much, if at all, since the 1850s.

In Buckinghamshire even the smallest water may harbour a few Moorhens. It is conceivable that when the Ouse valley was mainly swampland they were more a bird of reeds, but they do seem to be able to adapt to changing circumstances and readily associate with man. To a certain extent they complement the Coot: Moorhens prefer smaller waters while Coots are mainly found at the larger lakes.

The main concentrations of breeding birds are along streams, rivers and canals, but there are also many breeding records from wet ditches and small farm ponds. The introduction of piped water for livestock has meant that many farm ponds are no longer used and have been filled in, which may have led to a reduction in the Moorhen population. However, the species is still numerous in most parts of the county, though the map suggests that there are fewer in the Chilterns than elsewhere, presumably due to the lack of ponds and ditches on the chalky soil.

The Moorhen is remarkably adaptable when breeding. Nests

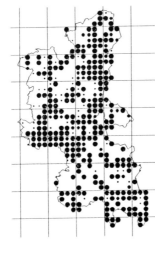

3,000 pairs

110

can be found at the waterside at ground level as well as quite high in bushes. Second and third broods often occur, particularly if the first one is destroyed, and it is common for females to dump eggs in the nests of other Moorhens.

Birds do move around a little but never go very far. The most distant recovery involving Buckinghamshire is of 81 km (from Surrey), although it is known that some birds bred on the Continent occur in Britain.

In winter, Moorhens can form small feeding flocks, but there are no major concentrations and the species only rarely gets a specific mention in BBC reports. The largest count reported in the 1980s was of 140 at Old Slade on 17 Oct 1982. The species may suffer quite heavily in hard winters and it is a fairly regular road casualty. A leucistic bird was seen on a pond at Gayhurst House on 18 Jul 1988.

NHFS

Coot
Fulica atra

Common resident and winter visitor.

The status of the Coot does not seem to have changed much since the 1850s. Earlier authors all considered it a fairly numerous breeding bird on ponds and lakes in the county, with numbers augmented considerably in winter.

It is clear from the breeding distribution map that the Coot is widespread in the county but much more restricted than the Moorhen to larger waters. The old gravel pits and other lakes in the north of the county, together with all the main rivers - Ouse, Thame, Chess and Thames - form the main breeding areas. Deeper water with a plentiful supply of submerged plants is a necessity, and many of the older gravel pits and other mineral workings are favoured. The Coot's breeding requirements are more conservative than those of the Moorhen, with nests nearly always over water.

In winter large numbers of birds arrive from the Continent, the intensity and timing of influxes apparently being linked to climatic conditions there. Waters such as Linford, Willen, and Caldecotte regularly hold 300-400 birds throughout the winter, and over 800 were recorded at Willen in November 1982 and December 1987. The south of the county usually holds rather fewer birds.

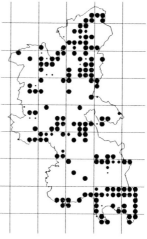

500 pairs

Coots which breed in Britain are mostly sedentary although local movements do occur. The farthest recorded by ringing

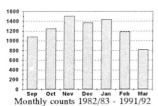

Monthly counts 1982/83 - 1991/92

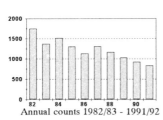

Annual counts 1982/83 - 1991/92

Coot

recoveries affecting Buckinghamshire is of a bird moving to Kent. There is no evidence of autumn moulting concentrations in the county.

NHFS

Crane
Grus grus

Very rare vagrant. There has been one record.

1987: adult or first-winter on 11 Jan, flying west over Withybridge (Slough) and two hours later over Dorney Common.

These two were originally accepted as two individuals (adult over Withybridge and first winter over Dorney Common) but there is clearly a strong possibility of only one bird being involved.

Waders

Of the 39 species of waders that have been recorded in Buckinghamshire only three are present throughout the year: Lapwing, Snipe, and Woodcock. Of these, Snipe are present in the breeding season in very small numbers and may no longer breed regularly. Four are breeding summer visitors: Ringed Plover, Little Ringed Plover, Curlew, and Redshank. Stone-curlews used to breed in small numbers but they became extinct in the mid 1960s and are now very rare vagrants.

Of the 31 species that have never bred in the county, three are regular winter visitors: Golden Plover, Jack Snipe, and Green Sandpiper. The first winters in the Vale of Aylesbury in flocks of several hundred, a discovery that was made during the 1970s. The other two species are found in very small numbers. Most records of Green Sandpipers in the county are of passage migrants.

The remaining 28 species are only recorded as either passage migrants or vagrants. Three have always been regular migrants: Dunlin, Greenshank, and Common Sandpiper, while ten are rare vagrants: Black-winged Stilt, Dotterel, Kentish Plover, American Golden Plover, Pectoral Sandpiper, Purple Sandpiper, Great Snipe, Lesser Yellowlegs, Grey Phalarope, and Red-necked Phalarope. It is noteworthy that seven were not recorded until at least 1976.

The mid 1970s were significant for many of the remaining

15 species. Only Ruff has more than four records prior to1974, and even this now frequently recorded species was not seen until 1959. All 15 are now recorded annually.

The reasons for this change are worth analysing. First, as with all birds, the increase in the number of observers has led to an increase in the number of observations. Second, the standard of bird identification has improved, and third, good quality telescopes did not become widely used until the early 1970s. The last two points may be significant to the identification of a group such as the waders which is notoriously difficult to identify and typically inhabits stretches of distant mud, although it must be said that there has been an equivalent increase in the number of records of Oystercatchers, a large, obvious species. Fourth, and perhaps of the most importance, a significant increase in the amount of suitable habitat for passage waders took place in Buckinghamshire in the mid 1970s.

In 1975 the south basin of Willen Lake was filled, followed in 1978 by the filling of the north basin. Work began at the gravel pits at Linford in the 1950s, but the bulk of the gravel was extracted between 1970 and 1984. These two sites are now the most important in the county for passage waders. In the early 1980s Stony Stratford Wildlife Conservation Area and Caldecotte Lake were created, although these sites are less

Willen Lake

important for waders. Altogether, the sites in the north of the county account for 88% of the records of the rarer migrant waders. Without these areas of wetland many waders would be very rare or unrecorded in Buckinghamshire.

The middle of the county includes Calvert Brick Pits, Weston Turville Res, and College Lake, while the south includes Shardeloes Lake, Chesham cress beds, Marlow GPs, and Old Slade Nature Reserve. These sites record only a few passage waders each year.

The sites mentioned cover more than 90% of the wader records in the county. The accounts assume that these are the sites involved, so they are not often mentioned. Less usual sites, such as flooded fields, are commented on.

Many wader sites are transient. For example, Hartigan's Pit, which was, in the 1950s, one of the most important wader sites in the county, no longer exists, while even the permanent sites can vary in their suitability from year to year. Thus Stony Stratford produced a number of wader records in the early 1980s, but a decade later, this site rarely features in the annual report. Similarly the chalk pit at Pitstone is now unsuitable for waders after a period when regular passage took place. The lakes at Willen and Caldecotte have become increasingly developed to the extent that there is now a road between the two basins at Willen, while the bays on the east side of Caldecotte now have vertical sides. On the other hand, College Lake Wildlife Centre, which did not exist until the late 1980s, is being managed, among other things, to provide areas of suitable mud, and is showing early promise.

The numbers of passage waders recorded in the county are very small relative to the numbers recorded in adjacent counties, particularly in the Thames basin and along the valley of the River Nene. It is likely that the county is peripheral to the main route by which waders cross England. Nevertheless, the waders that are recorded here can only be a small fraction of the total numbers that fly over the county, perhaps chiefly at night.

DMF

Oystercatcher
Haematopus ostralegus

Formerly rare, but now a regular migrant in very small numbers.

There are 6 records prior to 1975.:

1953: 1 on 24 Apr, Marlow GPs.
1957: 1 on 6 Aug, Hartigan's Pit, near Broughton.
1958: 2 on 10 Aug, over Drayton Beauchamp.
1961: heard 22 Jul, over Weston Turville Res.
1961: 1 on 2 Sep, over Weston Turville Res.
1968: 1 on 16 Oct, Hedgerley.

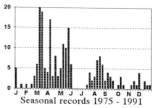
Seasonal records 1975 - 1991

Since 1975 there have been 108 records of 202 birds. They are shown on the histograms. Most records are of single birds, but a flock of 12-14 birds was at Little Marlow on 24 Dec 1987, and one of 9 birds was at Caldecotte on 4 Mar 1990. 161 birds were recorded in the north of the county, 28 in the middle, and 13 in the south. The increase in the number of records may be due to the increase in the British breeding population.

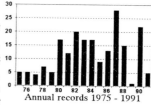
Annual records 1975 - 1991

The interesting double peak in the spring may be caused by different populations passing through the county. The birds breeding in the west and south-west of the European range return earlier than those breeding in the east.

Black-winged Stilt
Himantopus himantopus

Very rare vagrant. There has been one record.

1988: a pair of first-summer birds, 7-18 Jun, Willen. Copulation was observed on the 9th.

This is a typical date for this Mediterranean species.

Avocet
Recurvirostra avosetta

Rare vagrant. All records are given.

1975: 6 on 18 May, Linford.
1976: 1 on 21 Nov, Willen.
1979: 1 on 17 Jun, Willen.
1983: 24 on 27 Mar, Willen.
1984: 1 on 13 Mar, Marlow.
1984: 1 on 24 Mar, Willen.

Although an increase since the mid 1970s is a typical pattern for the rarer waders in Buckinghamshire, there is no doubt that the increase in the British breeding population has contributed. The flock in 1983 is an exceptional record for inland Britain.

Stone-curlew
Burhinus oedicnemus

Very rare migrant; formerly a local summer visitor.

Even in Clark Kennedy's time Stone-curlews were in decline. He states that they 'used to be numerous in the vicinity of Ivinghoe and Drayton Beauchamp'. Other sites apparently still used then included Aylesbury, Buckingham and Chesham. By the time of H & J they were in 'greatly reduced numbers, breeding very locally.' They seemed to have suffered a considerable decrease around 1910. Before this date they were numerous in the Skirmett/Turville Heath area and also bred at Fawley Park and Saunderton. In 1947 Price wrote 'regular summer visitor, breeding locally'. Since then there have been only four breeding records: in 1950 at Fingest, in 1956 at Wormsley, in 1959 again at Fingest, and again there in 1964. Between 1950 and 1967 birds were seen or heard at Saunderton, Fawley, High Wycombe, and Northend. It is unlikely that they bred at these localities.

There then followed a gap until a bird was recorded in late June and early July 1984 at a potential breeding site in the Chilterns, and the following year a bird was seen on 23 May at Caldecotte. This is the latest record.

As a bird on the north-western edge of its range it is likely that temperature is one of the limiting factors of its distribution. It may be significant that the birds slowly disappeared from the Chilterns first in the north around Ivinghoe and lastly in the south around Fingest and Wormsley.

But the major cause of the extinction is loss of habitat. Stone-curlews are birds of dry open spaces. In the county they occurred typically on Chilterns chalk grassland heavily grazed by sheep or rabbits. Sheep rearing has decreased considerably in the Chilterns and rabbits were decimated by myxomatosis during the 1950s. This has resulted in the chalk grassland becoming covered in scrub and thus unsuitable for Stone-curlews. This, coupled with ploughing, has reduced the amount of unimproved chalk grassland in Buckinghamshire to less than 300 ha. Because of public access very little of this is suitable for Stone-curlews. Many of the British breeding birds now nest on arable land, the chicks hatching in late May before the crop is harvested.

Stone-curlews are summer migrants. They arrive in Britain in March or early April and leave in September and October. There are two remarkable ringing records involving local birds. A nestling ringed at Fingest on 12 Jun 1959 was recovered at Landes, France on 14 Oct 1961, while its sibling, ringed three days later, was shot at Guipuzcoa, Spain on 31 Oct 1959.

DMF

Little Ringed Plover
Charadrius dubius

Summer visitor, breeding regularly in small numbers.

The Little Ringed Plover was first recorded breeding in the UK at the adjacent Tring Reservoirs (Herts) in 1938. In 1948 there was a sighting of this species at Slough STW which was then in Buckinghamshire. Breeding was first recorded in the

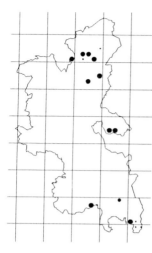

12 pairs

county at Marlow GPs with a nest and three eggs being found on 9 Jun 1949. Unfortunately this breeding attempt failed. Breeding occurred elsewhere in the county in 1953 (MTNHS). In 1976 F & Y described the species as 'breeding regularly in very small numbers throughout the area'. Since then the status has not changed significantly, the numbers no doubt being limited by suitable breeding habitat and perhaps competition with Ringed Plovers.

The distribution map essentially shows almost all the suitable breeding habitat in the county at the present time, this typically being flooded gravel workings where exposed areas of gravel provide the preferred nesting conditions. They also breed near more mature lakes where flat stony areas exist, particularly if a secluded nest site is available. Since the fieldwork was carried out at least one other site in the south of the county is now regularly used as well as the site at Old Slade (in the very south-east corner of the county). On the debit side the site just east of Slough has been lost as well as the site south-east of Beaconsfield which is now a landfill site. The preference for fresh gravelly areas can lead to pairs setting up territories in areas of active gravel workings, this sometimes leading to breeding failure as work progresses. The species is however known to replace lost clutches readily, sometimes up to three times (Parrinder 1964). Breeding success may also be affected by the presence of the more dominant Ringed Plover in the northern and central parts of the county.

Birds are usually seen in the county from the end of March (exceptionally from 10th March) with breeding territories being formed shortly after. The last records in autumn are typically the second and third weeks in September but exceptionally into early October. Small flocks can occur on passage, most often in April and May when up to 11 birds have been seen together. On leaving their breeding grounds many Little Ringed Plovers move south through France and down the east coast of Spain before crossing to North Africa and eventually reaching their winter quarters south of the Sahara (BWP).

JER

Ringed Plover
Charadrius hiaticula

Passage migrant and regular breeding bird in very small numbers.

H & J stated, using data based upon observations at the Tring Reservoirs, that the Ringed Plover was a 'regular bird of passage' with greater numbers seen in the autumn. However they do add 'used to occur not infrequently along the banks of the Thames'. Ringed Plovers remain a regular passage migrant within the county.

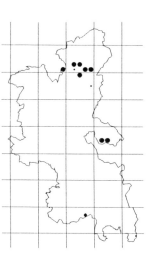

15 pairs

The first breeding record for the county was in 1975 at Willen Lake. Since that time a regular breeding population has built up in the north of the county and also at College Lake. This increase is very much in line with the national trend (Marchant et al 1990)

Ringed Plovers breed on areas of gravel or shingle adjacent to lakes or gravel pits and a large proportion of the county's population breeds on nature reserves or in protected areas such as Linford GP complex, Willen Lake, Stony Stratford NR and College Lake NR. At College Lake up to five pairs breed on just 300 sq metres of shingle which has been provided specifically for that purpose, while at Willen up to three pairs have bred on an island and on exposed gravel bars. In any one year between two and ten pairs usually attempt to breed in the county. To date there have been no breeding records from the south of the county.

Birds are normally seen passing through the county between early February and late May and between late September and mid November on the return passage. Larger flocks are normally seen in the spring with single flocks containing over 10 individuals recorded in most years. The largest flock recorded was 48 at Willen Lake on 7 May 1981.

Our breeding birds and their young leave their breeding sites shortly after breeding activity is finished. Inland Ringed Plovers usually are single brooded (the Breeding Atlas) so this movement can be from mid June onwards. These birds move to coastal areas, this being supported by a colour ringing project that took place at College Lake in the summer of 1987. Four breeding Ringed Plovers were caught and colour ringed. One bird ringed on 13 May 1987 was recorded in Swansea Bay, South Wales between 28 July and 3 October 1987. Another bird which was ringed on 30 June 1987, was recorded on the Taff estuary near Cardiff on 13 September 1987. At least two of the four colour ringed birds returned to College Lake in the spring of 1988 and one of the four was again seen on the Taff estuary in September 1988 (Kirby 1988). This example also demonstrates the site fidelity of this species. The only other ringing recovery was a bird ringed as a nestling at Pitstone on 21 July 1982 and controlled at Holme Pierrepoint, Nottinghamshire on 29 May 1984.

JER

Kentish Plover
Charadrius alexandrinus

Very rare vagrant. There has been one record.

1981: 1 on 13 Apr, Willen.

Dotterel
Charadrius morinellus

Very rare migrant. All records are given.

There are undated 19th century records for Aylesbury, Drayton Beauchamp, Boveney, and Beaconsfield.

The dated records are:

1857: a few shot in the spring, Burnham.
1862: adult male killed on 14 Aug, Ivinghoe.
1967: 4 on 3 May, near High Wycombe.
1985: juvenile on 23 Sep, Newton Longville.

The paucity of the records is in contrast to the situations in Hertfordshire, where it is a regular passage migrant, and Oxfordshire, where there have been 7 records since 1980.

American Golden Plover
Pluvialis dominica

Very rare vagrant. There has been one record.

1991: juvenile from 12-17 Nov, also 21 Nov, and 25 Nov, Broughton.

The bird divided its time between a field of winter cereals near Broughton and Cranfield Airfield in Bedfordshire where it remained into December. It was probably the same individual that was present at various Midlands localities prior to 12 November. This is one of the few inland records of this North American species (Ward 1991).

Golden Plover
Pluvialis apricaria

A locally abundant visitor in autumn, winter and spring.

Winter flocks consistently use several areas of mid and N Buckinghamshire. Flocks of up to 1,000 birds regularly occur and the maximum total numbers wintering in the county have probably exceeded 3,000 in most winters since 1980. At the turn of the century Golden Plovers were thought to be much rarer than formerly (H & R). However, they were certainly widely overlooked until the mid 1970s when Fuller and Youngman (1979) started to study the species in the Vale of Aylesbury. North of the Vale, knowledge of Golden Plover distribution is still incomplete.

Birds are occasionally reported from the Misbourne and Thames valleys but the regular wintering grounds are on the open farmland north of the Chiltern escarpment. Six tracts of farmland regularly hold substantial flocks in the Vale of Aylesbury: Shabbington/Worminghall; Berryfields/Quainton; Bishopstone/Ford; Haddenham; Marsh Gibbon; and Hulcott/Long Marston. These 'flock ranges' each essentially support one flock of Golden Plovers, although sometimes the birds may be distributed within the range in smaller 'sub-flocks'. Sites regularly used by Golden Plovers elsewhere include areas near North Crawley, Hillesden/Padbury, North Marston/Hoggeston and Edlesborough/Slapton. Smaller numbers have also been reported from widespread localities in the centre and north of the county.

Within flock ranges certain fields are strongly favoured for winter feeding, although the exact distribution of the birds can vary considerably from year to year (Fuller 1990).

The types of fields used by Golden Plovers in Buckinghamshire vary with the time of year and according to the activity of the birds. In the autumn and spring the birds do much feeding on cultivated land but in the colder winter months they feed almost exclusively on grasslands, especially permanent pasture. All the flock ranges in the Vale of Aylesbury support substantial tracts of permanent grassland. Interestingly, in the mid 1980s the Bishopstone/Ford site was largely deserted by both Golden Plovers and Lapwings, possibly because most of the favoured grass fields were converted to cereals (Fuller 1990).

Golden Plovers share their feeding fields with Lapwings and Black-headed Gulls, the latter pirating worms from both species of wader. At all times of the winter Golden Plovers roost and rest mainly on cultivated land, both on plough and short winter cereal crops.

Small flocks, perhaps passage migrants, are reported as early as August but substantial flocks do not arrive until October. However, some flock ranges support very few birds until midwinter when the major influx occurs, usually in December. Numbers remain high throughout the winter unless there is hard weather. Golden Plovers are deprived of their food in prolonged periods of severe frost and/or snow cover. The birds disappear very quickly at the onset of heavy snowfall but frost has to be continuous for several days before the birds move away. Such cold weather movements may be followed by a return, often to exactly the same fields, once a thaw has set in.

Flocks can be found as late as mid April. Many birds in spring are in full breeding plumage and these are certainly of foreign breeding origin, possibly Scandinavian, because British birds are on their breeding grounds by then. Whether these birds are the same individuals that are present in mid winter is unknown.

RJF

Grey Plover
Pluvialis squatarola

Scarce migrant.

Prior to 1974 there was only one record.

1819: 1 obtained 25 Nov, Dinton Hall.

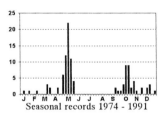

Seasonal records 1974 - 1991

Since 1974 there have been 58 records of 105 birds. They are shown on the histograms. Most were of singles but there was a flock of 9 birds on 7 May 1981 at Willen. 90 birds were recorded in the north of the county, 8 in the middle, and 7 in the south. Most of the birds appear at the usual wetland sites but 5 have been in the company of flocks of Lapwings and Golden Plovers on farmland.

There is a strong peak in late April and early May. This is similar to the pattern in Hertfordshire and Bedfordshire, but different to that in Oxfordshire where many more birds appear in the autumn and winter.

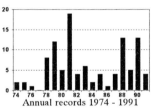

Annual records 1974 - 1991

Lapwing
Vanellus vanellus

A widespread breeding bird and common winter visitor.

Numbers of breeding Lapwings have almost certainly decreased in Buckinghamshire during the present century. Unfortunately there is no detailed historical information, although H & R state that Lapwings once nested on Coombe Hill, near Wendover, a site long since deserted. Breeding Lapwings are now widely but patchily distributedthroughout the county. The species is a semi-colonial breeder and several pairs will nest in one field where the habitat is favourable. Although they will nest on grass or tilled land, much of the

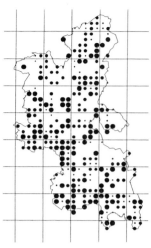

4,000 pairs

grassland in the county is now devoid of breeding Lapwings and most probably nest on cereal fields. Autumn-sown cereal fields with well-grown crops in the early spring are, however, scarcely used by Lapwings. The dense vegetation may reduce visibility for adults when incubating and is probably an unsuitable feeding habitat for the chicks. Lapwings usually select fields where the crop is low or sparse, sometimes as a result of winter flooding. By the 1980s spring-sown cereals were rare in the county but such fields presumably once provided an important nesting habitat for the species. The Lapwing is an opportunist, nesting wherever it can find suitable conditions. Consequently birds do not necessarily use the same fields each year. This is illustrated by observations of Lapwings breeding on fields near Wotton Underwood over a three year period (R. J. Fuller). In each year Lapwings nested in several of these fields; there was always a marked concentration in one, but not in the same field every year. In 1983 some 10 pairs nested in a patchy cereal crop which had much bare ground due to winter flooding. In 1984 this field supported a far better crop but few Lapwings were seen there and no nests were found. The majority were nesting in a short cereal crop nearby. In 1985 most birds moved once more, this time to a field which had recently been ploughed, where some 10 pairs nested. Not only will Lapwings use different fields in different years but they will even move their chicks away from the nest site to new fields more suitable for them to feed in (Redfern 1982). Lapwings nesting on cereals will sometimes move their chicks on to adjacent grassland soon after hatching (R J Fuller, H Galbraith pers comm).

Huge numbers of Lapwings winter on farmland north of the Chiltern escarpment. The Winter Atlas shows that Buckinghamshire lies in a part of central England which supports an exceptionally large concentration of birds at this time of year. Even so, there are large areas of farmland with few birds. In most winters since the mid 1970s the Vale of Aylesbury has probably held some 20,000 Lapwings in midwinter. The birds return each winter to use traditional wintering grounds, with the largest flocks centred on the same areas used by Golden Plovers. However, they are more widely distributed than Golden Plovers and greatly outnumber them. Winter habitat use is very similar to that of Golden Plovers. Arable fields are frequently used for autumn feeding but in midwinter the birds depend heavily on grassland, especially permanent pasture. Roosting is mainly on plough or cereal fields which have only a short crop. Lapwings do much feeding at night, even in midwinter, provided the weather is mild. At such times the birds spend much of the day loafing or roosting, with birds from a large area often gathering in one huge flock. Milsom (1984) has suggested that night-time feeding is most frequent around full moon periods but in Buckinghamshire large flocks of day-roosting Lapwings have been found during most stages of the lunar cycle (R J Fuller).

Flocks of Lapwings start to build up in June. These may include local breeders but the majority are probably immigrants from continental Europe (Imboden 1974). There are several records of birds ringed as chicks in Buckinghamshire being recovered to the south in the autumn and winter. One was found in Cornwall, 6 in France, 2 in Spain and 1 in Morocco, suggesting that locally bred birds often move away for the winter. Numbers in the county in winter appear to increase only gradually until the main midwinter immigrations. The timing of these influxes varies from winter to winter, presumably according to weather on the Continent and elsewhere in Britain. In two winters in the mid 1970s Fuller and Youngman (1979) reported major influxes in late December and January. In the 1980s, however, most midwinter influxes were in November or December, with the main arrival usually in early December. In mild winters numbers may remain high until birds suddenly depart in mid March. Prolonged periods of freezing weather or snow cause the birds to leave the feeding grounds. The birds appear to leave as soon as heavy snow falls, usually moving off to the south or south-west. Remarkably, they often return to exactly the same fields a week or so after the thaw has set in.

Seasonal trends in numbers of Lapwings in the county differ from those of Golden Plovers in several respects. Lapwings show a marked influx in mid-summer rather than in autumn, and few, if any, flocks of Lapwings stay into the spring. Where the Lapwings return to is not known for certain but recoveries of birds ringed elsewhere would suggest that N Europe and Scandinavia are likely destinations.

RJF

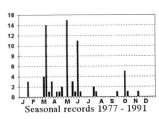
Seasonal records 1977 - 1991

Knot

Calidris canutus

Scarce migrant.

Prior to 1977 there were only 3 records:
1911: 1 on 28 Jan, Halton (specimen now in County Museum).
1937: 3 on 1 Feb, near Olney.
1960: 1 on 18 Sep, Emberton GP.

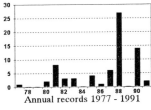
Annual records 1977 - 1991

Since 1977 there have been 32 records of 71 birds. They are shown on the histograms. 55 birds were recorded in the north of the county, and 16 in the south. Most were of singles but there was a flock of 14 or 15 birds on 15 Mar 1990 at Little Marlow and another of 11 birds at Willen on 8-9 Jun 1988. The majority of the records occurred between early March and the end of May, without any pronounced peak.

Sanderling

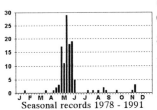
Seasonal records 1978 - 1991

Calidris alba

Scarce migrant.

Prior to 1978 there were only 2 records:

1956: 1 on 4 Feb, Bourne End.
1959: 2 on 22 May, Foxcote.

Since 1978 there have been 63 records of 118 birds. They are shown on the histograms. 108 birds were recorded in the north of the county, 6 in the middle, and 4 in the south. The majority of the records occurred in May with a distinct peak in the second week. This is similar to the situations in the neighbouring counties.

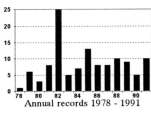
Annual records 1978 - 1991

Little Stint
Calidris minuta

Regular migrant in small numbers.

The first record within the present county boundary was not until 1964.

1964: 1 on 27 Dec, Foxcote.

There were no more records until 1975, but since then there have been 61 records of 140 birds. They are shown on the histograms. 130 birds were recorded in the north of the county, 1 in the middle, and 9 in the south. There is a small passage in the last week of April and May, and a larger autumn passage peaking in early September. Birds have normally gone by mid October, but one which appeared at Willen on 31 Oct 1990 remained until 16 Dec. The largest flock recorded was one of 13 birds at Willen on 19 Sep 1981.

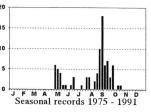

Seasonal records 1975 - 1991

Temminck's Stint
Calidris temminckii

Rare spring migrant.

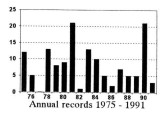

Annual records 1975 - 1991

All records were of single birds at Willen.

1980: 12-13 May, 18-19 May. 2 birds may have been involved.
1981: 19 May.
1982: 13-18 May.
1982: 1-3 Jun.
1984: 24 May.
1987: 24-27 May.
1989: 13-15 May.
1989: 25-27 May.

This series is remarkable for its consistency. Perhaps only one or two individuals were involved.

127

Pectoral Sandpiper
Calidris melanotos

Very rare vagrant. All records are given.

1988: 1 intermittently between 28 Sep and 9 Oct at Dorney Common. The bird spent much of its stay at Slough STW in Berks.

1989: 1 on 1 Sep, Linford.

These are typical dates for this North American/Siberian vagrant.

Curlew Sandpiper
Calidris ferruginea

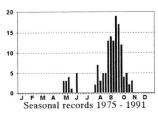
Seasonal records 1975 - 1991

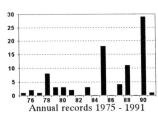
Annual records 1975 - 1991

Scarce migrant.

There are only two records prior to 1975.

1949: 2 reported on 2 Mar, Iver SF.
1959: 1 from 30 Aug-1 Sep, Hartigan's Pit, near Broughton.

There were no more records until 1975, but since then there have been records of 86 birds. They are shown on the histograms. 78 birds were recorded in the north of the county, and 8 in the south. Very few are seen in the spring, but there is a larger autumn passage with a distinct peak in mid September. The largest flocks recorded are one of 8 birds on 28 Aug 1978, and one of 7 birds on 9 Sep 1985, both at Willen.

Purple Sandpiper
Calidris maritima

Very rare vagrant. Both records are given.

1976: 1 on 27 Oct, Hambleden.
1977: 1 from 11-22 Nov, Willen, with 2 on 14 Nov.

128

Dunlin
Calidris alpina

Passage migrant seen in small flocks in all months of the year.

In 1920 H & J stated that Dunlins were a 'not uncommon passage migrant and occasional winter visitor' with the largest flock reported as 14. This situation did not change too much with F & Y in 1976 describing Dunlins as 'Recorded on passage in small numbers in most years. Has regularly been recorded during the winter in recent years'.

Despite this it is clear that earlier this century Dunlins were recorded less often in the county than now. The reasons for this are discussed in the introduction to the waders. Even in the 1960s and early 1970s the total number recorded in any one year was often no greater than 10 birds. Since the mid 1970s records of single flocks of this size, plus many other records, are received in most years.

Dunlins are seen throughout the county, primarily at lakes and gravel pits which have suitable muddy or sandy scrapes. Most birds are seen in the north of the county, Willen lake being the most important site with double figure flocks reported during most years.

Timing of migration through the county is confused somewhat by movements of wintering and non-breeding summering birds. Spring migration begins in March continuing until early June with 1-3 birds usually reported from a number of sites. At Willen flocks in excess of 10 are reported during most springs with single flocks of over 30 birds being reported in two of the last ten years. Autumn migration starts during July and continues until October, but birds are more widely reported during July and August. Larger flocks are however most likely to be seen between October and December, these probably being winter movements within the UK rather than migrant birds. The largest flock ever recorded in the county was at Quarrendon in November 1991 when approximately 70 were reported in a large mixed flock of wading birds in a waterlogged field. During the winter Dunlins are not infrequently reported on farmland, particularly when flooded, and are often with other wading birds such as Golden Plovers and Lapwings.

The extended periods of migration through the county are probably due to a combination of Dunlin from different races and countries being involved as well as winter movements. These are likely to be the races *arctica*, which breeds in NE Greenland and is believed to winter in NW Africa, and *schinzii*, which breeds in SE Greenland, S Scandinavia,

Iceland, and Great Britain, many of which spend the winter in NW Africa. To make matters even more complicated *schinzii* birds from different breeding areas pass through Great Britain at different times, as do adults and juveniles. Icelandic birds are the most numerous in the spring (BWP).

British birds are usually the first to pass through the county in the spring, this being from mid-March. Other *schinzii* birds are seen 2-3 weeks later and birds of the race *arctica* follow in late May. In the autumn, failed breeding birds are likely to be seen first with birds from Great Britain and Finland appearing any time after mid June. Birds from Greenland (both races) are usually seen between July and September, while juveniles from the Finnish populations may still be passing through in October (BWP).

Winter movements do apparently follow a pattern. Birds move westwards, away from the east coast in October and November (after moulting), and return between February and April before migrating to the breeding grounds (the Winter Atlas). This type of movement could well explain the regular winter records of relatively large flocks. It is likely that some or all of the winter records involve individuals of the nominate race *alpina* as these birds regularly winter in Britain. Three ringed birds of this race were recorded in the West Midlands in February 1976.

There are no ringing recovery data for this species in the county nor is there any information on the race or origins of birds seen in the county. Without more effort in identifying races this situation will not change. We will therefore have to continue to speculate as to the origins and destinations of these long distance travellers.

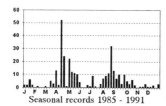

Seasonal records 1985 - 1991

JER

Ruff

Philomachus pugnax

Regular migrant.

The first record was:

1774: 1 shot 8 Aug, Dinton Hall.

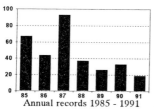

Annual records 1985 - 1991

Clark Kennedy records one killed near Chesham in the 1860s, but H & J give no records at all for Buckinghamshire. In fact there was only one more record within the present county boundary (a pair at Weston Turville Res on 16 Sep

130

1935) until 1957 when 4 were seen at Hartigan's Pit near Broughton on 29 Apr. Between 1958 and 1974 there were 32 records of 63 birds. In common with many of the Buckinghamshire migrant waders, Ruffs have become much more frequent since the mid 1970s with the filling of the south basin of Willen Lake in 1975 and of the north basin in 1978. In 1975 22 birds were recorded, but the following year saw a maximum of 18 birds at Willen on 18 Sep during the autumn passage in addition to 13 birds at other sites. 1981 saw the largest flock: 43 birds at Willen on 16 Sep, but two years later the autumn maximum was down to just 6 birds. The histograms show the records between 1984 and 1991 when 319 birds were recorded.

There appears to have been a change in migration patterns. Between 1964 and 1975 20 birds were recorded in spring and 63 in autumn, but between 1984 and 1990 160 birds were recorded in spring and 121 in autumn. This change has also been noted in Oxfordshire (Brucker at al 1992) and the West Midlands (Harrsison et al 1982) but not in Bedforshire (Trodd and Kramer 1991). There is no obvious explanation for either the change or the discrepancies between counties.

Birds are occasionally recorded in winter. The first winter record was of a bird seen at Bletchley SF on 24 Dec 1964, but the next was not until 31 Jan 1976 when a bird was recorded at Wendover SF. The largest winter flock recorded is one of 20 birds at Old Slade on 14 Jan 1977.

DMF

Jack Snipe
Lymnocryptes minimus

Regular winter visitor in small numbers.

The first record within the present county boundary is:

1936: 2 shot on 5 Feb, Olney.

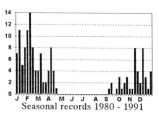
Seasonal records 1980 - 1991

In the 1950s 8 birds were recorded, in the 1960s 89 birds, in the 1970s c160 birds, and from 1980 145 birds. The maximum annual total since 1980 is 19 birds in 1989, and the minimum only one bird in 1984. Jack Snipes are unobtrusive birds and are certainly under-recorded, although their wetland habitat is often well watched. The increase during the first three decades since 1950 may be accounted for by increased observer activity, but since 1980 there appears to have been a genuine decrease. This is paralleled by a similar decrease

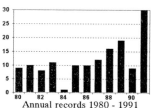
Annual records 1980 - 1991

131

which has been noted in neighbouring Oxfordshire (Brucker et al 1992). The records since 1980 are shown on a seasonal histogram.

Typical sites are Weston Turville Res, Chesham cress beds, Bletchley SF, and Aylesbury SF, as well as the normal wader sites. Most records have been of single birds, but occasionally up to 6 birds have been recorded. There is one exceptional record of 20 birds at Bletchley SF on 12 Feb 1975. Jack Snipes normally arrive in October and leave in March. The earliest arrival date is 5 Sep 1982 at Willen and the latest 13 Apr 1986 at Aylesbury SF.

DMF

Snipe
Gallinago gallinago

Breeds in very small numbers, fairly common on passage and common winter visitor.

The Snipe was considered by H & R to be 'common in suitable places' and H & J said that it had 'undoubtedly increased considerably in numbers in the Thames Valley'. The number of breeding birds has declined considerably in recent years, most probably because of loss of habitat. As Mead & Smith (1982) observed for Hertfordshire, the Snipe is now a bird which observers expect to see in winter but not in summer.

Birds are usually found in water meadows and along the marshy edges of streams and rivers. Suitable breeding habitat in Buckinghamshire has been reduced significantly due to field drainage over the last 30-40 years. In winter birds can be found in flooded fields, and muddy gateways seem to be especially favoured.

During the fieldwork for the county breeding survey, breeding was proved in only 1 tetrad and suspected in 13 others. The majority of these were adjacent to the River Thames, with none in the valley of the River Thame where they used to breed. The decline in breeding birds is probably still happening, as the Breeding Atlas recorded proved breeding in 8 of the county's 10-km squares in 1968-1972.

Spring passage appears to be most pronounced in March and April with very few records in early May, although birds in March could still be overwintering birds. There were 200 at Olney on 20 Mar 1982 and 450 at Marsh Gibbon on 16 Mar 1975.

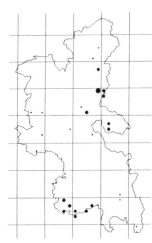

1986: 15 pairs
1991: 2 pairs

There are very few records from May to early July. The main autumn passage starts in late July and August with concentrations on flooded meadows and reservoirs, for example 42 on Aylesbury SF on 31 Aug 1980 and 60 at Willen on 7 Sept 1980. Numbers build up in the early part of the winter period and fluctuate according to weather conditions. Snipe tend to be found in the same sites as winter flocks of Lapwings and Golden Plovers at Marsh Gibbon, Bishopstone, Shabbington and Berryfields. Also in common with those species, Snipe move off the meadows during prolonged periods of cold weather when the ground is frozen. Maxima of 100 have been reported from several localities with over 700 at Marsh Gibbon on 24 Nov 1974, over 200 at Aylesbury SF on 25 Jan 1981, 150 at Berryfields on 20 Feb 1982, 100 at Willen on 26 Jan 1984 and 100 at Caldecotte Lake on 10 Nov 1984. Some of these birds are certainly immigrants from farther afield, as there are reports of birds ringed in Buckinghamshire being recovered in the Netherlands, France and near Moscow.

CEY

Great Snipe
Gallinago media

Very rare vagrant. There is one record.

1962: 1 from 23 Dec-17 Feb 1963, Alderbourne and Rush Green watercress beds, Iver.

This bird made the longest recorded stay of any Great Snipe in Britain. A record at Marlow in 1871 is reported rather tentatively by H & J, and should probably be disregarded.

Woodcock
Scolopax rusticola

Resident in small numbers and regular winter visitor.

It is evident from the early accounts that Woodcocks did not breed in the county until after the First World War. Clark Kennedy described its status as 'regular winter visitor, does not often remain to breed' while H & J did not give any breeding records at all, and wrote that it was 'nowhere very common' in winter. Price stated 'resident in small numbers, a few pairs breeding'. This equates with the national trend which suggests an increase during the late 19th and early 20th

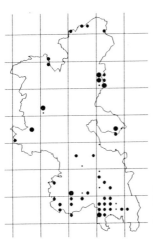

200 pairs

centuries until it was breeding in almost all English counties by 1930. The first recorded nest in the county was one found at Whaddon on 6 Apr 1926.

The national Common Birds Census shows a steady decline since the mid 1960s but local records are so sparse that it is very difficult to detect any trend, or to arrive at an accurate population estimate. There may be around 200 territories.

The map shows a concentration of breeding records in the south Chilterns, the Brickhills, and along the northern boundary. There are only two occupied tetrads for the broken band of woodlands in the Vale of Aylesbury. The optimum habitat for the birds is dry deciduous woodland with damp areas for feeding. There are large tracts of such woodland in the Chilterns, while the Vale of Aylesbury woods, which are wetter, may be less suitable. It must be noted that, although Woodcocks are not difficult to locate when they are roding, they are rarely seen at other times.

Woodcock are more widely scattered in winter, and are found in small numbers at places where they do not breed. In hard weather they may even be found in large gardens. The birds arrive in October and leave in March and may well include birds from N Europe. They tend to be found at sites that are well watched such as Newport Pagnell GPs, Willen, and Weston Turville. The Chiltern woods are rather avoided by birdwatchers during the winter and it is likely that many wintering Woodcocks are undetected. During a shoot at The Lee on 1 Jan 1979 20 birds were seen, which may give an indication of its true numbers in some Chiltern woods in winter. A flock of 18 flying north-west near Drayton Parslow on 21 Nov 1985 is noteworthy.

DMF

134

Black-tailed Godwit
Limosa limosa

Scarce migrant.

Prior to 1974 there were five records:

1941: 2 from 28-29 Aug, near Olney.
1955: 1 on 26 Apr, Marlow.
1957: 1 on 23 Apr, Hartigan's Pit, Broughton.
1961: 1 on 28 Oct, Bletchley SF.
1962: 1 on 11 and 18 Mar, Newport Pagnell GP.

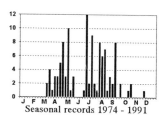

Seasonal records 1974 - 1991

Since 1974 there have been 76 records of 111 birds. They are shown on the histograms. 102 birds were recorded in the north of the county, 6 in the middle, and 3 in the south. The birds have been found in every month between March and November, though there is a four-week gap between mid May and mid June. The largest flocks have all been of 4 birds: on 30 Jun 1981 at Willen, on 28 Jun 1986 at Caldecotte, on 29 Jun 1988 at Willen, and 4 Aug 1990 at Linford.

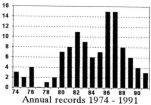

Annual records 1974 - 1991

Bar-tailed Godwit
Limosa lapponica

Scarce migrant.

Prior to 1974 there were five records:

1846: 2 in early May, Slapton.
1895: 1 shot in winter, Ivinghoe.
1947: 1 on 3 May, Fulmer.
1960: 1 on 4 May, Newport Pagnell GP.
1969: 1 on 12 Jan, Calvert.

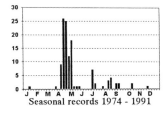

Seasonal records 1974 - 1991

Since 1974 there have been 47 records of 167 birds. They are shown on the histograms. 149 birds were recorded in the north of the county, 1 in the middle, and 17 in the south. Most birds are found in spring, with a peak in mid April. The largest flocks recorded are one of 25 birds on 30 Apr 1978 flying over Willen, and one of 14 birds on 16 Apr 1988 flying over Marlow GPs.

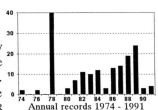

Annual records 1974 - 1991

Whimbrel
Numenius phaeopus

Annual migrant in small numbers.

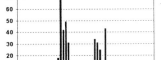
Seasonal records 1975 - 1991

Prior to 1975 there were four records:

1894: 2 shot in mid May, Ouse Valley, NE Buckinghamshire.
1941: 8 on 10 Aug flew over Buckinghamshire near Thame.
1960: 2 on 12 Aug, Newport Pagnell GP.
1961: 1 on 5 Sep, Marlow.

Since 1975 there have been records of about 387 birds. They are shown on the histograms. 214 birds were recorded in the north of the county, 117 in the middle, and 36 in the south. Most of the records were of birds flying over. The largest flocks recorded are one of c20 birds flying over Pitstone on 9 Aug 1981, one of 18 birds over Edlesborough on the same day, which may have been the same flock as that at Pitstone, one of 19 birds over Weston Turville Res on 30 Jul 1988, 18 birds which landed briefly at Willen on 17 May 1980, and another flock of the same size at Willen on 24 Apr 1987. The consistency in the sizes of the flocks is interesting. Birds flying over the Chiltern escarpment in late summer are a feature.

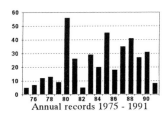
Annual records 1975 - 1991

Curlew
Numenius arquata

A local breeding bird and passage migrant.

The Curlew appears not to have bred in the county in the early part of this century, for H & R regarded the bird solely as a passage migrant. The first documented breeding was in 1946 at Kingsey. A survey of the main river valleys in 1982 found 26 pairs (Smith & Stone 1984) but this certainly overlooked some birds breeding away from the larger streams and rivers. The present population is probably less than 50 pairs.

Most of the county's breeding Curlews are along the Thame valley between Worminghall and Cuddington, and in the watershed region between the Ray and Thame around Dorton and Wotton Underwood. The upper catchment of the Ray between Ludgershall and Marsh Gibbon also holds several pairs in most years as does the upper catchment of Claydon Brook. Outside this area Curlews are scattered rather thinly. For example, they are absent from much apparently suitable habitat in the Thame valley to the north and east of Aylesbury and over most of the Ouse catchment.

All the strongholds of the Curlew in Buckinghamshire are areas with substantial areas of permanent grassland. The adult birds feed and nest in grassland, returning to the same fields year after year. Many of these traditional sites lie in valley bottoms which flood in winter. However, unlike Snipe and Redshank, the Curlew does not seem to require very damp conditions for breeding. The preferred fields usually have tussocky or fairly rank vegetation. Most are cut for hay and many show ridge and furrow. Heavily improved grassland, short-cropped grassland and silage crops are generally avoided. There are also no reports of any nesting attempts in cereal crops, although Curlew chicks occasionally move into such fields.

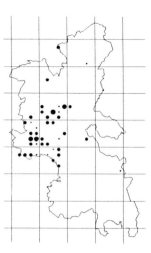

40 pairs

The fortunes of the Curlew, like the Lapwing and Redshank, are closely linked to the fortunes of farming. The species undoubtedly benefits from traditional methods of managing grass. It may be no coincidence that the expansion of the species into lowland habitats during this century, which occurred throughout the country (the Breeding Atlas), was in a period of economic depression when much farmland was run down. Recent years have seen intensification of drainage and grassland management throughout the county. As yet there has been no general decline of Curlews, although certain sites regularly occupied in the 1960s and 1970s no longer appear to hold birds.

Breeding Curlews are usually located by their bubbling song, performed in a display flight over the territory. Despite this far-carrying song, the Curlew can be surprisingly inconspicuous (Fuller 1981). Many of the possible and probable records on the map will certainly be nesting birds. When incubating, the bird often leaves the nest when the approaching observer is still some distance away. The chicks are extremely difficult to observe because they are usually hidden in long vegetation.

Most Curlews arrive on their Buckinghamshire breeding grounds in early or mid March but some may appear in late February. The birds have left many of the breeding fields by mid July but are sometimes seen along the River Thame meadows into August. Ringing recoveries suggest that the Curlews winter on the coasts of SW Britain or possibly of France or Iberia (Bainbridge & Minton 1978). The bird is a fairly regular passage migrant and is occasionally recorded in winter, but it is most unlikely that any overwinter in the county.

RJF

Spotted Redshank
Tringa erythropus

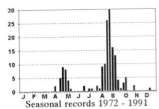

Seasonal records 1972 - 1991

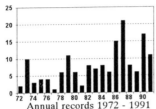

Annual records 1972 - 1991

Annual migrant in small numbers.

Prior to 1974 there were four records:

1960: 2 on 21 Aug, Emberton GP.
1961: 3 on 29 Aug, Emberton GP.
1973: 3 on 6 Sep, Linford GP.
1973: 5 on 16 Sep, Calvert.

Since 1974 there have been records of 156 birds. They are shown on the histograms. 138 birds were recorded in the north of the county, 13 in the middle, and 5 in the south. There is a small spring passage peaking at the end of April and a much larger autumn passage peaking at the end of August. The largest flock recorded is one of 13 juveniles on 23 Aug 1990 at Willen.

Redshank
Tringa totanus

Local breeding bird and regular passage migrant and winter visitor in small numbers.

Clark Kennedy described the status of Redshanks as 'uncertain visitants', but H & J wrote 'breeds in small numbers', a remark repeated by Price. This is consistent with the national trend which was of a steady expansion from the east of the country beginning around 1865 until 1940 when the population seems to have stabilised. Price's comment of 1947 still holds although a considerable change in the habitats used by breeding Redshanks has taken place.

Up to the end of the 1960s most of the Buckinghamshire Redshanks bred in damp meadows. Typical localities included Marlow Low Grounds (up to 7 pairs), meadows near Newport Pagnell (up to 9 pairs), Little Missenden, and Kingsey. During the 1960s drainage became widespread, which resulted in a considerable diminution of the habitat. For instance, the field near Newport Pagnell was drained in 1969 and since then no Redshanks have bred at this locality. A survey of breeding waders in wet meadows was carried out in 1982. A total of 40 sites covering approximately 5500 hectares were surveyed. 3 pairs of Redshanks were found, one of which was in a quarry. The other two were probably unsuccessful.

However, there does not seem to have been a reduction in the population. The creation of gravel pits has provided a

138

suitable substitute for the more natural meadows. Locations such as Willen Lake, Linford GPs, and College Lake now hold several pairs each of Redshanks. The total population may be around 20 pairs, which is probably a similar figure to the population in the first half of the century.

Birds arrive at the breeding sites at the end of February or in early March and leave in July. Peak numbers occur at the beginning of the season with the largest recorded number at this time being 35 at Willen on 3 Apr 1987. Outside the breeding season numbers are very small. The autumn passage rarely reaches double figures and occasionally no birds are recorded at all. A flock of c50 flying over Weston Turville Res on 16 Sep 1973 was exceptional. A small number of birds are recorded during most winters although stays of longer than a few days are unusual.

There have been 3 ringing records of birds moving outside the county. A bird ringed at Newport Pagnell on 15 May 1965 was recovered at Abberton, Essex on 30 Jun 1965; another bird ringed on the same day was recovered at Gironde, France on 29 Aug 1965; and a bird ringed at Weybridge, Surrey on 16 Jul 1934 was recovered at Dorney on 14 Feb 1937.

DMF

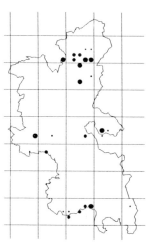

20 pairs

Lesser Yellowlegs
Tringa flavipes

Very rare vagrant. There has been one record.

1977: 1 from 15 Oct-5 Nov, Denham.

This record is rather late in the year for this North American vagrant.

Greenshank
Tringa nebularia

Regular migrant and very rare winter visitor.

Clark Kennedy described the status of the Greenshank as 'uncommon', but by 1947 Price was writing 'fairly frequent on migration'. It is now one of the more regularly recorded passage waders in the county.

It is likely that, in common with other migrant waders, numbers of Greenshanks have increased since the Second World War with the increase in the area of suitable mud caused by the creation of gravel pits and flood balancing lakes in the north of the county. Greenshanks, along with most

139

migrant waders, are still rather rare in the south of the county because there is very little exposed mud.

Numbers seen each year vary between 4 and c20. Flocks of up to 6 birds are regularly recorded in the autumn at Willen, but 11 birds were present on 6 Aug 1976.

Spring migration is between April and June with a peak in May. Autumn migration is from July to October with a peak in mid August. Numbers, which are swelled by juvenile birds, are larger in the autumn.

From 1974 to 1976 a bird wintered on the River Chess between Latimer and Chenies.

DMF

Green Sandpiper
Tringa ochropus

Fairly common passage migrant, most plentiful in autumn, and wintering in small numbers.

There appears to have been little change in numbers of birds on passage since H & J's time, but there has probably been an increase in the number of sites where wintering birds occur. H & J list only very few overwintering birds.

Green Sandpipers are found on the edges of quite small ponds, lakes, ditches and streams. They also occur on the banks of gravel pits, reservoirs and especially watercress beds which appear to be an ideal habitat.

There are some records in March, but the main spring migration is in April and continues with a few records in early May. There are virtually none in late May or early June. Numbers at most sites are usually only one or two; three at Stony Stratford on 19 Apr 1982, 5 at Caldecotte Lake on 27 Mar 1983 and 7 at Old Slade on 3 May 1980 are exceptions.

The return passage starts in late June and is most evident in July and August, with occasional concentrations in September and October. Maxima recorded are 14 at Old Slade on 18 Jul 1978, 11 at Bletchley SF on 8 Sep 1974 and 9 at Newton Longville on 9 Aug 1980.

Birds have been widely reported over the winter period from several sites and most years there are 1 or 2 at Chesham, Foxcote, Old Slade, Pitstone, Willen, Latimer Park, Shardeloes, Westcott and Linford GPs. Winter concentrations of 4 at Latimer Park on 7 Dec 1975, and 3 at Ilmer on 20 Nov 1984 and at South Iver SF on 6 Dec 1984 were unusual.

CEY

Wood Sandpiper
Tringa glareola

Annual migrant in small numbers.

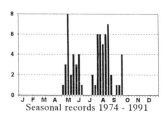

Seasonal records 1974 - 1991

There were only two records prior to 1974:

1965: 2 on 27 Aug, Shardeloes.
1971: 1 on 12 Sep, Bletchley SF.

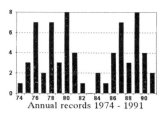

Annual records 1974 - 1991

Since 1974 there have been 57 records of 67 birds. They are shown on the histograms. 55 birds were recorded in the north of the county, 5 in the middle, and 7 in the south. Most of the records were of single birds, but up to three birds have been seen together. The bulk of the spring passage takes place during May and the majority of the autumn passage between mid July and mid August.

Common Sandpiper
Actitis hypoleucos

Scarce summer visitor, which has bred occasionally in the past; common passage migrant and rare winter resident.

H & J reported nesting at Colne near the River Chess and possibly along the River Thames, and a nest was found along the River Ouzel near Leighton Buzzard in 1929 by A. G. L. Sladen (OOS report). There has been no evidence of breeding in recent years, although birds are occasionally reported during the summer months. Most recently 2 were seen on the Thames near Medmenham during June 1977 but they might have been late spring or early autumn passage birds.

During the breeding season the Common Sandpiper primarily

inhabits upland streams, lakes and other watercourses. On passage it occurs regularly at reservoirs and gravel pits, and also along the banks of rivers and streams. In Buckinghamshire there are regular records along the Thames. The new lakes in the Milton Keynes area at Willen and Caldecotte have attracted small numbers in all recent years, while Linford GPs, Little Marlow, Foxcote and Summerleaze GPs also have a regular passage.

According to H & J the spring passage used to last from mid April to the third week of May, the same as in recent years, with only a few birds earlier or later. There are usually between 2 and 10 birds at most sites with maxima reported of 14 at Foxcote on 23 May 1977 and 15 there on 17 May 1980.

Only a few birds have been seen in June. The return migration starts in early July with the main passage from late July to early September and peak numbers occurring in August. The autumn passage is usually heavier than that in spring, some sites regularly holding between 8 and 10 birds. The largest numbers were 30 at Willen on 9 Aug 1981 and 12 at Old Slade on 10 Aug 1980.

Some birds remain into the winter, and 1 overwintered at Linford/Haversham in three consecutive years 1981/82 to 1983/84. Other sites that have held wintering birds include Old Slade, Willen, Tilehouse GP (Denham) and Foxcote.

A bird ringed at Marlow in May 1952 was recovered at Eton in April 1954 suggesting a regular passage of the same birds.

CEY

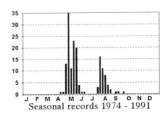

Seasonal records 1974 - 1991

Turnstone
Arenaria interpres

Annual migrant in small numbers.

There was only one record prior to 1974:

1959: 4 on 22 May, Foxcote.

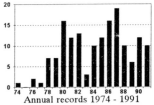

Annual records 1974 - 1991

Since 1974 there have been 84 records of 157 birds. They are shown on the histograms. 148 birds were recorded in the north of the county, 7 in the middle, and 2 in the south. The strong spring passage peaks at the end of April while the autumn passage peaks at the end of July.

142

Red-necked Phalarope
Phalaropus lobatus

Very rare vagrant. All records are given.

1978: female from 8-9 Jul, Willen.
1989: female on 1 and 3 Jun, Willen.
1992: juvenile on 19 Sep, Willen.

Grey Phalarope
Phalaropus fulicarius

Rare autumn vagrant. All records are given.

1866: 1 on 19 Sep, Halton.
1928: 1 found dead on 27 Oct, Dancers End.
1935: 1 on 16 Sep, Weston Turville Res.
1952: 1 found dead on 30 Oct, High Wycombe.
1985: juvenile on 8 Sep, Willen.
1987: 1 on 16 Oct, Weston Turville Res.
1987: 1 on 16 Oct, then 18th-19th, Willen.

The last two records occurred after the great storm of 15 Oct 1987 when many seabirds were blown inland into southern England from the Bay of Biscay.

Pomarine Skua
Stercorarius pomarinus

Very rare vagrant. All records are given.

There is one undated record for Crendon in Clark Kennedy.

The dated records are:

1859: 1 shot Nov or Dec, Chesham.
1982: immature from 13-15 Nov, Willen.
1985: adult on 11 Nov, Caldecotte.

Arctic Skua
Stercorarius parasiticus

Very rare vagrant. There have been two records.

1983: dark-phase adult on 28 Aug, Calvert.
1985: dark-phase adult on 23 Aug, Marsworth.

Long-tailed Skua
Stercorarius longicaudus

Very rare vagrant. There has been one record.

1982: immature from 12-17 Oct, Little Chalfont feeding in a freshly ploughed field.

Great Skua
Stercorarius skua

Very rare vagrant. There have been two records.

1983: 1 on 3 Sep, flew south-west into Buckinghamshire from Wilstone Res.
1987: 1 on 25 Aug, Willen.

Skua species
Stercorarius sp

1936: 2 on 20 Oct, Olney (a day after gales).
1990: 6 on 17 Aug, flew west into Buckinghamshire from Wilstone Res. They were either Arctic or Long-tailed Skuas.

Gulls
Larus spp

There are a number of generalisations which can be made about the five commonest species of gull, and these are made here so as to avoid unnecessary repetition in the individual accounts. Least common is the Great Black-backed Gull, followed in ascending order of abundance by Herring, Lesser Black-backed, Common, and Black-headed. All have increased greatly in the UK during the second half of this century, although the trend can be traced back to the 1920s at least. While conditions in Buckinghamshire have little significance for increased breeding success, many more birds pass through the county than formerly, and wintering inland has clearly become a successful strategy for surviving the harsher months for an increasing number. Key elements are the availability of food at rubbish tips and safe roosting sites on the larger stretches of open water.   Human refuse disposal has recently become more concentrated on fewer and larger tips or infill sites, the size of which allows birds to feed undisturbed for longer periods. Such sites are commonly based on complexes of disused excavations, with other pits nearby containing open water convenient for bathing and drinking. Gatherings at these locations are often vast, with numbers sometimes reaching five figures. Currently the largest sites in the county are at Hedgerley and between Bletchley and Newton Longville. By their very nature such sites are temporary, but while smaller ones may only be used for a couple of years, the largest may be used for several decades. The level and nature of disposal activity will determine a site's attractiveness to gulls.

Safe roosting sites are of prime importance. Flight lines of at least 25 km are easily identifiable and many birds must travel much further. The preferred roost sites are the largest available sheets of water, several of which are of fairly recent origin. Willen and Calvert are almost always in use from September to April. Caldecotte and Spade Oak are frequently used. Foxcote sometimes has a sizeable roost, but generally holds only a few birds, as does Linford. At the smaller sites there may be substantial gatherings which would appear to be roosts, only for the great majority to leave very late in the day to join a larger roost elsewhere. This behaviour has also been noted occasionally at more established sites and is most obvious in the three larger species. County boundaries are no barrier to any kind of roosting behaviour: birds which feed on the southern fringes of the county can be seen moving off towards the large London reservoirs, whereas Brogborough and Stewartby in the west of Bedfordshire and the Tring

Gulls at a waste disposal site

145

reservoirs in Hertfordshire attract birds from the east of the county.

Birds are by no means faithful to one site. Roosts may halve, double or treble from one evening to the next for no obvious reason. Very distinctively-plumaged or colour marked individuals and well described examples of rarer species have been noted at two or even three sites in quick succession. Other apparently suitable sites, such as Weston Turville Reservoir, are hardly used at all, and there is no really satisfactory explanation for this.

While regular watching of roosts has increased considerably in recent years, and some rarer species have been found with greater frequency, much potentially useful information is still not being collected. Gulls are almost totally ignored by most observers, and the published efforts of the rest are themselves meagre. Contempt born of familiarity may be a partial explanation of this situation. Another factor is that identification of the large species in some immature plumages is far from straightforward, especially in the gathering winter gloom. This not only deters some observers, but may also render some records liable to suspicion. The accounts which follow reveal the gaps in our knowledge. A considerable increase in records of all kinds is necessary. In particular, systematic roost counts, by species and by age, are vital if real progress is to be made.

AVH

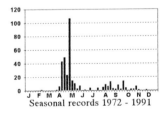

Seasonal records 1972 - 1991

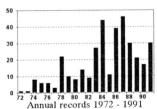

Annual records 1972 - 1991

Little Gull
Larus minutus

Occurs annually in small but increasing numbers as both a spring and autumn passage migrant.

The first county record was of an adult at Dorney Common between 6 and 25 Aug 1958. The steady and significant national increase between 1950 and the early 1970s, as traced by Hutchinson and Neath (1978), was not seen in Buckinghamshire, since the second record was not until 1970. The first record of more than two birds together and the first annual total in double figures occurred in 1978, since when there has been an upsurge in annual totals and multiple occurrences.

Old-style sewage farms were occasionally attractive to this species up to the mid 1970s, but since their modernisation all records have been from the larger lakes, reservoirs and gravel pits, with a resultant heavy bias towards the north of the county.

A gale-blown adult on 18 Feb 1990 at Willen Lake is the earliest record, but an immature on 29 Mar 1978 at the same locality is the first passage bird. In spring most birds move through between the second week of April and the third week of May. Immatures, almost always in first-summer plumage, have until recently predominated. Birds of this age sometimes stay for several days or even longer, whereas adults tend to move on rapidly. Midsummer records are few, with June and July producing only 4 records of 7 birds. The modest autumn passage is most obvious in August. It consists mainly of juveniles, and continues throughout September. There are a few October records and the latest are 2 adults with a first-winter bird on 1 Nov 1987 at Caldecotte following the 'Great Storm' of that year, and a first-winter bird at Willen Lake on 29 Nov 1982.

The following four records have transformed the general pattern. All were at Willen Lake. On 25 Apr 1983 19 adults in breeding plumage provided what the observers thought would be a unique sight for the county. However, in the following year on 1 May two flocks totalling at least 30 individuals were seen. On 2 May 1986 17 adults were present, and on 22 Apr 1987 three flocks, probably totalling 49 birds, moved through rapidly. It might seem that this marked passage is a very recent development, but it should be noted that flocks of similar size have been observed in adjacent counties for rather longer, for example in Northamptonshire in spring 1974. The timing and closeness of the four dates match the Arctic Tern passage (qv), and as with that species it is easy to see how the bulk of a swift passage can be missed. On the other hand it may be that in some years birds either by-pass or overfly the county.

A juvenile with largely dark upperwings, seen in company with two normally-plumaged birds at Willen Lake from 8 to 15 Aug 1984 (NBBR) would seem to accord with a rare variant plumage described by Grant (1986).

AVH

Mediterranean Gull
Larus melanocephalus

Rare but increasing migrant and winter visitor.

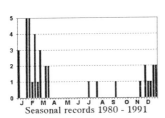

Seasonal records 1980 - 1991

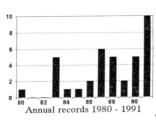

Annual records 1980 - 1991

The first record was:

1980: adult in summer plumage on 19 Mar, Hedgerley.

There have been a further 37 records. 17 of the total have been in the north of the county, 1 in the middle, and 20 in the south. The unusual proportion of records in the south of the county, which is counter to the situation with other rare gulls, accords well with the bird's southern distribution.

All the records are shown on the histograms. The dramatic increase in records is probably due to the increase in the species' breeding population in Europe and to the greater interest in gulls shown by some observers. All but three of the records have occurred between November and March with a peak in late January. Most records have been of single birds, but two adults were seen together on 2 Mar 1983 at Hedgerley, and three different individuals were seen on 2 Feb 1991 at three different sites in the south of the county.

Sabine's Gull
Larus sabini

Very rare vagrant. There have been three records.

1981: adult and immature on 13 Oct, Willen.
1987: juvenile on 17 Oct, flying NE over Colnbrook.
1987: adult on 21 Oct, 3 adults from 22-24 Oct, 1 from 26-28 Oct, Colnbrook.

The 1987 records occurred after the great storm of 15 Oct 1987 when many Sabine's Gulls were blown into southern England from the Bay of Biscay.

Black-headed Gull
Larus ridibundus

Abundant passage migrant and winter visitor, present in smaller numbers throughout the rest of the year.

H & R and H & J recognized this as the commonest gull in Buckinghamshire, though the largest flock mentioned, of 60 birds, is small by present-day standards. In former times it was more likely to be encountered on passage, particularly in spring.

As well as being by far the most numerous, this is the most widespread of the gulls because it is less demanding in its habitat requirements than any of the others. Larger stretches of permanent standing water, floods, rubbish tips, pasture and ploughed land provide the easiest feeding opportunities for large gatherings, though the opportunistic nature of the species allows individuals or smaller groups to forage elsewhere. They may be found patrolling the smallest watercourses, scavenging in urban back gardens early in the morning or, at the appropriate season, taking flying ants on the wing. A small party has even been observed locally forming an aerial queue to pluck rosehips.

There are no breeding records within the present county boundary though four pairs unsuccessfully attempted to breed at Slough SF in 1949. However, among the obviously immature birds which make up most of the small summering population there are always a few birds in adult breeding plumage. Whether these are early failed breeders or sexually immature despite their appearance, or even prospective colonists, is unknown. The last possibility should be kept in mind given that breeding has taken place in neighbouring counties. Numbers build rapidly from early July, and counts of over 3,500 have been made before the end of that month. From August to March numbers at any of the roosts may reach 5,000. The Willen roost is almost invariably the largest, the highest count being an estimated 20,000 on 30 Jan 1985. Optimal feeding opportunities on rubbish tips or farmland frequently produce flocks of 1,000-3,000 and sometimes more birds during the same period. By mid April far fewer are to be seen.

The thousands of birds which move into or through the county in early autumn are likely to be of British origin. Many of those which are seen in winter are thought to be of continental stock. This presumed shift in the population is largely based on national data, but local ringing also provides supporting evidence. Birds ringed as pulli in Belgium, Holland, Germany, Poland, and Finland have been recovered in the area. One bird ringed in its first winter at Marlow on 8 Jan 1968 was recovered in Copenhagen in July 1969.

Not surprisingly for such a large population, several examples of apparently leucistic, albinistic and melanistic birds have been discovered.

AVH

Ring-billed Gull
Larus delawarensis

Very rare vagrant. All records are given.

1991: adult on 24 Jan, Fulmer. This bird subsequently took up residence in Uxbridge.
1991: 2nd winter from 7-9 and 16 Nov, Little Marlow. What was probably the same bird was seen at Pickeridge Quarry on 23 Nov.

The first acceptable records for the county were long expected, but the species is still very rare in Britain away from favoured west and south coastal localities.

Common Gull
Larus canus

Common winter visitor.

In the past the Common Gull was well known but somewhat irregular in occurrence, but as with the other gulls, numbers have increased greatly in the post-war years.

This species has a more catholic taste in habitat than the larger gulls. While it is numerous at the established roosts and rubbish tips, it is often also found in strength on a variety of farmland. It was on agricultural land at Turville that a flock of 4,000, the county's largest, was recorded on 19 Mar 1983. Damp or flooded pasture and recently-ploughed land are most favoured, although like the more numerous Black-headed Gull, the bird is equally at home on playing fields and other urban open spaces.

A literal interpretation of the published records indicates that in the 1970s it was only found in large numbers in March and early April, but it seems unlikely that the situation could have changed so rapidly in a decade. A possible explanation is that birds moved into particular areas to feed because of flooding and agricultural activities at that time of the year, and that those who observed them there were interested enough to report them. There does, however, seems to be a passage, more marked than in autumn, between late February and mid April. Numbers drop off rapidly after this and from May onwards only small parties or single non-breeders move through or loaf about during their moult. The first real signs of a return become evident in September, and the current pattern is of a substantial influx in October and November, with regular counts of more than 500 at the expected roosts and refuse sites throughout the winter.

A bird ringed on Tylon Isle, Sweden in June 1937 was recovered at Hedgerley in April 1938.

AVH

Lesser Black-backed Gull
Larus fuscus

Numerous passage migrant and fairly common winter visitor.

H & R presumed, no doubt correctly, that the Lesser Black-backed Gull was a rare passage migrant in Buckinghamshire on the strength of sightings at the Tring reservoirs. H & J summarised similarly and noted as the first certain record for the county a bird at Bletchley in April 1910.

A manyfold increase at all seasons has taken place in the last fifty years. The wintering population manifests itself mainly at the larger rubbish tips and gull roosts, and three-figure counts at the latter are not exceptional. Some 500 birds at Hedgerley on 6-7 Jan 1987 might indicate that expansion is still taking place. However, this species is more often found in substantial numbers on agricultural land than Great Black-backed and Herring Gulls. In 1979 an increase in wintering flocks in the Vale of Aylesbury was noted, and in 1981 at Long Crendon 200 were seen. On 11 Jan 10% of this flock were identified as *L. f. fuscus*, but current thinking suggests that most birds with darker mantles seen in Britain are in fact *L. f. intermedius* while birds conforming to fuscus are a small minority (Grant 1986). A renewal of interest in this interesting, but problematical, subject in just the last few years is to be welcomed.

The transition from wintering to spring passage birds is difficult to detect but a general increase is obvious from late February to mid April, when flocks of several hundred are common. Flooded pasture is an important feeding habitat at this time of the year. Birds are reduced to a trickle in May, and in June only a few moulting individuals in various stages of immaturity are the norm. Thus 1,000 roosting at East Hurst End on 29 May 1991, and 1,500 there on 31st seems on first sight astonishing. About 10% were adults a few of which were judged to be too dark to be *L.f.graellsii*. Large numbers stayed in the area throughout June so this seems more than a fleeting phenomenon, which, it is to be hoped, will be followed up.

Autumn passage starts early in July and gatherings may be back into three figures by the end of the month. A year's largest counts may be made in any of the ensuing three months, but it is not clear whether this is due to the fickleness of the birds or of the observers. At all events, roosts may now hold over 1,000 birds (maximum 2,250 at Willen on 12 Oct 1974), and farmland flocks may be of similar size (1,500 at Saunderton in mid August and mid September 1980, and again in late September 1981). The main attractions are fields of burnt stubble and ploughed land. While the popularity of any one site may decline rapidly as the food supply diminishes, overall numbers only begin to dip substantially quite late in November, leaving (or perhaps being partially replaced by) the wintering population.

One bird ringed as a chick on Skokholm Island (Dyfed) in July 1960 was found dead at Broughton, Newport Pagnell on 2 Sep 1976.

AVH

Herring Gull
Larus argentatus

Locally common migrant and winter visitor.

Until 1920 Herring Gulls were noted only rarely near Tring Reservoirs and in the Thames Valley (and therefore presumably in Buckinghamshire), usually in association with bad weather. The subsequent considerable increase is presumed to have taken place mainly in the second half of the century. The steady rise in maximum roost counts indicates that this species has continued to increase even throughout the last decade.

The distribution of the species within the county is rather limited. While it is occasionally noted on flooded pasture or ploughed land, all larger flocks are closely associated with rubbish tips and roosting waters, or are noted moving between the two.

This is very much a wintering bird. Three-figure counts cannot be expected before late October or early November, though in some years peak winter numbers have been noted later in that month, or from the first days of December, for example 880 at Fulmer and 500 at Caldecotte. From the limited information available, however, it would appear that a second and more normal peak occurs in January and early February. The largest counts at other sites have been made at this time: 500 at Willen on several occasions, 1680 at Hedgerley, and 800 at Calvert. Gatherings of reasonable size may be noted up to late March, but thereafter the bird rapidly becomes scarcer. May to July records are noteworthy and there is no significant early autumn passage as there is with the Lesser Black-backed Gull.

In the last few years some attempt has been made to estimate what proportion of the wintering population is composed of the nominate race *L.a.argentatus*, which is a regular visitor.

The results are highly variable and it is too early to make sensible generalisations.

Yellow-legged Gull
Larus argentatus michahellis

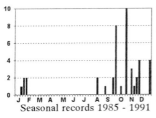
Seasonal records 1985 - 1991

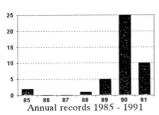
Annual records 1985 - 1991

Birds of a yellow-legged race were first noted in 1985: at Pitstone from 18-22 September and at Denham on 29 December. There were 43 records up to 1991, with a dramatic increase in the last two years. Though it is too early to make any clear pronouncements, there appears to be a passage in September and October. The race involved was probably *L.a.michahellis* which breeds in the Mediterranean area, rather then *L.a.cachinnans*, which breeds from the Black Sea eastwards. 33 of the records were in the south of the county, 10 in the middle, but none in the north, which accords with the bird's southern distribution.

AVH

Iceland Gull
Larus glaucoides

Rare winter visitor. All records are given.

1969: first-winter on 1 and 16 Feb, Calvert.

1981: second-winter from 12-13 Oct, Hedgerley.

1983: immature, perhaps third-winter on 21 Dec, Hedgerley.

1985: probably second-winter on 25 Jan, Hedgerley.

1986: first-winter from 30 Jan-1 Feb, Willen. Presumably the same bird was at Caldecotte on 12 Feb.

1987: first-winter on 18 Jan and 25 Feb, Langley Marish.

1988: second-winter on 13 Feb, Willen.

1989: first-winter from 30 Dec-3 Jan 1990, Bletchley Brick Pits.

1990: second-winter on 14 Feb, Willen.

1991: first-winter on 22, 26, 29, 31 Jan, Bletchley BP.

1991: first-winter on 31 Jan, Calvert.

The increased number of records is certainly due to the greater observer interest in gulls. The two 1991 records may have involved the same bird. Interestingly, an adult has yet to be recorded in the county.

Glaucous Gull
Larus hyperboreus

Rare winter visitor.

Prior to 1972 there was just one record:

1966: 1 on 24 Sep, Old Slade.

Since 1972 there have been 29 records of single birds. They are shown on the histograms. 14 were in the north of the county, 6 in the middle, and 9 in the south. The records have mostly been at the major lakes, though some have been at rubbish-tips.

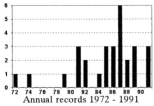

Seasonal records 1972 - 1991

Annual records 1972 - 1991

Great Black-backed Gull
Larus marinus

Fairly common winter visitor in appropriate habitat.

Both H & R and H & J presumed the Great Black-backed Gull to be a rare straggler to Buckinghamshire, based on less than conclusive evidence from just outside the county boundary. The steady increase which presumably took place from the 1940s until the beginning of the 1980s seems to be almost entirely undocumented, except for the most general statements. Despite a recent increase in the number of records submitted, these data are neither sufficient nor systematic enough to allow conclusions to be drawn about whether this growth is continuing or whether the population is steady or even declining.

Except for birds flying over, this species is rarely seen away from its preferred habitat on or close to large rubbish tips and the larger gull roosts. In this respect it is much more selective than the other large gulls.

Singles or small parties may be noted from mid March to early May and then again from the first half of August. However, in general few birds are seen outside the period November to early March and all the three-figure counts are concentrated in December and January. The Willen roost has been estimated at over 100 on several occasions in the 1980s, with a maximum of c300 on 20 Jan 1986. The highest single count was of c500 on 6 and 7 Jan 1987 at Hedgerley.

AVH

Kittiwake

Rissa tridactyla

Scarce annual visitor, with some evidence of passage in spring.

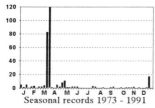
Seasonal records 1973 - 1991

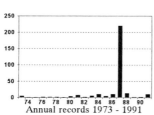
Annual records 1973 - 1991

H & R document the first record of Kittiwake as one killed at Dinton Hall on 11 Jan 1830. This century has seen a massive population increase nationally (Lloyd et al 1991), and the recent pattern of records for Buckinghamshire is an interesting one. The dramatic peaks on both the histograms are entirely the product of 1987. The pre-1987 trends should be examined separately; they are necessarily based on few records and should therefore be treated with some caution. An increase in January records may be due in part to the greater popularity among observers of seeking the scarcer species of gulls in roosts. A more convincing peak in April and May probably represents stragglers from a genuine cross-country passage, some of them late enough to make the three June birds seem less exceptional. The rest of the records are scattered through all months. At least in recent times there is little evidence of birds being storm-driven, as some literature suggests, though it may be adverse weather that causes birds to drop in at the larger lakes and reservoirs on which they are usually seen.

Three records in 1987 distort the picture completely. On 18 Mar an unprecedented 70-80 adults flew north-east from Willen Lake, and two days later 115 adults flew south from the same site. Each flock exceeded the entire pre-1987 county total, while 17 at Little Marlow on 20 Dec exceeded any previous annual total. Even discounting these records, two-thirds of the birds seen are adults. This bias would seem to be genuine given that immature birds have much more distinctive plumage and are therefore more likely to be detected. In contrast, all but one of the birds seen between mid June and late October have been immatures.

AVH

Caspian Tern

Sterna caspia

Very rare vagrant. There has been one record.

1992: 1 on 17 Apr, Willen.

This bird was also seen in Bedfordshire and Suffolk and was one of the earliest ever recorded in Britain.

Sandwich Tern
Sterna sandvicensis

Scarce migrant.

Prior to 1972 there were 7 records:

1895: 8 on 10 Apr, Great Marlow.
1935: 1 on 20 Apr, Shardeloes.
1953: 1 found dead on 7 Jun, Marlow GPs.
1956: 1 on 7 May, Hartigan's Pit, Broughton.
1960: 1 on 5 May, Newport Pagnell GP.
1960: 1 on 24 Jun, Newport Pagnell GP.
1961: 2 on 30 Apr, Newport Pagnell GP.

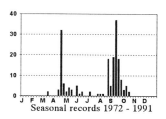

Seasonal records 1972 - 1991

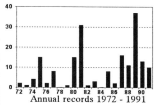

Annual records 1972 - 1991

Since 1972 there have been 48 records of c180 birds. They are shown on the histograms. 108 birds were recorded in the north of the county, 49 in the middle, and 23 in the south. The largest flocks recorded are one of 26 or 27 birds flying over Wavendon on 20 Apr 1989, and one of 13 birds on 22 Aug 1987 at Willen. The earliest record is of 2 birds at Little Marlow on 17 Mar 1991.

Roseate Tern
Sterna dougallii

Very rare vagrant. All records are given.

1944: 1 on 6 Sep, Marlow.
1982: 2 on 4 Jun, Willen.
1983: adult on 8 May, Mount Farm, Bletchley.

Common Tern
Sterna hirundo

Fairly common passage migrant which has recently become a scarce breeder.

In former times Common Terns were familiar passage birds, but far less frequent in autumn than in spring (H & J). However, there is no hint of breeding until much more recently. Breeding was first proved for the county in 1968 at Old Slade when a pair raised three young. Since then one to three pairs have been successful at this site in almost every year up to the present. Birds were successful at a second site, Little Marlow, in 1982, and two pairs bred there in 1983. Subsequently one pair has been the norm. In 1983 and 1985 single pairs bred at Willen. Thereafter this site has proved

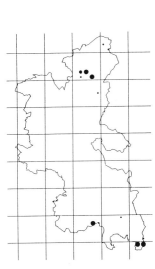

1986: 7+ pairs
1991: 30 pairs

very attractive, but also very difficult to count. Minima for 1986-91 are 17 fledged young in 1986, the same in 1987, 30 in 1988, 20 in 1989, 51 in 1990, and 60 in 1991. At Linford, birds were eventually successful in 1988 after several attempts. Other waters have had birds summering, displaying or copulating during the last decade or so, and presence in at least two summers has seemed a prerequisite to breeding. However, the key in Buckinghamshire would seem to be islands. Since 1974 at least, all successful nests have been on anchored rafts, as at Old Slade and Linford, or islands created during the digging of gravel pits or lakes, as at Little Marlow and Willen. Earliest flights by young birds reared in the county have been in the first few days of July, but birds have been successfully raised well into August, following earlier failure.

Leaving aside first and last dates, a number of factors obscure the pattern of other records. The arrival date of the birds which actually stay to breed is frequently confused by passage birds. Moreover, until the current decade, confusion over the identification of Common and Arctic Terns (qv) has led to the large majority being recorded as 'Commic'. Equally, a substantial increase in the numbers of breeding and summering birds, particularly in the north of the county, has made both the end of spring passage and the onset of autumn passage very difficult to separate.

In the last ten years the first birds have appeared between 6 (Willen, 1984) and 16 April. Usually single birds, but occasionally small flocks of 6 or 7, have provided the first record. Double-figure gatherings have not occurred until the last few days of April or the first ten of May, but even then 20 is exceptional (cf Arctic Tern). Passage appears to continue in small numbers into early June, but given the propensity of

158

the species to seek out new nest sites, some of the birds may well have been prospectors, even before summer residents obscured the picture. Since the establishment of the Willen colony even the smallest patches of water within 15 km have been visited occasionally during the summer, and gatherings in late July and August are likely to be attributed to that source. However, at times outsiders are clearly involved. The county's largest flock, of 90-110, about half of which were juveniles, at Willen between 15 and 19 Aug 1986 was not, it is assumed, entirely composed of local birds. These very recent developments apart, autumn passage usually involves far fewer birds than in spring and takes place between late July and mid September. However the peak date and overall number of birds are both variable. October usually sees a couple of records, the latest of which, in recent years, was at Old Slade on 23 Oct 1987.

There is one ringing recovery: a nestling ringed at Boston Fen, Lincolnshire on 14 Jun 1980 was found dead at Linford exactly 11 years later.

AVH

Arctic Tern
Sterna paradisaea

Passage migrant, often in large numbers in spring.

Historical sources only refer to records close to, or perhaps on, the county boundary. This lack of an early definite record is not surprising. Even in 1976 F & Y could find only a few certain records, and they recognised that difficulties in distinguishing Arctic from the very similar Common Tern were preventing its true status from being established. It was not until 1977 that the first substantial gathering was identified with certainty. There is no evidence that the upsurge in records in the last decade reflects anything other than increasing awareness and competence of observers. Therefore, to provide a reasonable portrayal, the accompanying histograms plot numbers only since 1980. During this period the pattern of occurrence has become established well enough to warrant confidence in the assumption that the great majority of any large concentrations of 'Commic' Terns in the early spring in previous years will have been Arctic.

Most of the records are from the north of the county, with its more extensive sheets of standing water. Two at Willen Lake on 9 Apr 1982 were particularly early. The bulk of the

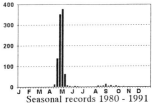
Seasonal records 1980 - 1991

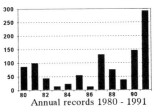
Annual records 1980 - 1991

spring passage is usually highly concentrated and often takes place over just a few days. Although flocks are often sizeable, with the largest being more than 60 on 22 Apr 1980 at Willen Lake, and over 62 on 1 May 1991 at Startopsend Reservoir, they may remain very briefly at the lakes or gravel pits on which they are seen. The speed of the passage may contribute to a low detection rate in some years when good numbers are noted in adjoining counties. Between one and three at Willen from 9 to 14 Jun 1988 are the only birds recorded in that month.

Autumn passage, mainly in August and September, is modest by comparison. All of the October birds have been juveniles, the latest being on 18 Oct 1987 at Marlow.

AVH

Little Tern
Sterna albifrons

Scarce migrant.

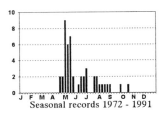
Seasonal records 1972 - 1991

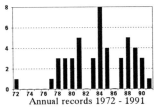
Annual records 1972 - 1991

There are undated records for the Thames and the larger reservoirs given by H & R.

There were four other records prior to 1972:

1850: undated, Slapton.
1946: 1 on 10 May, flying down River Thames at Little Marlow with Black Terns.
1958: 2 on 1 May, Hartigan's GP, near Broughton.
1971: 1 on 6 Jun, Marlow GP.

Since 1972 there were 38 records of 47 birds. They are shown on the histograms. 39 birds have been recorded in the north of the county, 2 in the middle, and 6 in the south. The largest flock recorded was one of 5 birds on 1 May 1984 at Willen. The majority of the records were in the spring with a peak in early May.

Black Tern
Chlidonias niger

Fairly common migrant on both passages.

There has probably been little real change in status since records began other than such as are explicable by the creation of more areas of standing water and a growth in the number of observers. 'Not uncommon' was the summary early this century by H & J. Although this species is liable to large fluctuations there were no 'good' years despite the increase in observer coverage. There was something of an upsurge in 1990, but the previous apparent decline may be more marked than the bare statistics imply. Whether it proves to be significant, or just a normal part of the population cycle, remains to be seen.

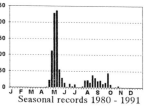

Seasonal records 1980 - 1991

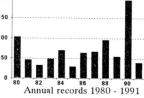

Annual records 1980 - 1991

The earliest recorded bird was on 11 Apr 1979 at Willen Lake. The peak or peaks of spring passage are somewhat unpredictable, occurring any time during the four weeks from 20 April, but the average peak is around the beginning of May. Odd stragglers may appear right up to midsummer and into July. At this time it is unclear which way birds are going, but the later individuals often show obvious signs of moult. What is clearly return passage can start as early as late July. Peak time in autumn is equally difficult to predict, and there is often no correlation with the numbers in spring. The largest recorded movement was on 15 Sep 1974 when a flock of 76 was observed at Calvert, but many more birds actually moved through that day. The scattering of October records includes 3 birds at Willen Lake on 28th in 1984 and an adult with damaged primaries at Weston Turville Res from 26th - 28th in 1987, after the 'Great Storm' of that year.

AVH

Guillemot
Uria aalge

Very rare vagrant. There has been one record.

1852: 1 caught in R. Ouzel, 13 or 14 Nov, Fenny Stratford.

A bird seen on 14 Nov, 1852 at nearby Simpson was almost certainly the same bird.

Little Auk
Alle alle

Rare vagrant, usually after storms. All records are given.

There have been 13 records, all of single storm-blown birds.

1893: Newport Pagnell.
1901 or earlier: Bulstrode Park.
1912: Quainton.
1912: Towersey.
1912: Ivinghoe.
1917: Wendover.
1917: Weston Turville Res.
1919: Skirmett.
1983: 14 Feb, Aylesbury.
1986: 2 Feb, found alive at Wingrave, released on Wilstone Res. where it stayed only a few hours.
1987: 25 Nov, Akeley.
1988: 28-31 Oct, Willen.
1988: 21 Nov, Medmenham.

Puffin
Fratercula arctica

Rare vagrant, usually after storms. All records are given.

There have been 11 records, all of single birds.

1881: 14 Oct, near Aylesbury caught after gales.
1914: 19 Nov, Oaken Grove, near Hambleden.
1918: 23 Nov, at Aston Clinton.
1923: picked up dying on 25 Nov, Kingsey.
1931: found alive on 31 Oct, Nash, was picked up but later died.
1947: picked up on 17 Oct, near Ivinghoe Beacon.
1955: a few days before 25 Oct, near Wycombe, kept for a few days then released.
1958: juvenile from 18-20 Oct, Shardeloes.
1974: juvenile, Loudwater, was picked up but later died.
1977: late Jun/early Jul, Quarrendon, Aylesbury, was later released at sea.
1979: 17 Feb, Amersham, was later released at sea.

Pallas's Sandgrouse
Syrrhaptes paradoxus

Very rare vagrant. All records are given.

1888: flock at Farnham Royal.
1896: 3 on 28 Aug flying overhead, near Halton.
1908: 7-8 on 1 Dec flew up from a turnip field near Buckland.

Although all the records are accepted, the 1896 record has rather less obvious substance than the others since it was not part of an influx into Europe..

Feral Pigeon
Columba livia

Resident, breeding in urban areas throughout the county.

At the beginning of the century Rock Doves were scarce in the county with H & R only referring to one colony near Marlow that bred on a high chalk cliff overlooking the Thames. In 1902 the possibility of these birds being 'infiltrated' by Feral Pigeons was considered a real possibility. Since then there is little doubt that the increasing number of Feral Pigeons that have colonised towns, villages and industrial areas have completely taken over any possible remnants of the Rock Dove. Feral Pigeons breed in urban areas throughout the county, particularly near the centres of towns where buildings such as churches and the older public buildings provide suitable nest sites in the form of ledges and holes. They also nest in other structures such as motorway bridges. As this species was not included in the fieldwork for the county breeding survey no map is provided.

JER

Stock Dove
Columba oenas

Common resident.

The status of Stock Doves in Buckinghamshire is significantly different from that earlier this century when H & R described them as nesting throughout the county 'where old trees afford nesting holes', and H & J described them as 'not rare'. However, there was a sudden decline in the number

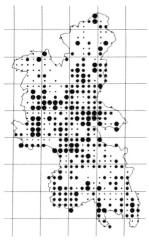

3,000 pairs

in SE Britain in the 1950s, which has been attributed to organochlorine seed dressings (the Breeding Atlas). Recovery from this was recorded by 1969. F & Y described the Stock Dove as 'fairly common and appears to be increasing'.

The local breeding population is probably controlled by the number of suitable holes for breeding. More intensively farmed areas such as N Buckinghamshire inevitably hold fewer pairs of Stock Doves as is shown on the map. There is, however, a higher concentration of breeding birds in the Vale of Aylesbury just north of the Chiltern escarpment, which no doubt reflects the availability of breeding sites in close proximity to food supplies (largely seeds, leaves, and buds).

Breeding commences during March, usually with two to three broods of two eggs each. Flocks of birds seen during March and April (50-200 birds are occasionally reported in Buckinghamshire at this time) are probably first-year birds and failed breeders. Breeding pairs will usually nest on their own or in a small colony, this being largely dependent upon suitable nest sites.

Following the breeding season Stock Doves flock together, and groups of up to 250 birds in the summer and autumn are not uncommon. During the winter months the maximum flock sizes reported in the county tend to be slightly larger (up to 400) with some influx of continental birds being likely (the Winter Atlas). They are also regularly recorded associating with Woodpigeons. It seems likely that most locally bred birds stay in the area all year. Murton (1966) states that 74% of ringing recoveries were within 8 km of the ringing site, with only 11% more than 40 km from the ringing site.

JER

Woodpigeon
Columba palumbus

Very common resident.

Numbers of Woodpigeons have probably not changed significantly this century, but in the 19th century a steady rise in numbers across the country was attributed to changes in agricultural practices (the Breeding Atlas).

The Woodpigeon breeds very widely and commonly throughout the county although in the more agricultural north they were noticeably under-recorded. Confirmed breeding is perhaps most readily achieved by locating the birds' easily seen and recognised platform twig nests. Since food for the fledglings is carried in the crop, confirmation by food carrying is not possible. Having fledged, young Woodpigeons may only stay in the immediate vicinity of the nest for a few days (BWP) thus making confirmation of breeding more difficult. It seems likely that many of the probable breeding records are actually of breeding pairs.

In Buckinghamshire, Woodpigeons use a wide range of habitats including woods, copses, farmland, hedgerows, towns, parks and large gardens. Nest sites range from medium-sized bushes to large trees. The preference for more wooded areas is shown by the higher level of records from the southern half of the county. Woodpigeons are frequent in gardens. The BBC Garden Bird Survey recorded them in 53% of gardens with a maximum flock size of 52.

50,000 pairs

The breeding season begins in April for some (mainly urban) birds, but much later (peak in July to September) for birds breeding in farmland habitat (BWP). At this time their territories are easily located by their gliding and wing-clapping display flight, and the familiar song. The estimated breeding population of 50,000 pairs makes the Woodpigeon one of the most abundant birds in the county. Because they are heavy birds, the mass of breeding Woodpigeons is greater than the mass of all the other breeding birds put together. Thus Woodpigeons have a greater effect on their environment than any other species in the county.

At the end of summer, flocks gather and may become very large in the autumn and winter. Flocks of several hundred are not uncommon in the county, the largest recorded number being 10,000 in November 1976. Woodpigeons do not usually travel far from their breeding area and our winter flocks are largely made up of birds from Buckinghamshire and adjacent counties, with fewer from further afield. Only a very few birds from the continent are likely to be present in a normal winter. There are however, a few records of birds having bred in and around Buckinghamshire travelling much further afield. A nestling ringed in Cookham (just across the county boundary in Berkshire) was recovered in Finistère, France. Winter flocks begin to break up in early spring when territories start to form.

The Woodpigeon is generally poorly recorded, probably since it is abundant throughout the year and because some people consider it to be a pest. Since winter flocks may give an indication as to the size of the local breeding population, perhaps an effort to record all larger winter flocks should be made in the future.

JER

Collared Dove
Streptopelia decaocto

Common resident.

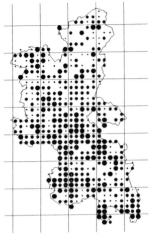

4,000 pairs

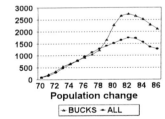

Population change

[← BUCKS → ALL]

The unprecedented rapid spread of the Collared Dove's range across Europe into the British Isles is well documented. The first breeding Collared Doves in Britain were recorded in 1955, with the first Buckinghamshire sighting in 1960 and breeding in 1961. For the next twenty years there was a steady increase in the local population, particularly in the more heavily populated southern part of the county. Even until the mid 1970s numbers in N Buckinghamshire were regarded as low in comparison with the southern half of the county (MTNHS) and this is shown in the Breeding Atlas. National Common Birds Census data for Buckinghamshire show a steady increase until the early 1980s followed by a period of decline, this pattern being similar for other nearby counties with similar habitat (see graph).

The Collared Dove's preferred habitat includes towns, suburbs, parks, large gardens and farms. In Buckinghamshire there were confirmed breeding records from most of the larger towns and villages. Some of the areas with no records are areas of unsuitable habitat, consisting largely of woodland or farmland with few breeding sites. Collared Doves often nest or roost in conifers and ornamental evergreen bushes which offer suitable shelter, and there are records of nesting on farm buildings in the north of the county. They are common in gardens. The BBC Garden Birds Survey recorded them in 76% of gardens where they fed fed on artificial food.

Breeding usually commences in March and may continue until September. Usually there are two eggs produced with as many as 3-6 clutches being raised in a year. Nests of Collared Doves are not so easy to find as those of Woodpigeons, because the nest trees are generally more dense. Breeding is perhaps most easily confirmed by the presence of recently fledged birds. Following breeding, Collared Doves may assemble in flocks. Gatherings of 100-200 birds are recorded annually with a maximum flock size of 500 being recorded in 1975. Dispersion from the breeding locality usually occurs the following spring when the birds are about one year old (BWP). The recovery of a bird ringed as a nestling near Aylesbury in May 1973 and found dead in Shropshire in February 1974 illustrates such a movement. Adult birds are thought to be more sedentary but there are some records of long distance travel. An adult bird ringed in the Netherlands in February 1971 was found dead near Aylesbury in January

1972.

In recent years this attractive dove has been only infrequently mentioned in county records, a dramatic change from its much talked about arrival a mere thirty years ago!

JER

Turtle Dove
Streptopelia turtur

Fairly common but decreasing breeding summer visitor.

A rise in the Turtle Dove population on a national basis in the 19th century was attributed to an increase in arable farming at that time (the Breeding Atlas). Numbers were steady during the period 1900 to 1940, but this was followed by another increase until the late 1970s. The Turtle Dove in Buckinghamshire was described in 1902 as 'a common summer bird' (H & R), while in 1920, H & J said they were 'not rare in well wooded places' with 'considerable numbers in the Thames Valley'. F & Y described them as common. During the 1980s there appears to have been a fall in the population with comments such as 'scarce' being used in the BBC annual reports. Certainly the maximum flock numbers recorded in the 1970s were much higher than recently. National Common Birds Census data from Buckinghamshire and adjacent counties support these apparent changes.

The current status of the Turtle Dove in the county is best described as 'not uncommon but decreasing'. There are generally more records of Turtle Doves just north of the

2,500 pairs

Chilterns but, surprisingly, rather fewer than expected in the arable north of the county, perhaps due to relatively poor coverage in that area. There is no longer evidence of high numbers in the Thames Valley as H & J had suggested.

Typical Turtle Dove habitat consists of woodland, copses, tall hedgerows, and areas of scrub and parkland. The nest site is not normally close to human habitation. The breeding season begins shortly after the birds arrive. This is generallyin May, but the earliest birds are typically seen in the second half of April. Birds may already be paired on arrival, thus enabling breeding to start almost immediately. Two eggs are laid in a platform nest of fine twigs, grasses and moss. Young birds leave the nest from around the last week in June.

Between July and September, post-breeding flocks of 20-30 were recorded most years in the 1970s. Since then the largest has been 20, but with no large flocks recorded in most years. During September the birds leave Britain to winter just south of the Sahara Desert. The last birds are usually seen in Buckinghamshire between the last week of September and the first week in October.

The Turtle Dove was a confirmed breeding bird in the whole of Buckinghamshire (and adjacent areas) during the Breeding Atlas survey period. In the Hertfordshire Breeding Atlas the Turtle Dove was found in 84% of the tetrads, while in Oxfordshire the figure was 51%. The Buckinghamshire percentage is 52. This low number in relation to the Hertfordshire figure may be party explained by the reduction in numbers since the Hertfordshire survey period and because Hertfordshire contains more suitable habitat, particularly in the well cultivated central and northeast areas. The most heavily cultivated areas in our county are in the north, where coverage for the survey was poorest.

The fall in population may be due to change in grassland use from hay to silage. The latter is typically treated with herbicides and fertilisers which inhibit the weeds, the seeds of which Turtle Doves eat in the early part of the breeding season.

JER

Ring-necked Parakeet
Psittacula krameri

Regular visitor in very small numbers and which has bred.

This species began breeding in the wild in Britain about 1969 and was admitted to the British list in 1983. There is now a population of 500-1,000 birds, mostly in Kent and the lower Thames Valley. The birds breed regularly in Wraysbury, just outside the county, and on the Berkshire side of the River Thames.

The first record in the county was of a pair producing three young at Dropmore in June 1974. The next records were of 7 on several dates in 1976 (but not in 1977) in Marlow, one on 10 Oct 1977 in Medmenham, and one from 26 Jul 1982 to late September at Stoke Mandeville. Since then they have been reported in ones and twos every year except 1985 as far north as Milton Keynes, although most of the records have been in the south of the county. The first record remains the only recorded breeding although a pair feeding young were found on an island in the Thames at Dorney Reach, but the nest-hole was two metres inside Berkshire.

There is evidence of a slow increase in the British population, and the species may yet become a regular breeder in the county.

DMF

Cuckoo
Cuculus canorus

Common summer visitor.

The Cuckoo was described by both H & R and H & J as common in Buckinghamshire in the early 1900s. They mentioned that Cuckoos needed hosts such as warblers and pipits in the county (H & R), and that in the Thames Valley eggs had been found in the nests of Garden Warbler and Reed Bunting, in addition to those of the more usual foster parents (H & J). The status of the Cuckoo does not appear to have changed much since then.

Cuckoos frequent a wide range of habitats and their distinctive, far-carrying call can be heard in towns, villages, farmland, woodland, reedbeds, and grassy downland slopes. The breeding distribution map shows them to be widespread, and the gaps, particularly in the north, are probably the result of under-recording. The ease of detecting Cuckoos by their

2,000 pairs

call shows in the fact that, while they were recorded in 64% of tetrads, only 5% of the records were of confirmed breeding. Dunnocks are the main hosts in farmland, woodland and around habitations, replaced by Reed Warblers and Meadow Pipits in freshwater and heathland habitats respectively (Glue and Morgan 1972), and this is almost certainly the case in Buckinghamshire. Other species that are occasionally recorded as foster parents vary from Blackbird to Wren in size; and Robin, Pied Wagtail, Sedge Warbler and Reed Bunting have all been recorded in Buckinghamshire.

Birds tend to return to the same habitat in which they were raised and parasitise the same host species that fostered them. A female Cuckoo watches potential hosts from some vantage point, seeking out birds engaged in nest building. Eggs are usually laid in the afternoon at intervals of two to five days and the process takes as little as nine seconds. The breeding season of Cuckoos is synchronised with the host species and young may still be found in Reed Warbler nests as late as the last week of August.

The last Cuckoos leave Britain during August and September to winter in Africa. In Buckinghamshire the latest dates recently recorded vary between 12 August (1975) and 19 September (1982). Ringed Cuckoos are infrequently recovered but two involving Buckinghamshire birds give some indication of timing and direction of departure in the autumn and, more importantly, the probable wintering area. These records are: Newport Pagnell (27 Jun 1965) to Loire, France (6 Sep 1965), and Marlow (27 Jul 1980) to Belgium (14 Sep 1980), and there is a record of a bird ringed just outside the county at Eton (23 Jun 1928) being found in Cameroon on 20 Jan 1930. In spring, returning Cuckoos are first reported in the county from as early as 14 Mar (1967) (Hudson 1973) but more usually from 7 April onwards, with widespread reports from 17 April.

RAM

Barn Owl
Tyto alba

Resident in small numbers.

H & R stated that the Barn Owl 'breeds commonly', but by 1920 H & J had modified this to 'by no means uncommon in suitable localities', and considered it decidedly less numerous than the Tawny Owl. Price in 1947 thought it to be a fairly common resident but much less so than in former years. By 1976 F & Y found it to be uncommon. They remark that 'there has been a marked decrease in recent years but numbers appear to be building up again'. Possibly this apparent recovery owed something to a series of mild winters, but whatever the cause it was short-lived. In 1978 extensive felling of elms killed by Dutch elm disease took place and the following winter was hard, with prolonged snow cover. A sharp downturn in the Barn Owl's status in the county appears to date from this time, and the birds have disappeared from many previous strongholds. This history closely follows the apparent national picture. Worst hit have been the more built up and intensively farmed areas of central and S England (Shawyer 1987), of which Buckinghamshire seems typical. Concern for the Barn Owl's future has prompted a variety of initiatives such as surveys, nestbox installation and captive breeding schemes, but in the long run these will fail unless there are fundamental improvements in habitat quality.

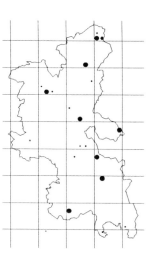

20 pairs

Barn Owls are very sedentary and are reluctant to move even if severe weather occurs. They are typically birds of open farmland. Rough grassy marginal land, as along hedgerows or river banks, provide valuable hunting areas within this habitat. Unfortunately, roadside verges also fill the birds' feeding needs admirably, but expose them to a high level of risk from traffic. Not at all a woodland bird like the Tawny Owl, none the less the presence of woodland edge is a useful feature, though in the Chilterns much of this is on higher ground where the Barn Owl fares less well in winter. Nest sites are another important factor. While Barn Owls will readily nest in buildings on farms and elsewhere, the majority of local breeding birds until recently used tree cavities. Old elms provided a rich source of these, and although many alternatives still exist it may be that the loss of a great number of elms within a few years during the 1970s was too rapid for the species to cope with.

At present the Barn Owl survives in the county in a number of scattered pockets, which are indicated by the map. Since the county breeding survey, there were no confirmed reports

171

of breeding until 1991 when birds were recorded breeding at 7 widely scattered sites. The long period without confirmed breeding may simply indicate that most nests are now in buildings. Such sites are difficult to locate and easily overlooked. These statements refer to wild birds. There are in addition a substantial number of feral birds originating from captive breeding schemes. The most ambitious of these is centred near Great Missenden. Following a pilot scheme in 1984, 22 pairs were released in 1985-86 on various farms in the district, all provided with nestboxes. A further 50 individuals were released in 1987. Four young were reared by one pair in 1984, 7 by 2 pairs in 1985 and 14 by 4 pairs in 1986. One of the successful pairs in 1985 consisted of an ex-captive female and a wild male.

Readiness to breed in captivity underlines an important feature of the Barn Owl's breeding biology. When conditions are good it has a greater capacity to respond with increased breeding effort than any other British bird of prey. Though 3 to 5 eggs are normal, many more are sometimes laid. H & R recorded clutches of 9 and 11 in Buckinghamshire. It is also the only owl in Britain which is capable of rearing more than one brood in a season, despite a fledging period nearly double that of the Tawny. The potential breeding season therefore spans much of the year, but August is perhaps the peak month for fledging in the county. Well grown young Barn Owls can sometimes be detected even in a deeply concealed nest site by their loud snoring hisses. The young disperse after a few weeks, but not usually far. Three quarters of recoveries have been within 20 km of the ringing site (the Winter Atlas).

Wintering Barn Owls roost in tree cavities or farm buildings. The latter are particularly frequented during hard weather, sometimes raising hopes that breeding will follow. Unfortunately such birds usually disappear with the return of milder conditions. East coast counties receive varying numbers of winter visitors of the darker continental race *T. a. guttata*, but there appear to be no records of them for the county..

PJKB

Little Owl
Athene noctua

Resident; breeds throughout the county.

Little Owls were unknown in Buckinghamshire a century ago. Following introductions into Yorkshire and Kent from Europe, large scale releases were made in the 1890s by Lord Lilford in Northamptonshire and by Walter Rothschild in Tring Park. The latter seem to have been unsuccessful, although the species now breeds there regularly. Presumably most of the first Buckinghamshire colonists originated from the Northamptonshire stock. H & R comment that 'Every year cages full are sent over from Holland ... many have been liberated and bred, though they are decreasing in numbers.' This theme, of an increase followed by a decrease, has been echoed by histories up to and including the Breeding Atlas, though the supposed timing of these changes varies. For an introduced species expanding into a vacant niche, such a sequence of events is perhaps to be expected, but there is clearly a subjective element in many accounts. Evidently, hard winters such as 1946/47 and 1962/63 had an adverse effect, and so, perhaps, did the pesticide problems of the 1950s and 1960s. Concrete facts and figures are scarce, and the effects of recent changes in agricultural practice on the Little Owl are poorly understood. An excellent Swiss study (Juillard 1984) could provide the basis for more detailed work in Britain.

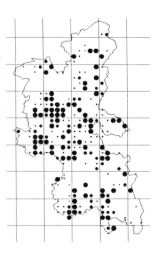

700 pairs

Within Buckinghamshire, more limited surveys over the past eight years suggest that over much of the county the Little Owl is the most numerous farmland bird of prey, and is maintaining its numbers. The national Common Birds Census data used to estimate populations puts Little Owl behind Kestrel, however. As the map indicates, strongholds are the Vale of Aylesbury and the Thames Valley, with a rather blank area along the well wooded Chilterns scarp, where Tawny Owls probably exclude the species to some extent. Open farmland is the principal habitat in the county, subject to availability of nest sites and invertebrate prey. The former are not difficult for the birds to find, except in some areas devastated by Dutch elm disease, but prey availability may influence habitat choice. Although rodents form a substantial part of the diet, invertebrates are also of great importance to this small predator (Hibbert-Ware 1937-38). Vital items are earthworms, best obtained from grassland, and dung beetles, especially *Geotrupes* spp, for which the presence of stock is essential. Consequently, extensive areas of cereal or other arable farming are unlikely to support high densities of Little

Owls.

Breeding may commence from early April, but most Buckinghamshire birds start at the end of the month or in early May. Breeding success can be adversely affected by cold weather in spring. Typical nest sites are narrow curving cavities in trees, with the eggs or young often hidden around a corner. Pollard poplar, abundant in parts of the Vale of Aylesbury provides many such sites, while willow, ash, oak, apple and the few remaining dead elms are all regularly used. Farm buildings, bale ricks, wood stacks, rabbit burrows and even a dense hawthorn hedge are some of the alternatives recorded in the county. Nest boxes are less readily taken here than by Tawny Owls and Kestrels.

Fledged by early July, the young disperse after four or five weeks, usually moving only a short distance. Most recoveries are under 10 km, and although occasional birds travel considerably farther, no such records involve local birds. A high proportion of recoveries in the county are road casualties. Persecution seems rare.

Winter roosts, which may be used throughout the year by established breeding birds, are generally on ledges or crevices in trees, giving shelter and a good view. They are betrayed by characteristic brownish pellets, spangled with glossy fragments of beetle elytra, and often also by accumulations of prey, sometimes referred to as 'larders'. Territories are established from February onwards, to the accompaniment of far-carrying 'kiew' calls, uttered by day as well as night. Data from S England (Glue and Scott 1980) indicate territory areas averaging from 35 ha (water meadows) to 38 ha (mixed farmland). Sites selected for nesting include some traditional cavities, used year after year, but changes are more frequent than with Tawny Owls and Kestrels. Consequently, breeding surveys of this species require extra effort in order to locate all new nest sites each season.

PJKB

Tawny Owl
Strix aluco

Resident, breeding throughout the county.

H & R reported that the Tawny Owl was 'common wherever there are large and old trees with hollows to breed in'. This essentially holds true today, but the loss of tree cover in the intervening years must have reduced numbers, although there was an increase in numbers in the first three decades of this century. Tawny Owls escaped the worst effects of the organochlorine pollution during the 1950s and 1960s, but the efficiency of modern rodenticides must have had an adverse effect through prey reduction. On the credit side, direct persecution is less than at the turn of the century, while active encouragement of the birds, for example by provision of nestboxes, has emerged as a positive factor.

The map for this species probably gives a rather distorted picture of the Tawny Owl's distribution in Buckinghamshire, largely due to the practical difficulties of covering all the Chilterns woodlands adequately for a nocturnal species. Thus, for example, it is shown breeding in some fairly built up areas but apparently absent from adjacent woodland in which its true numbers must actually be higher. Almost certainly its density in the Chilterns is considerably greater than in the Vale of Aylesbury where the population is patchy and dependent on scattered woodlands, thickets and hedgerows. Very open country is avoided, because the Tawny Owl hunts principally by dropping on to its prey from a perch, rather than quartering the ground. Nesting cavities could be a limiting factor, especially in commercial beechwoods where diseased growth is quickly eliminated, but old nests of squirrels, crows, Sparrowhawks and others provide alternatives which are probably under-represented by nest records. Chimney-type boxes installed in such woods have been readily accepted. In the Vale, cavities in ash, pollard poplar or dead elm are the usual sites. Boxes set for Kestrels are also used, though interestingly very few are ever used by both species. Eighteen local Kestrel boxes have been used by Tawny Owls and 56 by Kestrels, but only one has been used successfully by both species, with failed attempts in another two. Tawny Owls occasionally nest in bale ricks, but never in farm buildings as such, though individuals regularly roost in barns and sheds, leading to many spurious reports of 'Barn Owls'.

400 pairs

Being dependent on detailed local knowledge for hunting success, most established Tawny Owls are extremely sedentary. Breeding territories coincide closely with winter range, their size and boundaries depending from year to year on rodent numbers. In years of poor food supply, few pairs breed at all, and those that do tend to start later and have smaller clutches. The Tawny Owl is on average the earliest nesting British owl, with a mean starting date of 25 March (the Breeding Atlas). In 1985 at least one Chilterns pair started their large clutch of 5 eggs in mid February.

Monitoring of nestboxes and natural sites since 1980 has

shown marked differences in breeding success between populations in the Chilterns and the Vale of Aylesbury. As might be expected, Chiltern birds are more successful on average, but this is not so in all years. Unseasonal weather can have a serious effect on success, as when several monitored broods were killed during heavy snow on 25-26 Apr 1981. Successful broods mainly leave the nest during May. Most consist of 1 or 2 young but 3 or 4, and rarely 5, may be reared in a good year. The presence of fledged broods is betrayed after dark by insistent 'kewick' hunger calls. Full independence comes in the first autumn, during which time mortality is highest, with road deaths accounting for a high proportion of ringing recoveries in the county. Most young birds disperse no more than 10 km in their search for territories in which to establish themselves. During winter Tawny Owls roost by day in trees, with a liking for ivy-covered limbs. Occasionally their powers of concealment fail them, and noisy mobbing parties of small birds draw attention to their whereabouts. Courtship and nest cavity selection occur from December onwards, though some sites are chosen only just before breeding.

PJKB

Long-eared Owl
Asio otus

Uncommon resident and irregular winter visitor.

Early accounts depict this species as a regular, although not numerous, breeding bird in wooded parts of Buckinghamshire (H & R, H & J). Much later F & Y refer to these accounts as 'old nesting records', and describe the Long-eared Owl as an uncommon resident, rarely recorded. It may in fact be much overlooked as it is highly nocturnal, and an immense amount of skilled fieldwork would be required to form an accurate picture of its distribution in the county. That said, it does appear to have decreased this century, perhaps as a result of competition with the Tawny Owl. Ironically, it will also be less well recorded as a result of the decline in keepering, a reversal of the situation with many other birds.

Songs and calls associated with territory establishment and courtship begin in late winter, and provide the best means of discovering this elusive species. Coniferous woodland is a favoured habitat for nesting, though by no means the only one, and quite small copses and spinneys may be utilised. A nest in

the Vale of Aylesbury in 1975 was in a hedgerow poplar in open farmland (P J K Burton). Typically this was in the old nest of a Carrion Crow, though those of Sparrowhawks and Magpies are also commonly used. This habit is a further factor in making proof of breeding difficult to obtain. Breeding starts somewhat later on average than the Tawny Owl, and most young fledge in late May or June. For several weeks after this the presence of the young may be revealed by their 'unoiled gate' hunger cries. Thereafter they disperse randomly, and farther on average than Tawny Owls or Little Owls, with about a quarter of the birds ringed in Britain moving more than 100 km.

Birds from N Europe are more strongly migratory, and reach Britain in varying numbers each winter, sometimes almost on the scale of an irruption as was the case in 1986. The Winter Atlas mentions 26 foreign ringed Long-eared Owls recovered in Britain. One of these was a bird ringed at Vogelenzey in N Holland on 8 Jun 1932 and recovered at High Wycombe on 3 Nov 1932. Probably some visitors stay in Britain to breed, so increased vigilance following such influxes may reveal nesting pairs in new localities.

Birds have been found wintering more frequently in recent years. A roost of up to 13 birds was found in the Chilterns in January 1991.

PJKB

Short-eared Owl
Asio flammeus

Winter visitor in fluctuating numbers, of scattered and irregular distribution.

Early accounts (H & R, H & J) suggest a similar status in the past, but this could be misleading. The Breeding Atlas gives evidence of an increase in the British breeding population in recent decades, correlated with the spread of moorland forestry, so some overall increase in the wintering population is likely.

In Buckinghamshire wintering Short-eared Owls usually frequent open country, often in the vicinity of water or marshy areas, but also on chalk downland. Records may to some extent reflect the density of birdwatchers, as for example the regular sightings at Willen Lake, but such sites are in any case typical of this owl's habitat preferences. Rather less so is central Milton Keynes where one was seen in January 1984. In the years covered by the Winter Atlas survey, 1982/83 appears to have been a particularly good winter with many reports, while records were scarce in 1983/84. A possible instance of breeding in the south of the county was noted in 1980, but it seems unlikely that this will ever be more than a sporadic event.

Short-eared Owls start to appear in Buckinghamshire from early autumn onwards. Visitors doubtless include birds from British breeding areas, but also some from abroad. There are no ringing recoveries involving the county, but several birds from Scandinavia and Iceland have been found in Britain, as well as individuals from Belgium and western Germany. Short-eared Owls are highly nomadic outside the breeding season, their wanderings strongly influenced by food supplies, especially field voles. Occasional 'plague' levels of these rodents can attract spectacular numbers of birds. This does not appear to have happened in the county since detailed records have been kept, though some of the older farmers recall large gatherings of owls in the early post-war years.

In favourable habitat, Short-eared Owls are moderately gregarious, sharing communal roosts in scrub or rough grass. From these they venture out to hunt around dusk, though they are also often seen abroad earlier in the day. The latest lingering winter visitors have departed by mid May, so for any birds seen here from this time onwards, the possibility of breeding needs to be investigated.

PJKB

Nightjar
Caprimulgus europaeus

Rare summer visitor; migrant in very small numbers.

Clark Kennedy described the distribution of Nightjars as partially distributed throughout Buckinghamshire but nowhere numerous. He gives Gerrards Cross as a site. H & J remarked 'in suitable places by no means rare.' They list a number of sites throughout the county from Newport Pagnell and Bletchley in the north to Burnham Beeches, Marlow, and Hambleden in the south.

The history of Nightjars since the Second World War is one of a steady decline. In 1944 c8 pairs were recorded in the area bounded by Beaconsfield, Dropmore, and Wooburn. Between 1948 and 1963 up to four pairs bred at Littleworth Common, one pair at East Burnham Common, and three pairs at Bockmer. Birds may also have bred at Dukes Wood near Gerrards Cross, Penn Street, and Black Park. Many of these sites are now unsuitable due to the growth of trees in the breeding areas.

In 1965 four pairs were discovered in Brickhill Woods. This area remained a breeding site until the early 1980s when they seem to have died out. In the late 1970s birds were heard in Balham's Wood, near Stonor and may have bred for a few years.

The species is maintaining a very precarious existence in the county. Indeed it is possible that Nightjars no longer breed, and that the birds which are occasionally heard in the south of the county are passage migrants or wandering unmated individuals.

The 1981 BTO survey produced only two sites in the county, although during the mapping period Nightjars were found in

179

the Brickhills and at one site in the south. The map is not being being published because it is now no longer correct, and also to protect the few sites where it may still breed.

The primary habitat of Nightjars is heathland, a very rare and decreasing habitat in Buckinghamshire. They also utilise cleared woodland or recently planted conifer plantations, but this is a very transient habitat. The population decline in the county is paralleled by its decline in the country as a whole. As well as the reduction in habitat, this decline may also be linked to climatic change.

Attempts are being made to create conditions suitable for Nightjars in the south of the county. The heathland habitat is being invaded by birch and considerable work is required to create suitable conditions for breeding.

Passage birds are found in very small numbers. Since 1980 there have been four spring migrants recorded between 18 May and 3 Jun, and two in the autumn. One was on 12 Sep 1982 at Downley Common, and the other on 15 Aug 1988 at Langley Park.

DMF

Swift
Apus apus

Summer visitor, breeding throughout the county in towns and villages.

Clark Kennedy and all subsequent authors refer to the Swift as a regular or common summer visitor to Buckinghamshire, which it remains today.

The earliest arrival reported in the county between 1972 and 1991 was 15 Apr 1991, with the latest first arrival being 1 May 1976. Mass arrival generally occurs in mid May. The single-brood breeding cycle is very compressed, and the birds stay only three to three-and-a-half months before returning to Africa, south of the equator.

The breeding population remains fairly stable. As the birds are almost entirely dependent on buildings for their nest sites, only considerable replacement of traditional sites with unsuitable buildings is likely to upset the balance. Though they are seen throughout the county, breeding is not easy to prove - notwithstanding the assertion in the Breeding Atlas that 'locating breeding Swifts is easy because of their noisy chases'. Moreover, among the adults of breeding age are younger non-breeders - some possibly even three years old - which practise nest making, and this in itself makes it difficult at times to prove breeding. It is significant that tetrads showing only possible breeding are three times as numerous as those showing proved breeding. In Hertfordshire birds were proved to breed in 40% of tetrads and at least possible breeding was reported in 72% overall, compared with 12% and 59% respectively in Buckinghamshire. This may be because Hertfordshire is a more built-up county and therefore contains a larger number of suitable nest sites. The corresponding figures for Oxfordshire are 23% and 68%.

In the late summer some lakes and reservoirs attract quite large flocks. At Willen Lake more than 1,000 have been recorded. The main southward migration from the county usually starts in mid August. In 1976 most had left by the first week of August, which was considered early, but the good summer had obviously allowed the young to develop quickly. However, the following year the last birds were seen well into September. The latest reported was at Bletchley 2 Nov 1975, although Clark Kennedy noted one at Fawley on 22 Dec 1860. Only 70 Swifts were trapped and ringed between 1972 and 1986. One ringed at Weston Turville in May 1967 was recovered at Brazzaville, Congo in September 1968 and another, recovered when breeding at North Dean in June 1971, had been ringed as a nestling in Holland in June 1963 (BWP). Many local High and West Wycombe birds have been recovered in the same area, one after 11 years.

DBH

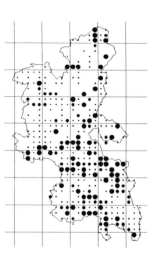

1,000 pairs

Kingfisher
Alcedo atthis

Resident, locally common in suitable habitat.

Earlier this century H & R stated that the Kingfisher was generally distributed where suitable habitat existed, while a few years later H & J wrote that Kingfishers were once quite numerous but reduced in numbers due to shooting, particularly on the River Thames. According to F & Y an increase occurred following the cessation of shooting and the introduction of the Protection of Birds Acts. The provision of new habitat, through the excavation of gravel pits, reservoirs, clay pits and canals, has also been beneficial to Kingfishers.

The present breeding distribution shows a very localised

100 pairs

pattern around streams, rivers, gravel pits, lakes and reservoirs, where a plentiful supply of minnows, sticklebacks and bullheads may be found. This shows the specific habitat requirements of Kingfishers. In the extreme south of the county Kingfisher distribution follows the meandering of the River Thames, and a concentration may also be found at the Wraysbury gravel pits bordering the Thames in the county's south-east corner. The central part of the county shows a few isolated breeding records, associated with the River Thame and its tributaries in the west, and the Grand Union Canal and Tring Reservoirs in the east. Very few breeding sites are found in the northern part of the county, with the exception of the Milton Keynes area where the Grand Union Canal, Rivers Ouzel and Great Ouse, and the gravel pits associated with them provide more suitable habitat.

Two or sometimes three broods may be reared in a season extending from March to September. Adult Kingfishers chase the young from the breeding territory soon after fledging. Movements of juvenile birds take place mainly from July onwards, in no particular direction. The birds usually travel less than 10 km but occasionally up to 250 km (Morgan and Glue 1977). Birds ringed in the county in autumn have been recovered in Surrey and Essex (via Northamptonshire), while others ringed at Chew Valley, Avon (149 km) and Knaresborough, Yorkshire (250 km) have been found in Buckinghamshire in November and August respectively.

Three major factors affect Kingfisher numbers: severe winters, pollution, and waterways management. Cold winters can cause very high mortality when access to open water is restricted by ice for long periods. Between 1962 and 1982 the winters of 1962/63, 1978/79 and 1981/82 reduced Kingfisher numbers considerably (Dobinson and Richards 1964, Marchant and Hyde 1980, Taylor and Marchant 1983). In extreme conditions some Kingfishers escape by moving to the coast. However, the high reproductive potential of the species enables a rapid recovery from heavy losses.

RAM

Bee-eater
Merops apiaster

Very rare vagrant. All records are given.

1866: 1 Dropmore.
1927: 1 in last week of Oct, Skirmett.
1976: 1 on 8 May, Buckingham.
1979: 1 on 27 Apr, Chalfont St Giles.

The record of 7 at Stoke Mandeville in June 1983 mentioned by Brucker et al (1992) was never submitted to the British Birds Rarities Committee, and cannot be substantiated.

Hoopoe
Upupa epops

Rare vagrant. Has bred once.

Clark Kennedy gives an undated record for Chesham.

The first dated record is:

1760: 2 shot at Ford.

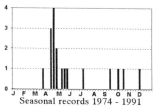
Seasonal records 1974 - 1991

Between 1838 and 1957 there were a further 11 records, including successful breeding in a garden at Taplow in 1916. There were another 12 records between 1962 and 1968, and 18 records between 1970 and 1990 with a maximum annual total of four birds in 1975. The records since 1974 are shown on a seasonal histogram. Hoopoes have been found throughout the county with most occurring at the end of April. Unusually, a bird was seen on 30 Nov 1990, and again from 7-8 Dec 1990 at Winslow.

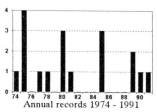
Annual records 1974 - 1991

Wryneck
Jynx torquilla

Scarce migrant which used to breed.

Clark Kennedy described the status of Wryneck as a 'common summer visitor', but there was evidently a reduction in the population by the early 20th century for H & J stated it was a 'regular summer visitor, but has recently decreased in numbers'. By 1947 Price wrote that it was a 'regular summer visitor, only breeding in the south-east'.

In the 1950s pairs bred at Penn, Marlow, and another site in the county. Small numbers of birds continued to be seen almost every year but there was no sign of breeding except for

183

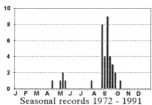

Seasonal records 1972 - 1991

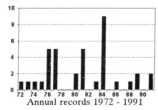

Annual records 1972 - 1991

a bird emerging from a hole in the Thames Valley during 1973. It was assumed that Wrynecks as a breeding bird in the county were long past until 1985 when a pair bred in a coconut hollowed out by Blue Tits in a garden in Chalfont St Peter. They were seen in the same locality during 1986 and 1987 but breeding was not proved.

Wrynecks require trees with suitable nest-holes, and areas of grassland where they can feed on ants, their major food. They found these conditions in old orchards, parkland, large gardens, and in the areas of scrub and grassland which are typical of the Chilterns.

The local decline is part of a general decline throughout England. From being a widespread summer visitor as far north as the Lake District they are now probably extinct. The reasons for the decline are not clear, but seem likely to be associated with the similar decline of the Red-backed Shrike and Woodlark. Wrynecks are a bird with a distinct south-east bias to their range in Britain, although birds from Scandinavia have visited Scotland in a similar manner to Red-backed Shrikes. It is likely that the birds, or their staple food supply, are at the edge of their climatic tolerance, so that any small decrease in mean temperatures could bring a reduction in the population. Many ants require hot conditions. The extinction of the Large Blue butterfly in Britain was due to a reduction in the population of the *Mycelis* ants on which the butterflies depended, which in turn was due to a lowering of the mean temperature of their grassland habitat. In a more local context, Adonis Blue butterflies, which also have a relationship with ants, began declining during the 1950s, and are now virtually extinct in Buckinghamshire after being fairly widepsread in the Chilterns. It is possible that the commoner ants on which Wrynecks feed have suffered a population decrease because of lower summer temperatures.

The histograms show the pattern of occurrence of migration during the years 1972-1991. During this period 37 birds were seen in 14 of the years. There is a very small spring passage and a slightly larger autumn passage which peaks in the last week of August and the first week of September. It is likely that these birds are drift migrants from Scandinavia. Wrynecks have been found throughout the county, but the central Chilterns seem particularly favoured at such places as Coleshill and Chartridge.

DMF

Green Woodpecker
Picus viridis

Locally common breeding resident.

H & R described this as probably the most plentiful woodpecker in the county: 'though nowhere numerous'. They wrote, 'it occurs wherever there are old trees in which it can nest.' H & J noted that Green Woodpeckers became scarce on the lower ground in the eastern part of the Thames Valley compared with their status in the beech woods of the western part.

Large-scale changes in distribution of the Green Woodpecker, which mainly concern the northern part of its range in N England and Scotland, are summarised in the Breeding Atlas. The breeding distribution map for Buckinghamshire shows the species to be widespread, though more numerous in the well-wooded southern half of the county. North of the Chiltern escarpment, which shows clearly on the map, the records are much more localised and the species is absent from much of the agricultural area lacking copses or hedgerows with mature timber. The chain of deciduous woodland running from Oakley to Middle Claydon, and the woodland areas of Brickhill Woods and Ashridge are centres of Green Woodpecker distribution here, most of the other scattered records relating to farmland breeding birds.

800 pairs

Green Woodpeckers are much less restricted to deciduous woodland than the other two British species of woodpecker, and while the map of their distribution is similar to that of the Great Spotted Woodpecker, the latter is not as widely distributed over the agricultural country lacking sizeable woods. Well timbered parkland, dry heath and well grazed chalk grassland are other favoured habitats of Green Woodpeckers, where they feed on the ground, especially on ants.

During the fieldwork for the county breeding atlas survey, Green Woodpeckers were recorded in 49% of tetrads but only confirmed in 8%, indicating how easy they are to detect by their loud 'yaffle' calls, but how difficult it may be to find their nests or newly fledged young. Nest holes are usually excavated in deciduous trees (especially ash, oak, birch and beech) at varying heights up to 15 m. Elms accounted for 8% of nest trees recorded on BTO nest record cards, with no difference in usage before or after the onset of Dutch elm disease (Osborne 1982). Eggs are laid from early April to early June (most commonly during May), with young in the nest in June/early July. Green Woodpeckers may travel some distance from the nest to feed at favourite grassland sites.

Green Woodpeckers are very sedentary birds and there is no evidence of long-distance movements within this country or the Continent. The most notable local ringing recovery is of a bird moving 45 km from Cheddington to Little Barford (Bedfordshire). In hard winters Green Woodpeckers are severely affected when they are unable to find food in the frozen ground. Some N Buckinghamshire woodland CBC plots reflect this. For example, following the cold winters of 1978/79 and 1981/82, the density of Green Woodpeckers at Linford Wood (Milton Keynes) dropped from 7 pairs per 100 ha in 1978 to none in 1979, and at Howe Park Wood (Bletchley) birds were present in three out of five years during 1970-1974, but not in either 1983 or 1984.

RAM

Great Spotted Woodpecker
Dendrocopos major

Locally common breeding resident.

In Britain as a whole the Great Spotted Woodpecker population has undergone some marked changes during the past 150 years. By the early nineteenth century it had all but disappeared north of Cheshire and Yorkshire. With the climatic amelioration that began in the latter part of last century a range expansion occurred, taking the species to the limit of suitable breeding conditions in N Scotland. The Breeding Atlas shows a widespread distribution in mainland Britain, and the population nationally has shown further recent increases. While the national Common Birds Census index for woodland remained stable from 1965-1971 it rose by 116% in the period 1972-1978. Osborne (1982) considered the most likely cause to be the greater availability of beetle larvae due to the spread of Dutch elm disease.

Historical information on the Great Spotted Woodpecker in Buckinghamshire is rather sparse, but H & J noted that it was scarcer than formerly, being less rare in the south of the county. The present situation parallels the national picture. Fieldwork for the county breeding survey showed that Great Spotted Woodpeckers now occur at a fairly high density in some of the deciduous woods in the north and west of the county and that the population has increased considerably over the last decade. At Linford Wood, Milton Keynes a density of 9.3 pairs per sq km was recorded in 1979 compared to 4.7

pairs per sq km in 1975. At Howe Park Wood, Bletchley the population increased from nil in 1971 to 16.7 pairs per sq km in 1983. The highest densities recorded in the county are from some W Buckinghamshire woodlands, where in 1984 15 pairs per sq km were found in old coppice and 20 pairs per sq km in high forest oak. These compare with an average density from a sample of national Common Birds Census plots in E England in 1983 of 8.3 pairs per sq km.

Location of Great Spotted Woodpeckers is fairly easy by listening for the loud 'tchick' calls and far-carrying drumming. Also, adults may be observed in courtship display: wing-quivering, tail-stretching and spiral chases around tree trunks. Nest excavation may begin as early as autumn but is most intensive during March. A sample of nest record cards from SE England showed the most frequent nest trees to be birch (33%), oak (15%) and elm (10%), with a wide variety of other tree species also used. Sites occasionally include telegraph poles and nest boxes.

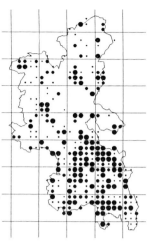

800 pairs

In autumn, family groups wander from the nesting area; isolated birds may be located in a wide variety of habitats including farmland, hedgerows and small gardens. Great Spotted Woodpeckers are attracted to fat and suet at garden feeders and the BTO's Garden Bird Feeding Survey has shown an increase in records between the 1970s and 1980s. British Great Spotted Woodpeckers are largely sedentary but continental migrants occasionally arrive during the autumn, and rarely on an irruptive scale as in 1949 and 1962. The Winter Atlas shows a similar distribution for the species in the winter months as in the breeding season, with records in 15 of 18 10-km squares of the county.

RAM

Lesser Spotted Woodpecker
Dendrocopos minor

Uncommon resident breeder.

The Lesser Spotted Woodpecker is described by earlier authors as 'fairly common in wooded areas', and all remark that it is commoner than generally thought. It is not easily seen, and is certainly under-recorded. This is largely due to its small size and its tendency to stay in the tops of trees. It is also very mobile within its local area. It may occur unexpectedly and rarely seems to be seen in the same place twice, except at nesting time.

100 pairs

The county breeding survey map seems to reflect all these features as only 8 tetrads had proved breeding out of a total of 78. Birds are thinly dispersed throughout the county with most in the central Chilterns and least in the Vale of Aylesbury and the north of the county. Lesser Spotted Woodpeckers avoid conifers but may be found in deciduous woods of any size and typically in lines of trees by rivers.

BBC annual reports did not discuss the status of the species in the 1980s but the MTNHS report for 1979 mentioned records from 22 localities, which was three less than in 1972. In the north of the county then the only records were from Milton Keynes and Stowe.

In 1978 it was suggested that the population had suffered a slight reduction and the loss of trees due to Dutch elm disease was put forward as a reason, a view repeated three years later. The national Breeding Atlas suggests that the consequences of Dutch elm disease were initially beneficial in providing an abundance of food in dead and decaying trees, though conceding that the eventual loss of trees might lead to fewer birds. There are not enough local records to detect any trend.

The Lesser Spotted Woodpecker breeds from late April into June, and is single brooded. Both sexes excavate the nest hole which is usually in soft or decaying wood, sometimes even on the underside of a branch. It can be up to 20 m above the ground, adding further to the difficulty of proving breeding.

Following the breeding season and moult, the species remains in the general breeding area. The birds may wander a little, even into villages and suburban areas, and they may be seen foraging in tit flocks. The BBC Garden Bird Survey mentions individuals in a couple of gardens and even taking artificial food, but these seem to be accidental occurrences rather than instances of birds being specifically attracted by food put out.

DBH

Woodlark
Lullula arborea

Previously bred; now a very rare vagrant.

Woodlarks bred regularly though rather sparsely in the middle and south of the county until 1961 when there was a last record of three birds on 16 Sep at Longdown Hill, Cadsden. The largest recorded flock during this period was one of 15-20 birds at Saunderton on 20 Nov 1949. There then followed a gap of 10 years before a pair was observed feeding young on 18 Jul 1971 at Bow Brickhill Woods.

Since then there have only been 4 records of single birds.

1973: 14 Feb, Iver GP.
1988: 23 Feb-8 Mar, Burnham.
1990: 30 Mar, Taplow.
1990: 21 Oct, Calvert.

The demise of Woodlarks in the county is part of a general decline in the population of Britain and N Europe. This decrease parallels the similar decreases in the populations of Wrynecks, Red-backed Shrikes, and Cirl Buntings, and may be linked to cooler and wetter springs and summers.

Skylark
Alauda arvensis

Common resident, migrant, and winter visitor.

The earliest accounts describe the Skylark as common, a statement that is still valid. The map shows a widespread distribution with gaps that are almost certainly due to under-recording. It is likely that Skylarks breed in almost every tetrad in the county.

After a long period of stability, Skylarks began declining nationally around 1980 so that the National Common Birds Census indices are now about half the 1980 figures. There are a number of reasons for this decline. The birds prefer fields whose vegetation is short enough to walk through. In the

189

1986: 20,000 pairs
1991: 10,000 pairs

breeding season this is found in newly-cut grass and spring-sown cereals. Autumn-sown cereals and oil-seed rape are only used in April, after which they become too tall. The change to winter cereals, which has become a common practice in the county, is thus detrimental to Skylarks. This change in farming practice has also reduced the area of stubble which is an important feeding habitat in winter. Spraying with herbicides is also a factor in the decline as this has reduced the amount of arable weeds which provide another important food source. It will be interesting to see what the effect of the increasing area of set-aside in the county will have on the Skylark population. Several large fields near Beaconsfield which were set-aside in 1987 have large numbers of breeding Skylarks while similar fields near Dorney Court have recently held very large wintering flocks.

In winter the resident population is augmented by visitors from NE Europe, though the lack of local ringing recoveries makes the source of the visitors only an assumption. During this period many birds form flocks. Flocks in excess of 100 birds are recorded almost every year, and flocks of 250 birds are not uncommon. The largest recorded flock is one of 500-600 birds at Dorney Court on 20 Feb 1991, while there were 350-500 birds at Little Marlow on 10 Feb 1991. Another large flock was of 450 birds at Boveney on 26 Dec 1984.

Large snow movements are occasionally recorded. On 31 Dec 1978 1,000 birds flew south-west over Marlow in 10 minutes, while on the following day a movement of 2,500 birds per hour was recorded.

DMF

Sand Martin
Riparia riparia

Very local breeding summer visitor, and regular migrant.

Sand Martins originally depended primarily on steep-sided river banks for nest sites, and their distribution in Buckinghamshire must therefore have been more restricted than it is today. Though nesting at sand and gravel excavations dates back at least to Clark Kennedy's day, the availability of this habitat has increased considerably in more recent times. Kennedy also alluded to breeding along the Thames and described the species as 'common everywhere during the summer months', but since he mentions no other colonies his assessment perhaps includes passage birds. H & R merely wrote of breeding 'in suitable places' while H & J only mentioned birds at Tring reservoirs in summer, and knew of no nearby breeding site. Other pre-war reports note a few Thames breeding colonies and occasional breeding at pits elsewhere.

Fluctuations in population size are greatly affected by human activity, notably gravel digging and subsequent flooding and filling in. The recent major decline, however, is thought to have been caused by the drought in the bird's main wintering area, the African Sahel. The numbers returning to Britain in 1969 were considerably lower than in 1968; for example, few if any birds were seen at a Milton Keynes pit which had held over 100 pairs, and numbers have remained low. The extent of breeding, especially at major sites, has been very poorly documented. No counts of more than 20-30 pairs were reported in the 1980s except for an estimate of at least 200 holes at a Newport Pagnell site in 1988. With few exceptions, breeding has always been confined to the south and the north-east of the county where the main gravel deposits lie. Some sites are used for many years while other colonies are short-lived. Sand Martins generally feed over (and breed beside) lakes or rivers, but sandpits some way from water are sometimes used. They also occasionally use other sites. For example, a colony at Olney used the masonry of the river bridge, and birds at the Stony Stratford Reserve have readily adopted metal pipes set into a concrete bank, designed to resemble natural burrows. Nesting may begin early in May, and as two broods are often raised, fledging dates often extend to mid August and even into September.

200 pairs

Gatherings of migrants begin to be reported in late July with peak numbers usually in August. The highest count of all was of 5,000 at Iver on 31 Aug 1963; several other flocks of 1,000 to 3,000 have been reported, but not since 1977. More recently, the largest number was at least 250 in an hour at Foxcote on 22 Aug 1980. Last sightings are usually in late September or early October, with the latest at Weston Turville on 24 Oct 1971.

Many Sand Martins have been ringed in the county, especially during the BTO enquiry in the 1960s. Much movement between colonies was recorded, with birds from Buckinghamshire moving to colonies as far as Durham and France. Although there were a few northward flights in summer, most dispersal was predominantly southwards. Birds from Ireland, N Scotland, Wales and many parts of England have been caught in the county, and Chichester reedbeds have provided a much used south coast staging post. Ringing also

191

reveals that movements begin in early July, well before a build up in numbers is seen. Eight birds have been recovered in NW France in August, while one ringed in Shropshire in 1979 was controlled at Linford in August 1980 and found in Spain 22 days later.

The earliest arrival dates are 24 Feb 1990 and 8 Mar 1952, and arrivals in mid or late March are recorded in most years. Larger numbers do not usually appear until mid April. Recent reports mention only two spring gatherings of as many as 150 birds.

HM-G

Swallow
Hirundo rustica

Common summer visitor and passage migrant.

Familiar to Clark Kennedy in the 1860s, the Swallow was regarded as very common everywhere by H & R early this century. Despite decreases in recent years it has remained widely distributed to the present time.

Swallows traditionally prefer to nest in stables or cattle-sheds where they evidently benefit from the associated supply of insect food. They may therefore have been affected by changes in agricultural practice and, in earlier decades, by the disappearance of commercial and farm horses. However, all kinds of farm buildings and other sheds may be occupied, and also out-buildings and porches of houses. The last types of site are occupied on a small but quite wide scale in leafy suburban roads or even near the centres of small towns. In addition some industrial sites are utilised: at the Pitstone cement works pairs nest both in buildings and a tunnel entry well below ground level. Occasional pairs nest under bridges over a brook or canal. In favoured places a number of pairs may nest near each other. While the Swallow's occurrence at a local level is obviously influenced by its dependence on man-made nesting sites, there can be few full tetrads within Buckinghamshire with no potential Swallow homes, and further fieldwork might well have revealed birds in many of the blank squares. At all events the species can be seen to breed throughout the county; problems of access to private buildings frequented by Swallows may explain why only 'possible breeding' was recorded in many tetrads.

In 1975 and again during the 1980s observers' comments on a drop in numbers, both of breeders and (latterly) of autumn flocks, were broadly in line with the national Common Birds Census, which demonstrated a decline beginning in 1973 (with some revival between 1975 and 1978). A connection with a drought-related deterioration of the African migration route and wintering habitat must be suspected. In cold, wet or windy weather, which occurs all too frequently in spring, Swallows congregate over lakes where insects are still available - and the earliest returning migrants are usually seen at such sites. In some years large beds of reeds, or sometimes other tall reed-swamp vegetation, are used as roosts by migrant flocks. Occasional roosting sites used by small to moderate flocks were a mixed hedgerow (1966), a wheatfield (1968) and a water culvert under the M40 (1978). Late summer gatherings on telephone wires are a familiar sight. Nearly all nests are within buildings, or under archways, typically built against a wall or beam, sometimes supported by some form of ledge. In dry spells, a lack of wet mud can delay nest-building, although old nests are quite often re-used. In warmer than average springs a few birds begin laying in late April, whereas in cool years breeding starts several weeks later. Even then many pairs manage two broods, since fresh clutches up to mid August are normal (if not numerous). Third broods are only occasional: a pair at Iver must have embarked on theirs around 23 Sep 1965, the young flying on 28 October.

5,000 pairs

Actual southward passage movements are seldom reported. Passage is frequently though irregularly manifested in the form of feeding concentrations and especially of roosts, but ringing has shown that the turnover of birds at roosts is rapid, and probably many birds leave their nesting quarters, or pass through the county, without forming or joining a local roost (in 1923 a June-ringed nestling was already found in Hampshire in July). Reedbed roosts vary from a few individuals or family parties up to (in Buckinghamshire) occasionally 3,000 birds. A roost of c300 at Aylesbury SF on 27 Jul 1976 was rather early; roosts in August (even c2,000

birds at Weston Turville in 1966) are not infrequent, but more often the large numbers occur during September with, as a rule, a rapid fall-off towards the end of the month, although Weston Turville still had 1,000 birds on 1 Oct 1962, and c700 on 3 Oct 1970.

Ringing at roosts has provided ample evidence of birds from further north in England passing through the county, as well as some from Wales and as far as Perthshire, at least between mid August and late September. Two birds made unexpected reverse flights to Shropshire in the autumn of 1967. The thousands of swallows mist-netted locally have only yielded one southern English recovery in the same autumn (in Dorset), suggesting that many of them may not make another stop before crossing the Channel. There is one October recovery in France, of a nestling ringed at Bourne End in July 1950.

Cool autumn days can result in spectacular feeding concentrations, notably 3,000+ birds at Calvert brickpits on 17 Sep 1973 and several thousand over Haddenham village on 11 Sep 1985. The latter is the only gathering of over 200 noted since the early 1980s. A few late October Swallows (occasionally up to a dozen together) are recorded annually, and there are plenty of November records, from the 1860s to the present. Single birds were observed in the county on 11 Jan 1974, 2 Dec 1974 and 1 Dec 1975. A full-grown May bird from Weston Turville was controlled in the Transvaal on 19 Mar 1969, while one ringed in the latter province on 20 Mar 1970 was controlled at Chesham on 15 Aug 1970.

Contrasting with birds tarrying in South Africa are the earliest arrivals in Buckinghamshire: 15 Mar 1981 (2 birds) and 19 Mar 1979. There are later March records (mainly in the last four days) from a number of years but sometimes the first sightings are in April, the most delayed being 13 Apr 1978. As a rule the species is not widespread until mid April, and generally late April, or occasionally early or even mid May, is the time of main arrival.

All-white or partial albino Swallows have been reported periodically. H & J describe a succession of mixed broods of white and normal Swallows reared by an Aylesbury pair from 1891 to 1895.

HM-G

House Martin
Delichon urbica

Common breeding summer visitor and migrant.

It is probable that the status of House Martins has not changed in the county since man began building and the martins moved from cliffs to artificial structures. Clark Kennedy wrote 'abundant' while H & J commented 'Common, though absent from many apparently suitable villages. Supposed to diminish steadily, but numbers fluctuate'. This is still an accurate statement. They noted that about a million(?) were seen over the river and pond at Great Marlow about 4-5 pm on 18 Sep 1896. The query is theirs.

Most birds occur in small, mobile colonies. This mobility means that the population at a particular site can vary widely from year to year, although the overall population probably remains stable. Their presence in suburbs depends to some extent upon the toleration of householders to the mess the nesting birds create.

The mobile, colonial nature of House Martins makes the population difficult to estimate. The figure of 9,000 pairs is very tentative. The county breeding survey found that birds were recorded in 62% of the total tetrads. This compares with 88% in Hertfordshire and 78% in Oxfordshire. The gaps in the north of the county are probably due to under-recording.

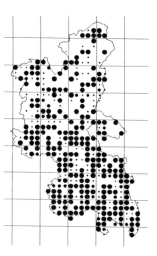

9,000 pairs

The first birds usually arrive in the first half of April, though one exceptionally early bird was seen on 29 Mar 1989 at Willen. The main arrival is usually in late April early May. Birds begin leaving in late September and early October, though an abnormally tardy pair were still feeding young on 7 Oct 1950 at Marlow. The last birds may linger to the first week of November with the latest in recent years being a bird seen at Chesham on 24 Nov 1986. The latest of all was a bird at Hartwell on 5 Dec 1874 (H & J).

House Martins are familiar migrants, often associating with Swallows. They can occur almost anywhere on migration, but, like Swallows, they tend to congregate over open water in poor weather. Flocks of several hundred are common, and sometimes flocks of more than 1,000 may be seen. Over 3,000 birds were seen near Denham on 9 Oct 1976.

There has only been one ringing record involving a bird travelling beyond Britain. A bird ringed in the county on 6 Oct 1974 was recovered in Herault, France on 15 Nov 1974.

Albino birds are occasionally recorded. The last was seen at Latimer on 25 Aug 1974.

DMF

Richard's Pipit
Anthus novaeseelandiae

Very rare vagrant. There are two records.

1967: 1 from 7-24 Oct, Dorney Common.
1990: first-winter from 28-30 Oct, Blue Lagoon, Bletchley.

These are typical dates for this Siberian vagrant.

Tree Pipit
Anthus trivialis

Breeding summer visitor to the more wooded areas of the county.

Tree Pipits occur within the county in open areas with bushes and scattered trees. They find the required habitat in young coniferous plantations and open areas of woodland. Such areas are most common in the Chilterns, Brickhill Woods, and Bernwood Forest as is shown clearly on the distribution map. In the Chilterns a few place names appear regularly in the records: Penn Woods, where birds were very numerous in 1974, Coleshill, Bradenham and Ashridge. However, earlier records suggest that it was probably rather commoner in the past, although not as common as the Meadow Pipit.

Tree Pipits were recorded in 82 tetrads, which is 14% of the total. This compares rather poorly with Hertfordshire (28%), but favourably with Oxfordshire (9%). A population density of 5 pairs per tetrad gives an estimated population of 400 pairs. Because of the transient nature of young conifer plantations the population may fluctuate from year to year. This probably masks any long-term trend, which, nationally, is slightly downwards.

First arrivals occur between 3 and 16 April with the main build-up from mid to late April.

Tree Pipits start to leave the breeding grounds in mid July. Last reports range from late August to mid October. There have been two interesting records involving locally ringed birds. Of two birds ringed as nestlings at Stoke Poges in June 1988, one was controlled at Alum Bay, Isle of Wight on 23 Aug 1988 and the other at Baldwin's Wood, near Wendover on 6 May 1990.

DBH

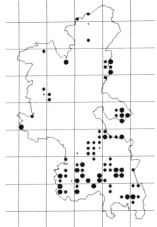

400 pairs

Meadow Pipit
Anthus pratensis

Scarce resident and uncommon passage migrant and winter visitor.

Countrywide, the Meadow Pipit is common and numerous, but Buckinghamshire is not one of its strongholds in the breeding season. It is a bird which prefers open country, so the wooded Chilterns hold no attraction for it. Even the open areas of the Vale of Aylesbury have very few breeding pairs. This confirms the findings of F & Y, but Clark Kennedy and H & R suggest that the Meadow Pipit was much commoner and more widespread in the 19th century. The former noted it as one of the commonest resident birds and H & R reported it occurring especially in lowland pastures. The map shows 43 tetrads where birds were recorded. A figure of 4 pairs per tetrad, which is far below the national breeding density, gives a population of around 200 pairs. In 1980 it was thought that '40 plus' pairs may have bred, but other recent years have reported far fewer breeding pairs. This may be because many sites are infrequently visited by birdwatchers. Chalk downland, such as at Pitstone and Turville Hills, are regular sites, while several pairs breed in the rough ground around Caldecotte Lake. Birds are sometimes present on sites that have only a transient attraction, such as waste ground by the John Lewis superstore at Booker.

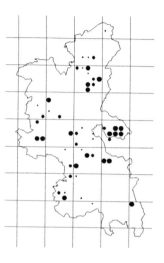

200 pairs

The species is more numerous on passage and in winter, although the birds may disappear completely during cold spells. Most flocks are of 10-20 birds but there are records of up to 200 in January and February, and passage movements of up to 300 in October and March. Most flocks occur near water or on the downland of the Chiltern scarp, although the Bishopstone area occasionally attracts quite large flocks, for example in 1977 and 1986. Only single birds have been recorded in the BBC Garden Bird Survey.

There was a large passage in October 1992 when 350+ were recorded passing through Little Marlow STW on 20th, and c2,000 at the same site on 27th when 115 birds were caught and ringed using a tape lure.

It is likely that many birds come from the north, and some may winter in the same area in successive years. Possibly the bird ringed near Chesham in January 1972 and recovered there in December 1973 was one such. The only other noteworthy ringing recovery involves a bird ringed at Abberton in Essex in October 1957 recovered at Chenies in January 1960.

DBH

197

Rock and Water Pipits
Anthus petrosus and *A. spinoletta*

Rock and Water Pipits were split into two species in 1986 (BOU 1992). Hence for records prior to 1986 it may not be absolutely certain that the identification is correct. There is still quite frequent confusion between brighter examples of the Scandinavian Rock Pipit *A.p.littoralis* and Water Pipit in spring. Thus it would not be surprising if a number of birds recorded as Water Pipits in March or April were in fact Scandinavian Rock Pipits.

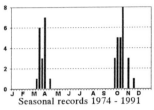

Seasonal records 1974 - 1991

Rock Pipit
Anthus petrosus

Scarce vagrant.

There are three records prior to 1974:

1932: 1 on 16 Oct, Startopsend.
1960: 2 on 23 Apr, Newport Pagnell GP.
1970: 1 on several dates in Feb, Marlow GP.

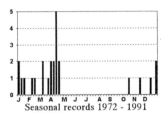

Annual records 1974 - 1991

Since 1974 there have been 40 records of 43 birds. They are shown on the histograms. Most of the birds have been recorded at Willen with a few at Caldecotte and Linford. Records have increased markedly since 1986. As the usual sites for this species are very well-watched this is likely to be a genuine increase. The reasons are not known.

Water Pipit
Anthus spinoletta

Scarce vagrant and winter visitor.

There are four records prior to 1972:

1960: 1 on 18 Apr, Newport Pagnell.
1962: 1 on 25 Mar, near Chesham.
1971: 1 from 28 Jan-11 Apr, Chesham.
1971: 3 on 30 Mar, Latimer Park.

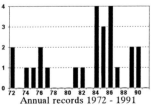

Seasonal records 1972 - 1991

Annual records 1972 - 1991

Since 1972, there have been 23 records of 25 birds. They are shown on the histograms. Localities have included the margins of the usual lakes, and Chesham cress-beds where wintering occurred from 1971 to 1977. The largest gathering was of three birds at Willen on 12 Apr 1986 and the three at Latimer noted above.

There is an interesting contrast with Rock Pipits. As can be seen from the histogram, Water Pipits are mostly found from January to April, with a peak in April, while Rock Pipits are found in both spring and autumn, with a peak in October.

Yellow Wagtail
Motacilla flava flavissima

Passage migrant and summer visitor, breeding mainly in the lowland areas of the county.

There has been a marked contraction in the range of this species in the country since 1930 (BWP). In 1947 Price stated 'The British race (*M.f.flavissima*) is a regular summer visitor, found in low-lying meadowland and near rivers' while in 1976 F & Y remarked 'Breeds in small numbers in low lying meadows near rivers'. These statements still hold true today despite a reduction in the number of breeding pairs in the country since 1976 (Marchant et al 1990).

The preferred breeding habitats of Yellow Wagtails are damp water meadows and marshy fields along river valleys, sewage treatment works, reservoir margins, flooded gravel pits, and sometimes drier areas such as market gardens and industrial waste land (the Breeding Atlas). Yellow Wagtails have been recorded breeding in all these habitats within the county. Chalky areas are avoided by this species (the Breeding Atlas) this being borne out by the Buckinghamshire map where there are virtually no birds breeding within the Chilterns. The distribution map compares well with that published in the Breeding Atlas where breeding was not proven in three of the 10-km squares in the Chilterns.

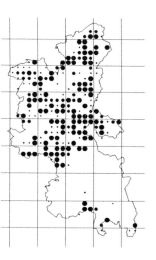

900 pairs

The species is usually recorded in the county between the end of March and the second week in October with the main movements normally in the last two weeks of April and between the third week of July and the end of September. The earliest recorded arrival date is 23rd March and an exceptional late record was a bird at Old Slade on 23 NOv 1973. Larger flocks are more frequently recorded during the autumn migration when flocks of 50+ are not uncommon and 150+ recorded occasionally. On 31 Aug 1980 up to 375 were recorded at a roost at Aylesbury STW. During the spring flocks tend to be somewhat smaller with 100 being exceptional.

Once our Yellow Wagtails leave us in the autumn they head southwards via SW France and Portugal before crossing into Africa and on to their wintering grounds in tropical Africa

(BWP). This is supported by a juvenile Yellow Wagtail which was ringed at Newport Pagnell on 26 Aug 1973 and recovered at Estremadura, Portugal, on 23 Sep 1973. Other ringing records show recoveries in Jersey and Landes, France (one month after ringing). Recoveries within Britain include a bird ringed in West Yorkshire on 14 Aug 1976 and controlled in Buckinghamshire on 10 Sep 1977.

Blue-headed Wagtail
Motacilla flava flava

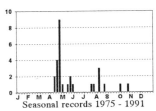
Seasonal records 1975 - 1991

A scarce passage migrant, most often recorded in the spring.

This subspecies is nowadays perhaps more often seen than earlier this century when Price (1947) stated 'The continental race, known as the Blue-headed Wagtail, is a scarce passage migrant; since 1920 recorded on several occasions in April and May at Slough Sewage Farm' (then part of Bucks). It is now a scarce passage migrant, recorded several times in most years. This may be due to an increase in the population in Fennoscandia, and to an increase in the area of suitable habitat, for instance, Willen Lake, where it is often recorded, did not exist before the mid 1970s. The accompanying histogram shows a clear peak at the end of April. It may be that birds are recorded more often in the spring because of the identification difficulties posed by birds in non-breeding and juvenile plumages.

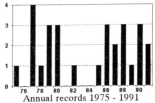
Annual records 1975 - 1991

The following subspecies are less clear-cut. They may well be hybrids rather than true examples.

Spanish Wagtail
Motacilla flava iberiae

In 1980 a male bird resembling this subspecies was first seen on 25 May at Aylesbury STW after which it was seen paired with a normal female and observed carrying nest material. No young were seen. This subspecies normally breeds in SW France, Iberia and the Balearics.

Sykes' Wagtail
Motacilla flava beema

A bird showing characteristics of this subspecies was seen at Willen from 1-3 Apr 1983. This subspecies breeds in SE Russia.

Ashy-Headed Wagtail
Motacilla flava cinereocapilla

A male resembling this race was seen at Weston Turville Reservoir on 16 Apr 1988. This subspecies breeds in Italy, central Mediterranean islands, S Austria, and NW Yugoslavia.

Grey-headed Wagtail
Motacilla flava thunbergi

A male was seen at Caldecotte on 4 Jun 1991. The date is typical for this subspecies which breeds in N Fennoscandia.

JER

Grey Wagtail
Motacilla cinerea

Scarce resident and winter visitor.

There has been a gradual expansion of breeding range into southern and eastern England, most noticeably since 1950 with breeding becoming regular in areas where it had previously been erratic (Marchant et al 1990). Price described this species as 'Chiefly a passage migrant in autumn and spring; a few remain for the winter, and some pairs remain for the summer'. In 1976 F & Y stated 'Breeds in small numbers by some rivers and lakes. Numbers supplemented during the winter by visitors from the north. Numbers greatly reduced during the 1963 hard winter but now fully recovered'. More recently, and on a country wide basis (Marchant et al 1990), a decline was reported following the hard winters of 1978/9, 1981/2 and 1984/5 (during our survey period) and although some recovery has been made the species has not reached the population levels of the mid 1970s.

Grey Wagtails are essentially birds of fast flowing streams in upland and hilly country. In Buckinghamshire they are usually found by rather more slow moving streams but they do pick territories containing faster flowing water such as weirs, narrows, waterfalls, and even locks. The map clearly shows

50 pairs

a higher concentration of Grey Wagtails in the Chilterns where the habitat requirements are more often met. The dots on the map mostly follow the lines of the rivers, the main concentrations being along the rivers Wye, Chess, Misbourne and Thames with a few also along the Thame. However since the fieldwork has been completed a serious lowering of the water table has reduced the flow of all the Chilterns rivers and streams and undoubtedly caused a reduction in suitable breeding habitat. This is particularly true of the Misbourne which flows through Great Missenden and which has dried up along much of its length in recent years. The cause of this is largely due to the lower rainfall in recent years, but is no doubt further exacerbated by excessive water extraction by local water companies.

Grey Wagtails usually build their nest above water on a rock or ledge, in exposed tree roots, or in ivy growing on a tree or bridge. They have been recorded breeding in industrial areas in the High Wycombe area, one nest being in a drainage pipe.

The Breeding Atlas clearly shows Buckinghamshire placed on a line running north-west to south-east with breeding taking place in most 10-km squares to the south-west but very few to the north-east. This compares well to the map shown here.

During the winter Grey Wagtails are recorded more widely in the county. This is very much in line with the Winter Atlas, which shows a much wider distribution with records received from most 10-km squares in Buckinghamshire and the surrounding counties. BWP suggests that British Grey Wagtails are usually resident with mainly local dispersion, and only 25% of ringing recoveries over 100 km. However the Winter Atlas states that some birds move south, sometimes even as far as France and Iberia to be replaced by birds from further north and occasionally even from the continent. There are however no ringing recoveries for this species from birds ringed or controlled in the county to support this.

In hard winters when streams and rivers are frozen many Grey Wagtails may perish (the Breeding Atlas). This was noted in the severe winter of 1963 when numbers were 'greatly reduced' (F & Y). However some birds move into sewage treatment works and into towns where food is more often available (the Breeding Atlas). Sewage treatment works account for many of the Buckinghamshire winter flock records for this species although flock sizes larger than six are rarely recorded. A gathering of 20 birds at Marlow STW on 15 Aug 1981 was exceptional.

JER

Pied Wagtail
Motacilla alba yarrellii

Common resident and migrant.

Just after the turn of the century, H & R considered the Pied Wagtail to be 'nowhere rare' in the county. At the time, the species was regarded as generally migratory but with single pairs seen in every month. Since then numbers have increased, possibly because of the spread of industry and urbanisation into areas which were previously woodland or farmland with few buildings.

The Pied Wagtail breeds in a variety of habitats including farmland, quarries, gravel pits and industrial sites. It nests in crevices or holes in walls and embankments, on or under roofs and in buildings. Although sometimes associated with damp habitats, it may be found breeding more than 6 km from the nearest pond or river. The distribution of breeding records shows the bird to be present in most of the county, absent only from large tracts of woodland in the Chilterns and parts of the Vale of Aylesbury that are rural areas with few buildings and far from water. The blank areas on the map in the centre and north-west of the county largely indicate under-recording.

There are considerable differences in breeding densities. One suburban tetrad near Burnham had 6 breeding pairs; one covering mixed farmland near Dorney had 5; and many Chiltern tetrads had only a single pair. This contrasts with some rural Scottish tetrads with up to 11 breeding pairs.

In Buckinghamshire the Pied Wagtail usually starts breeding

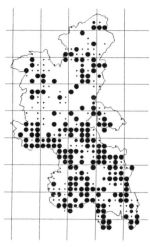

2,000 pairs

from the second week in April, normally raising two broods and occasionally three. Roosts of all male birds from breeding pairs have been observed in May and June, but after the breeding season, from mid July, the birds begin to flock and to use the autumn reedbed roosts.

These flocks are augmented from mid September onwards by migrant Pied Wagtails from N Britain. Two records from Scotland (May and August) and two from Yorkshire (August) involving birds in Buckinghamshire in October and November are indicative of this. The recovery of a bird ringed near Buckingham in October 1976 on a ship in the Skaggerak off Denmark in March 1977 suggests that continental birds may also winter in the county. Most adults remain in S England for the winter, although first-year birds usually go further south to the Atlantic coasts of Portugal, France and Spain. Local breeding birds tend to make only short-distance movements, but some in their first winter also move to the Continent (Davis 1966); a Pied Wagtail ringed at Eton on 18 May 1923 was recovered at Tovias, Portugal during November 1923.

During severe weather up to three-quarters of wintering birds may migrate to areas with more clement conditions. The individuals which remain are hard pressed to find enough food and sometimes continue to feed in suburban areas for up to an hour after sunset. National Common Birds Census data show a drop of between 25% and 66% in the population after a severe winter. In winter, flocks of feeding birds may be found on agricultural or common ground where the cereals and grasses are less than about 40 cm tall. Although flocks numbering up to 200 are seen occasionally, groups of 10-20 are not uncommon. There are several large roosts within the county, particularly at Dadford (up to 400), Chesham (c150), Amersham (c100), Weston Turville Res (c125), and a pre-roost of over 1,000 birds at South Iver. The majority of the birds from south of the Chilterns roost one km outside the county, near Burnham; this roost also contains birds from Middlesex and Berkshire, and has held up to 3,400 birds (December 1982).

White Wagtail
Motacilla alba alba

The European race is recorded annually in small numbers on spring passage, particularly at Willen, Foxcote, and Old Slade, and rarely in late summer and autumn. A pair bred near Latimer in 1902 (H & R).

JK

Waxwing
Bombycilla garrulus

Scarce winter visitor.

The first records are for the winter of 1849/50 when birds were observed 'in several parishes'. The second records, also given by Clark Kennedy, were in 1867 when an 'immense number' were shot in the spring of 1867 around Buckingham. Surprisingly, H & J do not give any further records for Buckinghamshire, but one is recorded in *The Countryman* for 1883.

Between 1921 and 1950 Waxwings were recorded only in 1921, 1944, 1945 and 1949. The largest flock in this period was one of 14 birds at Drayton Beauchamp on 8 Mar 1944. From 1951 to 1970 they were recorded in 9 years. Notable flocks during this period were 19 at Aston Clinton on 8 Feb 1959, 20 at Amersham in January 1966, and up to 30 birds at Beaconsfield from 4 Dec 1970 to the end of the year. From 1971 birds were recorded in 10 years with a maximum of 11 in 1988.

Birds have been recorded between November and March.

Dipper
Cinclus cinclus

Rare vagrant.

There are old undated records for the River Chess and the canal near Drayton Beauchamp.

The first dated record is:

1894: 1 near High Wycombe

There were no more records until 1941 when a bird was seen from 4-11 May on the River Chess below Chenies. The next record came in 1966. Between that year and 1972 there were 8 records, but then nothing until 1975. There followed three more records: in 1984, 1989, and 1991. Five of the 14 records were identified as birds of the continental Black-bellied race, *C.c.cinclus*. There have been no definite records of the British race *C.c.gularis*.

Localities include Shardeloes, the River Chess, and the River Wye. Birds were seen between 13 Aug and 20 May but there is no pattern to the occurrences. The longest stay was achieved by a bird at Shardeloes from 5 Nov 1967 to 6 Mar 1968.

Wren
Troglodytes troglodytes

Very common resident throughout the county, with occasional passage visitors.

The Wren's status in the county has not apparently changed much since Clark Kennedy and H & R. It is one of the most numerous and widespread species in the British Isles. Yet, because it is not normally gregarious and skulks around in the undergrowth, it can prove remarkably elusive. A two-hour walk without seeing one is quite possible and a sighting may well be simply a small brown ball whirring between bushes. It is more likely to be heard than seen. The national Common Birds Census suggests that the underlying trend is now a slight increase (Marchant et al 1990), but the species is very susceptible to severe winters. Numbers then drop considerably, but equally they can recover quite rapidly. The county breeding survey shows that the Wren was recorded in 83% of all tetrads. Some of the gaps in the north are likely to be due to under-recording, as many of them are rural tetrads where the species might be expected; but there are other gaps in dense urban areas which, if there are no gardens, are unlikely to be suitable habitat.

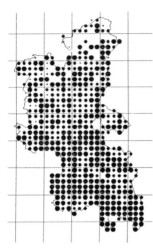

40,000 pairs

Wrens normally produce two broods in a season between April and July. The nest can be almost anywhere, constructed in bushes or ivy with a dome and side entrance, or simply placed in a hole or crevice in a rock or a tree. In 1974 a nest in a squirrel's drey was reported from Great Kingshill.

Outside the breeding season the Wren often remains territorial, but it is very adaptable. It is able to collect food from all kinds of small nooks and crannies and will even penetrate under the snow if necessary. In winter and especially on colder nights it roosts in holes, and it is then that many birds will huddle together. MTNHS records a roost of 42 Wrens in one Denham nest box in the cold winter of 1978/79.

Wrens use gardens quite extensively in winter. They were reported from 75% of the gardens in the BBC Garden Bird Survey, but no more than 4 birds were seen at any one time. Natural food was preferred to that provided on bird tables.

The majority of the county's Wrens are resident, but continental birds do migrate through the eastern side of Britain and may reach as far inland as Buckinghamshire. A few British birds wander as well. One bird ringed in Lane End in October 1965 was recovered at Cageux in France in February 1968. It is not known whether this was a locally-bred bird or a continental migrant moving through.

206

Wrens have been ringed in quite large numbers, but the only other reasonably long-distance recovery noted was a bird ringed at Moulsoe Wood in November 1982 being retrapped at Gibraltar Point in Lincolnshire in September 1983, a distance of 133 km.

DBH

Dunnock
Prunella modularis

Very common resident throughout the county.

Despite the Dunnock's neat but dull brown appearance, and its rather unobtrusive behaviour, it is a fascinating bird. Comparison with old records suggest that its status has not changed much over the years, although the national Common Birds Census shows that there has been a slight decline over the last 10 years or so. Nevertheless, it is one of the commonest and most widespread birds both nationally and in Buckinghamshire. On the map, most of the gaps in the north-west and north of the county are likely to be due to under-recording. Dunnocks are very common in woodland borders, farmland, hedges, and rural and suburban gardens; and they will even penetrate into urban areas if there are suitable bushes.

The Dunnock has one of the more bizarre breeding systems yet known. Every combination of one to three males with one to three females is known, and researchers admit that keeping track of all the goings-on can be difficult even with colour-ringed birds. Whether the complexities of the behaviour extend into habitats other than gardens is not known.

30,000 pairs

In the winter, the BBC Garden Bird Survey found it in 89% of gardens, with a maximum of 11 birds at any one time. Natural foods were used about as much as foods which were put out, and the birds normally remained on the ground to take bits that had fallen rather than fly up to a table.

A highly sedentary bird, the Dunnock often remains in the same territory throughout the year. Over 2,600 Dunnocks have been ringed in the county but all recoveries and retraps show only very local movements. A total albino raised a brood of 4 at Prestwood in 1972.

DBH

207

Robin

Erithacus rubecula

Mainly a resident, found throughout the county, but numbers augmented by some passage migrants.

50,000 pairs

The British national bird is fairly well represented in Buckinghamshire, being recorded in 84% of tetrads during the county breeding survey. This is probably an underestimate and the scarcity of records in parts of the north of the county is likely to be due to under-recording rather than a complete lack of birds. The Robin is tolerant of most habitats which offer a reasonable amount of cover, be it scrub, hedge or wood. So, although it is found most commonly in woodland, it is probably best known because of its adoption of gardens, both rural and suburban, and town parks. Its status does not seem to have changed at all since Clark Kennedy's time.

Breeding territories are set up around March and breeding continues until midsummer, with perhaps 3 or even 4 broods. Territories are held around the year, however, the sexes holding separate ones through the autumn and winter.

During the winter, Robins often visit bird tables, tending to be aggressive to other birds wanting to feed. The BBC Garden Bird Survey showed the species to be in the top five of garden visitors and feeders on artificial food. It was seen in all gardens in the second year of the survey, one garden having eight simultaneously. Robins showed a marked preference for the food provided on bird tables. Their adaptability, however, was shown one summer when a bird was seen to have learnt the knack of plucking tadpoles from a garden pond (D B Hamley). There are two interesting recoveries of birds ringed in the county. One bird ringed at Frieth in June 1964 was recovered in December 1965 at La Chevrolière, Loire Atlantique, in France; another ringed at Drayton Beauchamp in October 1979 was retrapped five days later in London and found dead at Ashford, Surrey in April 1980.

DBH

Nightingale
Luscinia megarhynchos

Scarce breeding summer visitor.

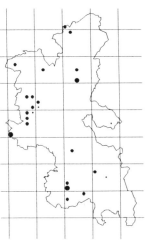

100 pairs

Nightingales have slowly declined this century. H & J stated that they were generally absent from the hills and drier beech woods, but were found in many places in the low-lying fertile districts. While the habitat preferences are still valid, 'many places' would now be considered too optimistic.

The 1976 BTO survey found 64 singing birds in 21 sites. As 12 former sites were not visited it was considered that the true total may have been about 100 birds. The survey was repeated in 1980 when 50 birds were found, 16 of them in just 2 sites. Again the true total was considered to be around 100 birds. The map shows records in 21 tetrads, 3 of them with only possible breeding. As this probably represented the true picture it can be considered that a slight population decrease had taken place. Since then there appears to have been a considerable decrease, though this will certainly be in part due to under-recording.

Although the map shows the Nightingale to be a scarce breeding species in the Chilterns, it seems that they now only occur in this area as a migrant. Nightingales are virtually confined as a breeding species to the discontinuous band of woodlands stretching from Bernwood Forest on the boundary with Oxfordshire to Salcey Forest on the Northamptonshire border. These woods are mostly pedunculate oakwoods with a hazel shrub layer, the primary habitat of Nightingales in

Britain. The population decline is certainly due the cessation of coppicing as a woodland management practice. It has been shown (Stuttard and Williamson 1971) that Nightingales prefer coppicing on a twelve to twenty-five year cycle with the five to eight year old stools providing the most suitable habitat. Only three of the Buckinghamshire Nightingale woods are managed with conservation in mind; elsewhere coppicing ceased during the Second World War.

The fate of Nightingales in the county may be linked with that of the Black Hairstreak butterfly, an insect which has an almost identical range, within Buckinghamshire, to the Nightingale's. It has been suggested (Heath 1984) that Black Hairstreaks are confined to the woods of the East Midlands because of the long coppicing cycles practised and that the reduction in population is due to the ending of coppicing. The unmanaged woods are now completely grown, so the present populations of both Nightingales and Black Hairstreaks may well have reached a stable minimum.

The first Nightingales are heard during the last week of April, with the bulk arriving in early May. A few birds are seen most years in spring at sites where they do not breed, eg in scrub by Little Marlow GPs. Signs of autumn passage of this unobtrusive bird are very rare. One was trapped on Steps Hill on 14 Jul 1985 and another was seen in a garden at Westcott on 28 Jun 1991. The only significant ringing recovery is of a bird ringed at Portland Bill on 10 Sep 1955 which was recovered at Newport Pagnell on 27 Apr 1956.

DMF

Bluethroat
Luscinia svecica

Very rare vagrant. There are two records.

1969: 1 on 31 Aug, Aston Clinton SF.
1983: female on 21 May, Great Linford GPs.

These are typical dates for this European species.

Black Redstart
Phoenicurus ochruros

Irregular summer breeder and uncommon migrant.

There are 10 records prior to 1972:

1909: female or male of the year on 11 Jun, near Wooburn.
1938: one October, Olney.
1961: single birds 5, 25, 26 Oct believed to be 2 different birds, Stoke Park.
1965: male on 22 May, Marlow nurseries.
1965: male on 13 Aug, Sands, High Wycombe.
1965: pair with 3 juveniles, seen on several dates up to 22 Sep, Booker, High Wycombe. It seems likely that they bred in the area. The male seen at Marlow and Sands may have been the male of this pair.
1965: 2 on 10 Oct, Frieth.
1969: female March, Chesham SF.
1969: 1 on 18 Mar, Princes Risborough.
1970: 2 on 10 Apr, 1 on 11 Apr, High Wycombe.

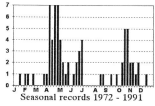
Seasonal records 1972 - 1991

The records of migrants between 1972 and 1991 are shown on the histograms. There have been five further attempts at breeding, three of which were successful:

1973: nest containing 2 eggs found in old brick kiln at Newton Longville Brick Pits but was later deserted.
1975: 4 young fledged at Bradwell on 25 Jun.
1978: female with 2 recently fledged young on 18 Jun at Pitstone.
1982: successful breeding in mid Buckinghamshire.
1983: unsuccessful breeding at Bletchley.

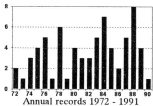
Annual records 1972 - 1991

Black Redstarts first bred in Britain in the 1920s on the south coast and in London. They gradually spread until there are now rather less than 100 pairs as far north as Northumberland. In many places, including Buckinghamshire, they are erratic breeders. They prefer industrial sites, which birdwatchers tend to avoid, so they may well be under-recorded. Typical breeding sites include derelict factories and power stations. During the county breeding survey they were recorded in two tetrads - in SP91H where it was confirmed to have bred, and SP84V where the species was present.

The histograms show a concentration of records in the early spring. The birds may be found throughout the county, but the centre appears to be particularly favoured.

DMF

211

Redstart

Phoenicurus phoenicurus

Rare summer visitor and uncommon migrant.

It is evident from earlier accounts that Redstarts have always been local in the county. H & J described them as 'generally not rare, but appears to be scarce in the Chilterns and uncommon in beech woods, though more frequent in the neighbourhood of rivers.' They give as river localities the Ouse near Newport Pagnell, Castlethorpe, the Chess, and the Thames. It is likely that they nested at these sites in pollarded willows. Parkland sites they mention are Stowe Park, Chequers, and Mentmore, and other sites given are Burnham Beeches, Buckingham, Aylesbury, and Amersham.

Even allowing for the fact that Redstarts are often elusive, and undoubtedly under-recorded, the range has contracted in the last seventy years. In 1946 12 pairs were found nesting in pollarded willows between Long Crendon and Waterperry in Oxfordshire, but they are no longer present. Birds are regular only at Burnham Beeches where up to six pairs have bred (in 1960), Ashridge, where up to five males have been present (in 1982), and the Brickhill Woods, where at least six territories have been held (in 1976). Numbers may have declined at all these sites, with only one or two pairs at Burnham Beeches in 1987, four at Ashridge in 1990, and four in the Brickhills in 1988. There have been no records at Burnham since 1987. Other sites have included Ravenstone Woods, where three pairs bred in 1960, Black Park, Stockgrove, where four pairs bred in 1964, Cublington, and Coombe Hill. Redstarts apparently no longer breed in the county alongside rivers, and hardly at all in parkland. The site in Burnham Beeches comprises mainly ancient beech trees, but the other major sites are areas of pedunculate oakwood within large mixed woods. They nest in tree-holes which they have to occupy in competition with other hole-nesters. It is thought that, although Redstarts do not take readily to nest-boxes, provision of artificial nest-sites helps the birds as it reduces the competition from other species. None of the major breeding sites has any nest-boxes, and this may be a factor in accounting for the county's very small population. 1967 saw two unusual nest sites. A pair bred near Marlow in a gravel bank, even though suitable tree-holes were present nearby, and on the Oxfordshire border a pair nested below the floorboards of a gypsy-type caravan.

Nationally there was a significant decline in the population between 1968 and 1972, but since then the population has

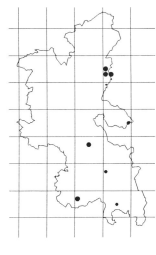

10 pairs

212

steadily increased until it has now reached its level of the mid 1960s. The decrease was due to drought conditions in its wintering area, the Sahel region of Africa. It is very difficult to detect any parallel trend locally because of the tiny numbers involved.

It is interesting that Redstarts and Wood Warblers, which are usually found together in the sessile oakwoods of western and northern Britain are also found together in Buckinghamshire, even though both species are rare in the county. Ashridge and the Brickhill Woods are the principal sites in the county for Wood Warblers, while the third important site for Redstarts, Burnham Beeches, appears to have lost both its Wood Warblers and Redstarts at about the same time.

There are small passages in both spring and autumn. In the 8 years between 1983 and 1990 62 birds were recorded in the spring between 3 Apr and 7 May, and 37 birds in the autumn between 12 Jul and 29 Oct. The peak passages are in the last week of April and late August and early September. Migrants are likely to turn up anywhere in the county, but regular sites include Campbell Park in Milton Keynes, and the usual well-watched wetland sites.

DMF

Whinchat
Saxicola rubetra

Regular passage migrant in small numbers; no longer breeds.

Clark Kennedy described the status of Whinchat as 'sparingly distributed' and gives Dorney Common and Chesham as sites. H & J were more detailed. They wrote 'somewhat locally distributed, and rare or absent from the hills or drier districts, but regularly breeding along the Thames Valley, though not in any numbers, also by Ouse, Chess, in the Vale of Aylesbury, and in the north of the county.' Price wrote 'regular summer visitor, breeding in small numbers'.

None of these statements is now correct. By the late 1950s breeding was restricted to the escarpment near Ivinghoe and probably Westcott. In the 1960s there were pairs at Haversham, near Kimble, and Calvert. By the mid-1970s breeding had become restricted to just 3 sites, but in 1978 breeding was not recorded. One or two pairs have bred since but the last positive breeding was at Aylesbury SF in 1983. The decline in the population of Whinchats in the county is part of an overall decline in lowland England which seems due to the destruction and degradation of its favoured habitat. Whinchats prefer weedy uncultivated land such as neglected fields, road-verges, and railway embankments. Now fields are largely cultivated, roads have become busier, and railway embankments are overgrown. It will be interesting to see if the increase in the area of land set-aside from cereal production will improve the situation.

Whinchats are regular passage migrants through the county. Spring passage occurs between mid-April and the end of May while autumn passage is from the end of July to the end of September. The spring passage usually consists of single birds, or two together, but parties in the autumn, which are swelled by young birds, may be larger. The biggest congregations recorded are 17 birds at Dorney on 1 Sep 1982, and at least 16 birds at Marlow GPs on 21 Sep 1980. Birds have been recorded throughout the county but regular sites include Willen, Caldecotte, Westcott, and Dorney Common.

There has been one ringing recovery. A bird ringed at Mentmore on 7 Sep 1965 was recovered in Logrono, Spain on 16 Oct 1965.

DMF

Stonechat
Saxicola torquata

Winter visitor and migrant in small numbers which no longer breeds.

H & J described the status of Stonechats as 'Now rather local but one or more pairs nest on most of the commons, where gorse abounds.' They remark that a few pairs nest in the south of the county and give Burnham Beeches as a locality. Price wrote 'a scarce summer visitor, breeding in small numbers. Some remain for the winter.'

Since then there have been no confirmed breeding records. Stonechats have suffered a substantial decline in inland counties due in the main to fragmentation of habitat. The species prefers heathland but will use areas of waste ground, particularly if gorse is present, a habitat which has become scarce in the county because of ploughing. This fragmentation of habitat has tended to isolate Stonechat populations and make them susceptible to extinction during severe winters. During the atlas period the species was recorded in one tetrad, SP80I, where breeding was considered to be probable.

Stonechats still appear in winter. During the early 1970s

between 8 and 17 birds were seen annually but there was a large influx in October and November 1976 when birds were found at 45 localities, including 7 birds at Marlow GPs. The following year a pair with 5 juveniles was present on 11th Sep at Old Slade, although they were not thought to have bred in the county. Since then numbers fell, reaching a low of only 3 birds in 1987. The following year saw an increase to 9 birds, and in 1989 and 1990 c16 birds were seen in both years. Typical localities are normally those that are well-watched, such as Willen, College Lake, Blue Lagoon, and Calvert. Wintering birds usually arrive during October and leave in February. There is also a very small passage in March and September.

A female present during February 1992 at Aylesbury SF had been colour-ringed as a nestling the previous June near Donaghadee, Co. Down, N Ireland. The bird reappeared at its birthplace on 11 Apr, 1992 where it mated and laid eggs.

DMF

Wheatear
Oenanthe oenanthe

Regular passage migrant in small numbers; no longer breeds.

Wheatears have declined as a breeding species in the county since the beginning of the century. H & J wrote 'apparently less frequent than it used to be.' They mention as breeding sites Coombe Hill and Whiteleaf Cross, but also that it had ceased to breed on Ivinghoe Beacon 8-10 years previously and at Halton 20 years before. Price described the status as 'a regular summer visitor, breeding in small numbers.' Since this was written there has only been one breeding record. A pair reared 7 young at Hartigan's GP, near Broughton in 1954.

The reduction in the Wheatear population in the county is part of a general decline in south inland England where breeding Wheatears are now extremely rare. The decline is certainly due to habitat loss. Wheatears breed in open country with short grass, a habitat that was plentiful in the 19th century when sheep grazing was commonplace. Since then the numbers of sheep have fallen considerably, and rabbits, which also help to keep the grass short, have been decimated by myxomatosis. Furthermore, much of the grassland has been ploughed, particularly since the Second World War.

A strong double passage occurs through the county. The spring passage usually begins in the third week of March and ends in mid-May. The autumn passage begins in mid-July and continues to mid-October. Very small numbers of the Greenland sub-species have been seen, usually towards the end of the migration periods.

Wheatears may be found at suitable localities throughout the county but certain places seem favoured. These include Lane End, Wescott, Oakley, Dorney Common, Old Slade, and the Chilterns escarpment. The largest congregations recorded are c25 at Lane End on 24 Apr 1963, 20+ at the same locality on 4 May 1967, 20+ at Wescott between 9 and 19 Sep 1974, and 21 at Downley Common on 5 Apr 1987. An exceptionally late record is of one at Willen on 4 Nov 1978. There have been six records of single birds in June.

DMF

Black-eared Wheatear
Oenanthe hispanica

Very rare vagrant. There is one record.

1992: male on 25 Apr, Chearsley.

This bird, one of the few to be recorded in an inland county, was a pale-throated male of probably the eastern race *O.h.melanoleuca*.

Ring Ouzel
Turdus torquatus

Annual migrant in very small numbers.

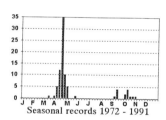

Seasonal records 1972 - 1991

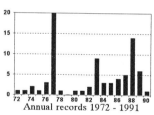

Annual records 1972 - 1991

There are old undated records for the middle of the county. The first dated record is:

1840: 1 shot, Risborough.

Between 1862 and 1960 only 10 birds were recorded, while between 1961 and 1971 17 birds were seen. Since 1972 the frequency of recording has increased markedly with 84 birds being identified. These last records are shown on the histograms.

The largest flocks were of 7 birds on 9 Apr 1977 at Steps

Hill/Ivinghoe Beacon and of 8 birds on 17 Apr 1988 at Steps Hill. Most of the records have been on the Chilterns escarpment with rather fewer in the north of the county. There have been only 7 records for the south. The seasonal histogram shows a brief spring migration with a marked peak at the end of April. A few birds are seen in October.

Blackbird
Turdus merula

Very common resident, migrant, and winter visitor.

70,000 pairs

All the early accounts describe the Blackbird as one of the commonest species. Blackbirds diversified from their natural woodland habitat to towns and villages during the 19th century and are now found throughout the county. They reach their highest population densities in suburbs with mature gardens where there can be over 250 pairs per 100 hectares.

It is probable that Blackbirds breed in every tetrad in the county and that the gaps are due to under-recording. The estimated population of 70,000 pairs makes the Blackbird the most numerous breeding bird in Buckinghamshire. Large areas of the county are a mosaic of woods and towns and villages that are very favourable to the species. The only threat to the population comes from the removal of hedges and from changes in farming practices. Spring tillage is helpful to Blackbirds as it enables the birds to find food more readily during the breeding season. Winter cereals, which are commonly planted in the county, have the effect of reducing the area tilled during spring and this may have an adverse effect on Blackbird populations (O'Connor and Shrubb 1986). This may be balanced by the change from hay to silage which involves many cuts during a season and thus increases the amount of time when the vegetation is short enough to be available as feeding areas.

Blackbirds were recorded in 99% of the gardens participating in the BBC Garden Bird Survey, which, with Blue Tit, is the highest percentage recorded. This figure has remained almost unchanged during the 6 years of the survey. A maximum of 22 birds have been seen at one time.

The local population is augmented in winter by birds from elsewhere. Most ringing records outside the county have been from other parts of S England, although a bird ringed at Weston Turville Res on 30 Aug 1964 was recovered in Dyfed on 4 Nov 1965, and another bird locally ringed on 8 Dec 1974 was recovered on 14 Jan 1977 in Co.Fermanagh.

There have been 25 recoveries in Europe of locally ringed birds. All were winter visitors to Buckinghamshire but only 7 were recovered in the breeding season. Of these, two were found in Germany, and one each in the Netherlands, Belgium, Denmark, Sweden, and Finland. A further 7 birds were recovered in March, when the birds could have been migrating. Two were found in the Netherlands, and one each in Germany, Belgium, Denmark, Finland, and Norway. The remaining 11 birds were recovered in autumn or winter. Three each were found in the Netherlands and Germany, two each in France and Sweden, and one in Finland. It seems from this that Blackbirds are not particularly faithful to their wintering areas. No foreign-ringed birds have been recovered in Buckinghamshire.

DMF

Fieldfare
Turdus pilaris

Common winter visitor.

The status of Fieldfares appears not to have changed since Clark Kennedy wrote 'regular winter visitant'.

The earliest autumn record is of a single bird at Willen on 17 Aug 1983, 3 weeks before the next earliest bird, one at Middle Claydon on 7 Sep 1981. Birds are not usually noted in any numbers until October, and sometimes not until November. The timing of departure of birds from their Scandinavian breeding grounds is dependent upon the abundance of rowan berries. Very large flocks are not usually present in Buckinghamshire until the new year, but an exceptionally large flock of c15,000 birds in the Haddenham-Aston Sandford area was recorded on 18 Nov 1981. Movements of birds during the winter are very variable and are dependent upon the availability of wild fruit crops and the weather. This is reflected in the considerable variation in the maximum numbers that are recorded each year. For instance the largest recorded flock size in 1980 was 500 birds, but the following year saw the huge flock at Haddenham. Feeding flocks of more than 1,000 birds are recorded in most years, and flocks greater than 2,000 birds are not unusual. Only two feeding flocks of more than 10,000 birds have been recorded: the one already mentioned, and another in the same locality on 23 Feb 1990.

Fieldfares roost communally, usually in trees. The largest

roost in the county is in Bernwood Forest which regularly holds in excess of 10,000 birds. On 25 Mar 1984 15-20,000 birds were estimated to be present.

Birds begin to leave the county in April and are usually gone by the end of the month. The latest record is of a single bird at Broughton on 28 May 1978, but there are two early summer records. A bird was present in Amersham from 28 Jun to 3 Jul 1978, and another bird was seen at Moulsoe on 12 Jun 1990, but there were no indications of breeding.

There are 12 recoveries of birds ringed in Buckinghamshire, 7 in the summer and 6 in the winter. The summer recoveries were in Norway (3 birds), Sweden (2), and Finland (2). Five of the winter recoveries were in France and the other was in Belgium. It seems that Fieldfares do not necessarily return to the same wintering areas, and indeed that they can move considerable distances during a winter, as shown by a bird which was ringed at Calvert on 26 Jan 1986 and recovered in Finistere, France on 3 Apr 1986. The ring of a nestling ringed in Karelia, Russia on 8 Jun 1974 was found at Denham on 24 Jun 1988. This is one of only three Russian-ringed Fieldfares reported from the British Isles.

DMF

Song Thrush
Turdus philomelos

Common resident, migrant, and winter visitor.

Evidently the status of Song Thrushes has changed considerably since 1920 when H & J described it as 'even more numerous than Blackbird' because there is no doubt now that Blackbirds are much the commoner birds.

This change in relative numbers is part of a national trend. The Song Thrush population began declining during the 1940s and is still doing so. This can be explained in part by a succession of winters which had an above average number of days when the ground was frozen (Baillie 1990). The decline has also been attributed to changes in farming practices (O'Connor and Shrubb 1986). The area of land which is tilled in spring has been reduced owing to the preponderance of winter cereals, so that birds breeding in farmland now have a smaller area in which to feed during the breeding season. However, this does not account for all the decline for the birds are decreasing even in urban areas.

It is well known that Song Thrushes eat snails. It is possible

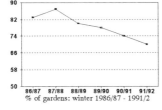
% of gardens: winter 1986/87 - 1991/2

220

that the use of slug pellets has had an adverse effect on Song Thrush populations either through direct poisoning or by causing a reduction in mollusc populations. This may account for the reduction in the percentage of participating gardens in the BBC Garden Bird Survey reporting Song Thrushes. This figure has fallen from 87% in the winter of 1986/87 to 70% in the winter of 1991/92. The decline is shown in the accompanying graph. A maximum of 6 birds have been seen at one time.

It is probable that Song Thrushes breed in every tetrad in the county and that the gaps are due to under-recording. The population in the 1970s may have been around 30,000 pairs, falling to 15,000 pairs in the mid 1980s, and falling again to perhaps 12,000 pairs in 1990.

In winter the population is augmented by birds from other regions. It also seems that Buckinghamshire birds winter in other parts of Britain and in S Europe, possibly in response to freezing conditions. No British ringing recovery of a locally ringed bird has been made further north than Shropshire, but birds have been found as far east as Lincolnshire and as far west as Devon. There have been five foreign recoveries, four in France and one in Spain. All were recovered between October and February.

1986: 15,000 pairs
1991: 12,000 pairs

DMF

Redwing
Turdus iliacus

Common winter visitor.

The status of the Redwing has changed little since H & R wrote 'Fairly common, sometimes very numerous'. H & J wrote 'On 11th March 1906 a flock estimated to be 38,000 were spread thickly over eight acres of grassland near Skirmett,' and 'In 1918 Redwings were generally very scarce. Hartert saw none until March'. In 1976 F & Y gave the Redwing's status as 'common winter visitor with numbers varying from year to year.'

This has not changed. The largest flock recorded in some years is only 150 birds, but in others flocks of over 1,000 birds are common. The largest recent flocks were of 5,000+ birds at Ford/Bishopstone on 17 Dec 1977 and another of 4,000 birds at Hughenden on 21 Dec 1989. This annual variation is due to birds not regularly wintering in the same area or even the same country. Birds which come to Britain

one year may winter in Italy the next. Similarly the numbers of Redwings in the county are rarely the same throughout a complete winter. When few birds have been recorded in the first half, an increase can often be expected towards the end of the winter.

The first Redwings normally arrive in Buckinghamshire between 27 Sep and 3 Oct. Many early records are of birds heard calling while flying over at night.

Redwings commonly roost with Fieldfares and other thrushes. Gatherings of 200-300 are fairly common, but roosts of up to 2500 have been found at Bacombe, Wendover, 2000 at Shenley Wood, Bletchley, and at Lady Villiers Gorse, Drayton Parslow. During severe weather most birds usually migrate with the remaining few frequently succumbing to the cold. At these times some birds move into gardens to feed. The cold winter of 1854, according to *The Field*, destroyed Redwings and Fieldfares by tens of thousands. H & J also state 'In the cold winter of 1917 all or nearly all Redwing which were in the county at the time perished. Redwings were then scarce in 1918 and were probably as common as before the 1917 frost in 1919'. Most are gone by early April.

There are three records of Redwings in summer: one shot at Harleyford on 28 Jul 1871 (H & R), one at Old Wolverton on 16 Aug 1983, and one trapped Steps Hill on 21 Jul 1984. The Wolverton bird was thought to have been present for some time as it was in heavy moult.

Redwings ringed in the county have been recovered in Italy (3 birds), Belgium (2), France (2), and one each in Sweden, Germany, Spain, and Portugal.

JK

Mistle Thrush
Turdus viscivorus

Common resident.

Early writers described the Mistle Thrush as common, although H & J also remarked that 'it was not in any great numbers in the Thames Valley.' The situation has probably not changed as Mistle Thrushes can be found throughout the county although not in any great numbers. They favour wood edges, farmland with hedges, and urban and suburban areas. Open areas for feeding are essential. In urban areas this is provided by parks and sports fields, while elsewhere farmland is used.

Nationally there has been a slight decline, although this has not been obvious locally. To some extent, Mistle Thrushes are dependent upon the area of land which is tilled in spring for feeding during the breeding season. With the trend towards winter cereals this area has decreased. On the credit side the change from hay to silage, which is cut earlier, has probably been beneficial as short grass suitable for feeding is available during this species' early breeding period.

4,000 pairs

The map shows several large gaps in the north of the county, which are probably due to under-recording. The gaps are larger than those on the Song Thrush map and may be caused by the much smaller Mistle Thrush population, which results in the birds being harder to find. It is likely that Mistle Thrushes occur in every tetrad in the county.

The species has been recorded in 25% of the gardens participating in the BBC Garden Bird survey with a maximum of five being seen at one time.

Post-breeding flocks can be quite large. A flock of c72 birds flew over Coleshill on 31 Oct 1989, while 48 birds were recorded at Chesham on 30 Jul 1990. A large winter flock was one of 45 birds at Great Missenden on 25 Feb 1981.

The local Mistle Thrushes seem remarkably sedentary. Of the 34 ringing records involving birds either ringed or recovered in the county in only three cases had the birds travelled more than 10 km.

DMF

Cetti's Warbler
Cettia cetti

Rare vagrant.

1967: 1 adult trapped on 22 Jul, Weston Turville Res. It was retrapped on 29 Jul and 9 Sep.
1977: 1 on 24 Jul, Linford GPs.
1985: 1 male from 2 Nov-9 Jan 1986, Weston Turville Res (trapped).
1989: 1 on 12 Aug, Old Slade.
1990: singing male on 28 Apr, River Colne near Tilehouse GP.

The first occurrence was the third British record. It is disappointing that only four have been recorded since.

Grasshopper Warbler
Locustella naevia

Local summer visitor.

In the 19th and early 20th century the Grasshopper Warbler was, much as today, considered to breed sparsely though widely in Buckinghamshire. Combining past and current information in 1920, H & J knew of only ten places where it had occurred, including three which were on or just outside the county's present boundaries. However, the species was probably more under-recorded then than it is now. Numbers appear to have fluctuated over the years. The older statements, though very vague, suggest at least one period of decline earlier this century. Thus Clark Kennedy's 'not very plentiful' in 1868 and H & R's 'generally distributed' in 1905 contrast with H & J's 'rather rare' in 1920, while Sage (1959) writes of a 'decrease during recent years in Hertfordshire'. The MTNHS reports show birds present in a good many places during the 1950s, without commenting on abundance. By 1964 the species was 'widespread in all suitable localities'; and increases were recorded over the following three summers, with numbers remaining high to at least 1969. In 1972 and subsequently a marked drop was noticed. The 1973 report attributed this to the local maturation of conifers, with consequent habitat loss, but both the rise and subsequent decline locally corresponded closely to changes in annual numbers of migrants at coastal bird observatories (Riddiford 1983), suggesting that the local changes were in fact part of a nationwide pattern. No clear trend was recorded in the 1980s, though there may have been some resurgence.

The Grasshopper Warbler inhabits low scrub and rank herbage, in both dry and damp situations. Thus it may be found in areas of rough, tussocky grass, as in damp and neglected fields, or where such herbage is interspersed with low brambles and bushy growth on waste or common land. This can include chalk downland, if not heavily grazed, and field hedges and ditches. Song is sometimes heard, and breeding perhaps takes place, in growing crops. A locally important habitat is provided by forestry plantations and felled but regenerating woodland, where there are young trees and tangled undergrowth. Plantations have been available on a larger scale and more regular basis in recent decades than formerly, and they acquire sizeable populations of Grasshopper Warblers for the few seasons when they offer ideal conditions. How far such new sites may compensate for scrubland lost through intensification of agriculture, and sometimes urbanisation, is however not known.

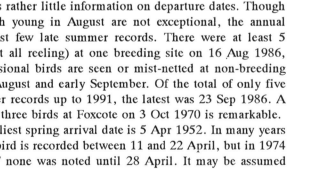

100 pairs

First clutches are often begun around mid May and there may be two broods. Nests are notoriously difficult to find. It is therefore not surprising that breeding was only proved in four tetrads, while many of the 'probable' breeding records may simply relate to reeling males. Since the birds sing mainly around dawn and dusk, it is likely that some birds were missed, but against this must be set the frequent reports of birds reeling on just one or two dates, apparently during pauses on their migration. Also, as the map was compiled over 6 years it may exaggerate the distribution in one year because some sites may only be suitable for a year or two.

There is rather little information on departure dates. Though nests with young in August are not exceptional, the annual reports list few late summer records. There were at least 5 birds (not all reeling) at one breeding site on 16 Aug 1986, and occasional birds are seen or mist-netted at non-breeding sites in August and early September. Of the total of only five September records up to 1991, the latest was 23 Sep 1986. A report of three birds at Foxcote on 3 Oct 1970 is remarkable.

The earliest spring arrival date is 5 Apr 1952. In many years the first bird is recorded between 11 and 22 April, but in 1974 and 1977 none was noted until 28 April. It may be assumed that most local birds arrive during late April or early May, but precise information on this very secretive species is hard to gather and the arrival of females must go largely unnoticed.

HM-G

225

Moustached Warbler
Acrocephalus melanopogon

Very rare vagrant. There is one record.

1965: 1 trapped on 31 Jul, Weston Turville Res.

This was the fourth British record of this Mediterranean and East European species.

Sedge Warbler
Acrocephalus schoenobaenus

Locally common summer visitor, primarily to damp habitats, and passage migrant.

Past accounts, back to Clark Kennedy's time, are essentially in accord with present-day observations in describing the Sedge Warbler as generally distributed along large and small watercourses, as well as by pools and lakes. It is also found in drier sites.

The species exploits a wider variety of more or less luxuriant vegetation than the Reed Warbler, and the map shows it to have a correspondingly wider distribution. Since Sedge Warbler pairs are quite strongly territorial, concentrations like those often formed by Reed Warblers do not occur. The national Common Birds Census shows the breeding population to have been high in the mid 1960s but to have declined markedly (albeit with fluctuations) from 1969 to the present, the decrease coinciding with drought conditions in the African wintering range. Observations in the annual reports for Buckinghamshire mostly support these findings, though the bird was still thought to be numerous in the county in 1970. Nevertheless, one of the highest counts of territories was in 1978 when Linford GP held at least 50 singing males. At Weston Turville 24 males were singing in 1963 and some 50 birds were recorded there as early as 20 Apr 1968. By contrast, during the 1980s fewer than 10 pairs, and sometimes only three, were located at this site.

While most pairs breed within about 100 m of water, single pairs or small loose groups can occur by tiny pools or wet ditches, which may even dry out during the summer, and birds can then quite easily escape detection. Some birds settle well away from water, though often still in its general vicinity. Birds heard singing in completely dry sites, including gardens, probably include wandering males, but there is evidence of occasional nesting in young plantations and on farmland.

Apparent breeding in rape fields has been observed in neighbouring counties (Bonham and Sharrock 1974). Clearly some breeding sites are transient in nature, affected perhaps by waterway management and farming. The waste ground around gravel pits, for instance, is often ideal while it remains at the open scrub stage. However, there are some long stretches of watercourse which lack suitable vegetation and hold no Sedge Warblers.

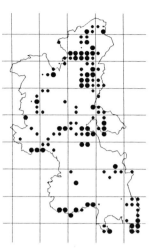

2,000 pairs

Breeding generally starts in mid May, though sometimes earlier, and second or repeat clutches can be found up to mid July. While some birds live up to their names by building in sedge tussocks in marshes, and a few build in Reed Warbler fashion among reed stems, far more nest in brambles or other shrubs and in herbage such as nettles and willowherb. They are usually in extensive areas of herbage, but sometimes by hedges. Once a pair is breeding the male sings very little, and the parents sometimes contrive to approach and leave the nest entirely under cover. They become more conspicuous again when tending fledged young.

Autumn passage usually gets under way towards the end of July or even in mid month. It is mainly observed in wetland areas, though not exclusively (eg a bird was found dead in the centre of Medmenham on 8 Sep 1976). Evidence of the substantial numbers that can be involved is provided by the 128 birds, at least 90 being juveniles, which were ringed at one site in the last week of July 1963. Passage probably reaches its peak in August but diminishes markedly thereafter. Nevertheless, 10 birds were still noted in the MTHNS area on 19 Sep 1976 and two were observed at one site on 13 Oct 1974. The latest county record is of a bird at Willen on 22 Oct 1989.

Several ringing recoveries illustrate the timing and direction of autumn movements. A nestling ringed at Newport Pagnell on 19 Jun 1977, had flown 65 km south-east to Essex by the end of the following month. A juvenile ringed on 21 Jul 1963 was on the Sussex coast on 16 August, one ringed on 25 Jul 1965 was already in SW France 16 days later, and a later juvenile reached Sandwich Bay, Kent within five days of being ringed on 5 Sep 1964.

Two very early Sedge Warblers were located at Ham SF (now in Berkshire) on 29 Mar 1974. The earliest within the present county boundary was on 2 Apr 1961 at Weston Turville Res. There are five other early April records, but more commonly the first report comes during the second week of April. At Weston Turville Res early arrivals typically remain hidden in *Phragmites* beds, uttering only infrequent and subdued snatches of song. Major influxes or passage movements occur between mid April and early May, depending on the season, and can continue into late May (see MTNHS report for 1978).

HM-G

Aquatic Warbler
Acrocephalus paludicola

Very rare vagrant. There are two records.

1990: 1 on 2 Aug, Blue Lagoon, Bletchley. Probably also on 3 Aug.
1990: 1 on 26 Aug, Botolph Claydon.

It is of course remotely possible that the two records refer to the same bird. The first record is one of the earliest dates for this eastern European species in Britain.

Marsh Warbler
Acrocephalus palustris

Very rare vagrant which has bred. All records are given.

1931: bred Chalfont Park.
1956: 1 on 18 May, Shardeloes.
1960: 1 singing on 26 Jun, near Wendover.
1974: 1 on 26 May, Weston Turville Res.

The absence of recent records accords with the decline almost to extinction of the Britsh breeding population.

Reed Warbler
Acrocephalus scirpaceus

Summer visitor to suitable riparian localities, also passage migrant.

Early this century the Reed Warbler was 'abundant where reed abounds'. The rivers Thames, Ouse and Colne, and the reservoirs at Tring and Weston Turville received specific mention, as well as ponds with osiers. Since then, the additional habitats provided at new waters, mostly formed during mineral extraction, have allowed further areas to be colonised. However, although old records do not specify where along the Thames the bird bred, the near absence of records from there during the county breeding survey seems to imply a loss of Reed Warbler habitat.

The Reed Warbler's distribution is fairly strongly bound up with that of the reed. Yet even where reeds are present, pairs often breed in a variety of other riparian herbage as well as in willow and sallow scrub. Wandering birds sometimes sing in gardens or farmland, but no nests in such habitats have been recorded in the county. Nearly all the tetrads where the species was found contain some wetland. As a rule, Reed Warblers breed colonially, the densest concentrations apparently occurring in vigorous, recently formed stands of reed. In limited patches of suitable habitat such as the short strips of reed scattered along the smaller rivers, colonies are necessarily much smaller, and single pairs may be found. These pockets probably constitute the nearest Buckinghamshire possesses to a natural Reed Warbler environment.

Bigamy is known in this species, and instances have been suspected at Weston Turville Res, with occupied nests only two or three metres apart (H Mayer-Gross). The species is also regularly parasitised by Cuckoos, but with no noticeable

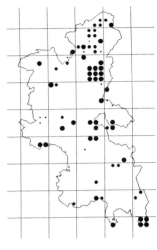

200 pairs

impact on numbers. As well as sharing with the host species such hazards as predation, young Cuckoos in nests over water can drown on fledging; this has been witnessed once and suspected on other occasions (H Mayer-Gross).

It is clear that Reed Warblers in Buckinghamshire are heavily dependent on man for the provision and preservation of their main breeding areas. Colonies quickly establish themselves wherever suitable plant growth develops at newly dug waters, whereas operations to straighten stretches of river inevitably eliminate Reed Warbler sites, at least in the short term.

The male Reed Warbler has a readily recognisable song, and as the species has a long breeding season (the first birds laying before mid May and the last broods fledging in early September), location is usually straightforward, although the odd isolated pair may have escaped detection. NE Buckinghamshire had the highest density of occupied tetrads, closely associated with the meanderings of the Great Ouse, whose tributaries the Ouzel, Claydon Brook and a small brook at Bradwell provided further pockets of habitat to the south and west. Beside the Great Ouse lie the Newport Pagnell and Great Linford gravel pits. The former especially, with associated riverside reeds, has long formed a stronghold, with estimates of 40 pairs in 1954, 62 in 1972 and 50 in 1981. Counts for the Great Linford complex are sparse, though 17+ pairs were located in 1981. The population at both groups of pits was lower during the period of fieldwork for the county breeding survey than in the preceding decades, mirroring the national decline but also due to the effects of management. There are no recent figures for Gayhurst Park, where some 25 pairs were present in 1954. What may at first sight seem a remarkable concentration of colonies was recorded in the environs of Milton Keynes. It should, however, be noted that this area contains old gravel pits, brick pits (where the thinner reedbeds hold fewer birds), new balancing lakes (where Reed Warblers quickly found the planted reeds), as well as the River Ouzel already mentioned. Isolated pools at Dadford and Wing also hold reedbed colonies.

In mid county there is a small colony at the calcareous fen and fishponds fringing a former chalk quarry at Pitstone. The large colony at Marsworth Reservoir (Herts) just extends into Buckinghamshire. The population at the major colony at Weston Turville Res was put at 34 pairs in 1985 and 52 in 1986, although it had been an estimated 100 pairs in 1962. In part at least, this reduction was due to maturation of vegetation. A pair sometimes nests on the nearby Wendover

Canal, and 10-13 pairs are spread through three tetrads on the Grand Union Canal by Aston Clinton. Small groups also breed along stretches of the River Thame, one extending on to the adjacent Aylesbury Sewage Works for a few seasons before the marsh vegetation was cleared. At the Wotton Lakes reedbeds the last estimates of population were of 25 pairs in 1977 and 'good numbers' in 1981. Colonies south of the Chilterns, on the Thames and Colne in particular, are generally small and there is some evidence of a decline over the last 15-20 years.

The Reed Warbler's lifestyle makes it particularly amenable to ringing studies, and a wealth of interesting recoveries is to be found in the annual reports, especially since 1963. A selection of these, along with fuller ringing data from Weston Turville Res and N Buckinghamshire, illuminates the picture of migratory movements obtained by visual observation. There are numerous records of adults and young birds returning to the same breeding colony, and also of birds breeding in colonies at some distance from their birthplace. While most of the latter concern youngsters, there are occasional instances suggestive of adults changing colonies. For example, one ringed at Colnbrook on 6 Jun 1968 was controlled at Weston Turville Res on 24 Jun 1973, and one ringed at Wilstone Res, Hertfordshire on 19 Jun 1980 was controlled at Weston Turville on 18 Jul 1983. A few others have been proved to reach at least 6 years of age, including one ringed in Spain on 11 Sep 1967 found breeding in the county in 1972 and 1973.

Most records of 'autumn' migration come from reedbed breeding sites, but some birds stop on passage at other localities, even well away from water. Being unobtrusive, such birds are more often than not detected during mist-netting, though occasionally they are found dead. Visual observations of passage have been recorded from mid July, for example in 1963, and in several seasons the population at Weston Turville Res has been found to be markedly diminished during early August (H Mayer-Gross). Small numbers, however, remain well into September. Late records include six in October since 1967, and two in November 1977. Ringing indicates that August is the peak passage month for locally bred birds. There appears to be an initial rather random dispersal, including many juveniles travelling a few kilometres west, but all longer August and September movements have been in directions between south and east. The earliest long movement from within Buckinghamshire was of 89 km to Chichester by 23 August, and another juvenile was controlled in Kent on 29 August, 144 km from its colony. September recoveries, both short and long distance, are still quite plentiful. A 1985 recovery concerned an adult ringed at Weston Turville Res on 1 August which reached Portugal by 2 September, and three more birds ringed in the county were recovered in Iberia between 29 September and 12 October, while one ringed as a nestling was taken in Portugal as late as 8 December - if the finder is to be believed. Better progress was shown by a juvenile still at West Wycombe on 15 Aug 1964 which had reached SW Morocco on 25 September.

The first spring arrivals have nearly always appeared between 11 and 24 April, though the earliest post-war date was 9 Apr 1961. In 1962 no bird was seen until 28 April. Observations indicate large-scale arrivals from the second week of May onwards, with birds at least sometimes still arriving early in June. A Weston Turville bird at least two years old was still in Morocco on 6 May, a Newport Pagnell bird of similar age had reached Portland, Dorset in its northward journey on 16 May, and 4 birds caught between 11 and 19 May were still between 7 and 30 km from their breeding colonies.

HM-G

Great Reed Warbler
Acrocephalus arundinaceus

Very rare vagrant. There has been one record.

1946: 1 singing 27 Apr on the northern edge of Marsworth Res.

Lesser Whitethroat
Sylvia curruca

Fairly common summer visitor.

The Lesser Whitethroats which fell to the Rev. Lightfoot's gun at Bulstrode, and were illustrated by Latham in 1787, were the first to be recorded in Britain. Authors from 1868 onwards have described the species as widespread though not very abundant, and so it remains today. Even though it is less conspicuous than the Whitethroat, statements indicating that prior to 1969 it was less numerous are surely correct. In the absence of numerical data, not too much weight should be attached to H & J's comment that the Lesser Whitethroat was much more plentiful in Middlesex than in the adjoining parts

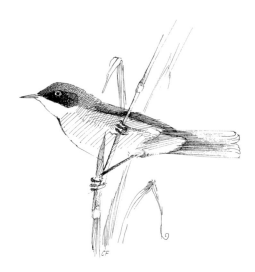

of Buckinghamshire, unless there were habitat differences to account for the variation.

The national Common Birds Census shows numbers in England to have been at a peak in 1966 and to have fluctuated at around 45-75% of that level during the next 20 years. The early 1980s saw the bird at its lowest numbers.

Observers' comments on annual changes in abundance in MTNHS and BBC reports have often, but not always, concurred with the CBC findings. Breeding pairs are scattered enough to be counted easily, provided the song is known, and sometimes they are sufficiently numerous to give quite good counts. Thus at least 8 males were singing near Great Kingshill in 1960, and 9 nests in the Haversham/Linford area in 1983 indicate flourishing populations there.

While habitat requirements overlap considerably with those of the Whitethroat, the Lesser tends to prefer taller bush vegetation and its territories mostly contain scattered trees. It is therefore found along reasonably dense or bushy thorn hedges on farmland as well as in bush scrub, whether on waste land, in overgrown gardens, or in young deciduous or coniferous plantations. CBC work, quoted in the Breeding Atlas, indicates that the highest density of breeding pairs occurs on chalk downland, given that the scrub community is at an ideal stage. This was evidently the case on Steps Hill, where at least some of the census study was carried out, and

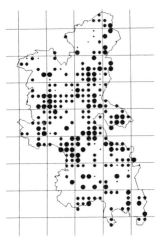

1,500 pairs

may in part explain the presence in a high proportion of Chiltern tetrads. However, even allowing for the bird's avoidance of open farmland where hedges are either cut very low or have grown into open tree-lines, it is likely that the species was considerably under-recorded in some parts of the county. It is also likely that nesting actually did take place in most, if not all, of the tetrads where only possible or probable breeding was noted; though some observations may have involved passage birds or song from unmated males.

As the summer progresses, and certainly by mid July, the species becomes more widespread, appearing in rural and riparian scrub, for example. This spread doubtless begins with local post-breeding dispersal, but later records may well involve an increasing proportion of migrants. Passage in late July can be quite strong, as shown by the 25 birds ringed in a week at Weston Turville Res in 1966. August is generally the main passage month, but movement continues into September, and in 1963 peak counts of around 20 birds were noted between 9 and 15 September at Weston Turville. In some years the final sighting is soon after mid September, though there are some late September observations. Even later records refer to 7 Oct 1985, 22 Oct 1973, and a very late bird on 8 Nov, 1987 at Valley Farm, Linslade.

The earliest recent date for a spring migrant is 10 Apr 1981 at Denham, though the pooled pre-war Berkshire, Buckinghamshire and Oxfordshire records include a bird on 8 Apr 1912 (OOS Report for 1936). In most years the first bird is recorded between 12 and 28 April. First records as late as 3 May 1970 and 6 May 1965 may indicate genuinely delayed migration or perhaps emphasise how easily Lesser Whitethroats are overlooked. In 1962 the species was reported, presumably on the basis of birds ringed, as 'numerous on spring passage' at Weston Turville Reservoir, and in 1968 various observers commented on newly arrived birds not staying. Otherwise the annual reports do not mention spring movements, apart from noting early May as the time of main arrival at breeding sites. A bird ringed at Weston Turville on 2 Sep 1961 was recovered in Lebanon on 22 Mar 1962 during its return from the East African wintering area.

HM-G

234

Whitethroat
Sylvia communis

Widespread and fairly common summer visitor (formerly far more abundant), and passage migrant.

In 1868 Clark Kennedy wrote that the Whitethroat was one of our commonest warblers, and in 1905 H & R went further, calling it 'one of the commonest birds in hedgerows, gardens, woods and commons'. One might in passing question whether gardens or mature woods really were particularly favoured habitats, but the species certainly continued to be abundant into the 1960s, when it was still possible to find nests in similar numbers to those of the ubiquitous Willow Warbler. However the population returning in the spring of 1969 proved to have fallen drastically from the level of previous years - by 70% on four local census plots - and (despite optimistic perceptions of increases by observers unfamiliar with pre-1969 numbers) it has essentially fluctuated around this much lower level until the time of writing. Even so, this remains a reasonably common species and it may be added that numbers in the county have probably been somewhat unevenly distributed in the post-1968 period, with some localised, possibly short-lived, pockets of relative abundance. The population crash is attributed to the great deterioration of habitat produced by prolonged drought over the Whitethroat's winter quarters in the Sahel region of tropical Africa, and should a sustained climatic improvement take place there, a recovery by Whitethroats (and other species wintering in the same zone) might be expected.

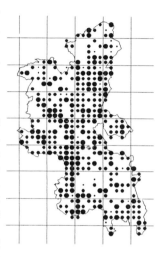

5,000 pairs

The preferred breeding habitat is essentially lowish bush scrub interspersed with rank herbage. In Buckinghamshire this occurs most widely in the guise of hedgerows on less intensively managed farmland and by country roads, with thick flanking vegetation on a verge, ditch-bank or field-corner forming a well-nigh essential feature. This type of landscape, as the Breeding Atlas points out, has only existed since the agricultural enclosures of two centuries ago, whereas ancestral territories may have been restricted to woodland clearings; these were still occasionally utilised by Whitethroats when numbers were high, for example in Ashridge Forest. Patches of wasteland, both small and large, are also classic Whitethroat habitat, as is such bushy common land as the county contains. Breeding also takes place in young plantations. During dispersal or on passage later in the summer, birds often visit gardens and wetland sites where they do not breed.

The relative sparsity of atlas registrations in southern parts of the county, which generally had good observer coverage, probably reflects a genuine scarcity there, especially in wooded areas lacking much suitable Whitethroat habitat. In the somewhat less well covered north of the county, much of the farmland contains potential Whitethroat territories and if, (with the population at a low ebb) relatively few were occupied, the species could easily have been overlooked in a number of tetrads.

Past annual reports contain no information on the timing of the main autumn departure, but it is likely that movement takes place chiefly during late July and August. A juvenile ringed at Weston Turville on 7 Aug 1961 was recovered in Portugal on 21 Sep 1963. Even dates of final sightings are lacking for some recent years, and occasional 'last' records in early September are unlikely to represent the true picture. However in a number of seasons birds were noted in the second half of September (four at one site on 27 Sept 1978) and there are three October dates, the latest being a bird in song at Newton Longville on 5 Oct 1975.

Winter observations are exceptional; the 1936 OOS Report records a bird at St Leonards on 17 Nov 1936 (and one in W Oxfordshire two days later!), while a bird was ringed on 11 Dec 1982 at Little Marlow SF and remained for a week.

Arrival dates for the first spring migrants were earlier before the 1969 crash than they have been since. Earliest of all was a bird at Colnbrook on 24 Mar 1952, while one reached Slough (now in Berkshire) by 2 Apr 1950; a number of arrivals between 5 and 10 Apr were also noted in the years 1949 to 1965. In the more recent period the dates of earliest sightings have ranged from 11 Apr 1981 to 28 Apr 1972 (with the majority in the third week of April). In some years singing males are widespread by the last week of the month, but the main influx is generally considered to take place from early to mid May.

HM-G

Garden Warbler
Sylvia borin

Summer visitor, fairly common and widespread.

A bird with no strong distinguishing features, the Garden Warbler tends to be under-recorded; but the older accounts, from Clark Kennedy onwards, agree with current assessments in considering it not particularly common but generally distributed in suitably wooded habitats throughout the county.

Both annual and longer term fluctuations have been noted. The national Common Birds Census registered a marked decline during the 1970s, initially in the more marginal farmland habitats but later also in woodland, followed by a recovery in the 1980s. As a rule this species is considerably less abundant than the Blackcap, though periodic exceptions occur. These are perhaps local. One example was at Lane End, where in May 1966 Garden Warblers apparently outnumbered Blackcaps by five to one, though the report does does not state whether the birds all settled to breed.

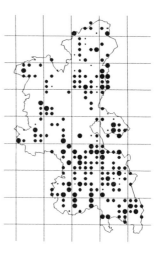

1,500 pairs

The Garden Warbler primarily inhabits woodland and spinneys, particularly clearings and margins or where the wide spacing of trees permits undergrowth to flourish. Bush scrub is also utilised, provided some taller shrubs or trees are present in the vicinity. With the same proviso, the thorny thickets which often develop for a few years in young conifer plantations are also favoured. Despite its name, the bird seldom nests in gardens, except ones containing sizeable patches of wilderness, though it may visit them on passage.

Little has been published about the local breeding population's departure. The 1963 and 1964 MTNHS reports indicated light passage taking place in late July, with August being the main passage month. This is supported by two ringing recoveries. A juvenile caught at Weston Turville Res on 30 Jul 1965 was found in the Côte d'Or, France on 10 Aug 1966, and a juvenile ringed at Marlow SF on 16 Jul 1988 was found in S France on 3 Sep. Another bird ringed at Marlow SF on 22 Aug 1987 was recovered in Ghana on 6 Dec 1988, indicating the wintering quarters.

Dates of last sightings are available for only 15 years, mostly since 1972. Eight were between 10 and 23 September with a further three at the end of that month, and there were observations on 1 Oct 1979, 11 Oct 1985 and 21 Oct 1978 - this last bird ringed at Wraysbury, now partly in Berkshire. Some of the passage records, especially the later ones, could well concern individuals hatched or breeding outside the county, perhaps even Continental drift migrants.

Dates for the earliest spring arrivals are quite variable, in most years falling between 9 and 30 April. An exceptional record was of a bird seen along with some other migrants at Newport Pagnell GP on 13 Mar 1977, almost seven weeks before the next bird was reported that year. The second earliest sighting, on 2 Apr 1960, was also at Newport Pagnell. On the other hand the first birds in 1972 were not noted until 1 May, and in 1976 not until 7 May. Except in very forward seasons, the main influx of local breeders probably takes place in the first half of May.

HM-G

Blackcap
Sylvia atricapilla

Common summer visitor and passage migrant, and a small but increasing wintering population.

Clark Kennedy found the Blackcap to be generally dispersed, more numerous than the Garden Warbler but not so common as many other warblers. The species was described as common in suitably wooded localities by H & R and H & J. None of these writers mentioned overwintering, but F & Y in 1976 knew of 'several' wintering records. In contrast to most other warblers, numbers have been maintained since the 1960s and have risen markedly on farmland (Common Birds Census), and it is probably now the second commonest warbler in the county.

The breeding season map shows the species to be widely distributed in tetrads containing woodland but often absent from areas of very open farmland, although some gaps in the north are probably due to under-recording. No tetrads appear to be so urbanised as to exclude it. Blackcaps breed in most types of woodland, spinneys and scrub, and also not uncommonly in mature gardens. They require undergrowth or bushes and so are absent from dense conifers and closed-canopy beechwoods. Scrub, both low and tall, mixed with large trees is especially favoured.

The dispersal of local birds begins in July, and more visits to rural gardens and other non-breeding areas are recorded from then. The timing of the main passage is hardly mentioned in local reports. 'Surprisingly large' numbers were ringed at Weston Turville Res in late July 1965, and movement certainly extends through August and generally well into September; for example, some 15 birds were seen on Pitstone

Hill on 19 Sep 1970. In most years occasional migrants are seen into October, even late in the month. All such occurrences, perhaps significantly, have been since 1972 and could involve winter visitors arriving from continental Europe. However, some birds are very likely to be passage migrants, as there are breeding season ringing recoveries in Cheshire and Cambridgeshire of birds ringed in the county in September 1963 and 1981 respectively.

The first definite record of a wintering bird in the county is of one in Rectory Wood, Amersham on 22 Jan 1932. Although the MTNHS area produced single records in the early months of 1946, 1952 and 1953, regular wintering in the county apparently began considerably later. One bird was seen in November 1963, there were records between November and February in 4 of the next 8 seasons, including five birds in 1969/70, and since 1972/73 birds have been seen every winter. Numbers have slowly and rather erratically built up, sometimes producing 30 reports a winter by the mid 1980s. The true totals must be substantially greater. The BBC Garden Bird Survey recorded Blackcaps in 8% of gardens.

6,500 pairs

Snow and Snow (1988) have shown that various wild berries are taken while they are available in the autumn, and the birds move more into gardens from late December onwards when the berry stocks have dwindled. It is thought that bird tables play a key role in enabling this new wintering population to survive the coldest months (Berthold and Terrill 1988). Studying mainly scrubland in Buckinghamshire and adjacent parts of Hertfordshire, Snow and Snow saw 24 males and 26 females during four winters and consider that the frequently recorded preponderance of males arises through their 'defending' garden feeding stations, and keeping the less aggressive females away. The actual numbers may well be about equal. There are instances of birds remaining up to 27 March, and there is circumstantial evidence of a few remaining into April, with a hen feeding on ivy berries on 18 Apr 1984 very likely being the same bird seen feeding there 10 weeks earlier (B K Snow).

Problems arise in distinguishing early summer arrivals from wintering individuals. Thus a number of 'arrivals' were recorded between 5 and 12 Mar 1977, whereas in 1965 a small spate of mid March records was attributed to wintering birds on the move (MTNHS reports). Since rather few Blackcaps reach the south coast observatories before April (Riddiford and Findlay 1981) it seems likely that most March records are late wintering birds, either local or passing through from the south-west, the main wintering area in

Britain (Leach 1981). In many years first 'arrivals' occur in late March or early April but widespread arrivals, initially mainly of males, usually do not begin until the second, third or even fourth week of April.

Adults ringed in the county have been recovered in S Spain in March and Morocco (2) in April.

HM-G

Yellow-browed Warbler
Phylloscopus inornatus

Very rare vagrant. There is one record.

1966: 1 on 9 Oct, Holmer Green.

This is a typical date for this Siberian species.

Wood Warbler
Phylloscopus sibilatrix

Local summer visitor and rare passage migrant

It appears that Wood Warblers have always been local in the county. H & J described them as occurring in the Chilterns and Brickhills, but being scarce in the Thames Valley. There seems to have been a decline as they were considered to have been formerly plentiful in Burnham Beeches, a locality where they are now rare. Price described the status as 'a regular summer visitor in small numbers' a description which is still accurate for today. An increase was noted in the late 1960s, but since then the species has slowly declined.

The birds now breed regularly at only two sites: Ashridge and Brickhill Woods, where they breed in mature deciduous pedunculate oak woodland. 12 singing males were present at Ashridge in 1980 but this fell to only one in 1987. Numbers rose to four in 1988 but there were none in 1990 after the storm of January 1990 which felled around 10,000 trees in the Ashridge Estate and changed the appearance of much of the area. Two birds were singing in 1991.

Numbers in the Brickhill Woods have fluctuated between one and three singing males since 1980. Wood Warblers do not breed regularly in Chesham Bois Woods even though there was confirmed breeding at this site during the survey period. The former breeding sites of Burnham Beeches, Penn Woods, and Bledlow are apparently no longer occupied though a bird was singing at the first site in 1988.

The two main sites also hold very small numbers of breeding Redstarts, which is an equally local breeding species within the county. Wood Warblers and Redstarts appear to require woods with sparse shrub and field layers. While most of the Chiltern beechwoods meet this requirement it may be that beech is less suitable for the species than oak. The oakwoods in the middle of the county have a very dense shrub layer of old coppiced hazel and are unoccupied by the birds.

Wood Warblers are occasionally found on passage in the beechwoods of the Chilterns. It is likely that most of the records in this area refer to passage birds. A few birds appear in late April but most are not seen until early May. Autumn passage is very rarely recorded. A bird seen at Yiewsley GP on 25 Aug 1990 is the only autumn record in recent years.

The one ringing record is of a bird ringed as a nestling at Burnham on 12 Jun 1924 and recovered at Potenza, Italy on 23 Sep 1924.

DMF

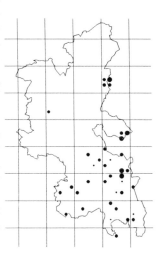

10 pairs

Chiffchaff
Phylloscopus collybita

Common summer visitor and passage migrant; a very few winter.

In 1868 Clark Kennedy mentioned the Chiffchaff's early arrival and late departure but made no comment on its abundance. It was probably common then, as writers early this century certainly found it in suitable localities.

As the map shows, the species remains common and fairly widespread, especially in the better wooded parts of the county. According to the national Common Birds Census index, numbers were higher from about 1966 to 1973 than before or since. Local observers supported the census findings that 1976 and 1984 were particularly poor years; 1977, however, was considered poor locally while the census showed an increase. Fluctuations are doubtless nothing new: in 1930 birds were fewer than the year before at Chorley Woods, though reportedly 'numerous' at Whaddon (OOS reports).

Chiffchaffs are birds of woods, spinneys and woodland scrub, so long as the canopy is sufficiently open to permit the continuance of a field layer of bramble, nettles and similar rank herbage for breeding. They are thus particularly associated with clearings, rides and margins, with nests often to be found beside paths or boundary ditches. In woodland sites they can outnumber or entirely replace Willow Warblers. Breeding regularly takes place in young plantations and sometimes by bushy hedgerows or in gardens, but usually when there are tall stands of trees nearby. Low brambles are a typical site for the domed nest, generally placed 15-30 cm above the ground, though other rank vegetation is also used.

Tall field hedges, gardens and riparian scrub are more extensively visited during migration. The wintering records come mainly from lower-lying wetland areas with willow scrub and thick bush cover, or cress beds; a January bird at Marlow GP was seen feeding on a manure heap, presumably taking insects. There are, however, occurrences in less sheltered habitats, as at The Lee, 195 m above sea level.

Singing males are particularly easy to locate, and as they take little part in nesting duties they continue singing through the summer. Song is also frequently heard in spring and late summer from passage migrants and even wintering birds from distant populations, so 'probable breeding' registrations which simply indicate a singing bird must be viewed with caution. On the other hand since nests are well hidden and breeding females generally inconspicuous (though observers familiar with the 'hweet' call can readily locate them), the map will on balance give a fair indication of breeding distribution.

Remarkably for a migrant, the Chiffchaff often begins laying in the third week of April and further nesting-starts, either repeats or second broods, continue until early July. After breeding, adults moult completely before moving south.

Autumn passage is strong during August, perhaps particularly in the latter half, and continues through September, with small numbers of birds still regularly observed in early and even mid October. Movements revealed by ringing, mainly of full-grown birds, which fill out this picture include two from Weston Turville to Dungeness, Kent (26 Sep 1974) and Spain (30 Sep 1968). Initial north-eastward movements were shown by three birds handled in summer in Berkshire and Wiltshire, and in Buckinghamshire in September. A 1923 nestling from Dorney (now just in Berkshire) was found in Portugal in October 1924. Two wintering areas used by birds from the county are indicated by recoveries of July-ringed individuals in S Spain in November and Mali in February.

Some of the Chiffchaffs seen in late October or even November could be straggling passage birds. However, in two or three cases there is evidence of such individuals wintering, the clearest being one seen at Old Slade from 23 Oct 1969 to late March 1970. Records of birds which were presumably wintering in the S Midlands go back at least to 1887 (county unspecified; OOS Report for 1936), with another at Wilstone in 1913 (Sage 1959). The next record seems to be from Horton (now Berkshire) on 13 Nov 1954, after which winter observations in or close to Buckinghamshire become increasingly frequent. At least two, and often far more, birds have been recorded annually since 1968/69. This may in part be due to raised observer awareness, though the scrub around gravel pits and the Milton Keynes lakes may be enabling more birds to find feeding sites. Equally, such places may simply be attracting those birds which would in any case be staying within the county. Overwintering does, however, appear to have become more common. Two winters of 1974/75 and 1982/83 stand out, the latter producing some 25 birds.

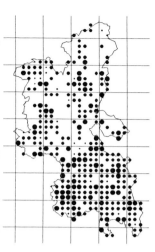

5,000 pairs

The winter birds are considered to be of eastern origin, and a minority have in fact shown plumage typical of some populations of the 'Siberian' Chiffchaff *P. c. tristis* and uttered distinctive 'chiv-it' calls. The Wraysbury GP complex has been a good site for eastern-type birds. This form can show a slight wing-bar (as did one at Mursley in 1988), and elsewhere in Britain such birds have on occasion been misidentified as Greenish Warblers *P. trochiloides*. Winter records are well distributed from November to February. After this it becomes increasingly difficult to distinguish the birds from spring arrivals, though a few individuals are known to have sojourned well into March, with one until 10 April (1975). It is not known whether a *tristis*-type bird singing at Taplow on 14 Apr 1986 had wintered locally, but it seems likely.

Observations in early March of birds which could be returning breeders are infrequent. In most years the first such migrants appear during the second to fourth weeks of that month. In 1977 birds were already 'at many localities' on 13 March and widespread arrivals later in the month are common, but major influxes in the first half of April are also observed. A bird ringed at Lane End on 29 Aug 1965 was controlled near Dorking, Surrey on 16 April the following year, presumably travelling north; and a male at Maple Cross, Hertfordshire on 7 Apr 1984 was en route to Drayton Beauchamp where it was controlled that summer.

HM-G

Willow Warbler
Phylloscopus trochilus

Very common summer visitor and passage migrant.

The Willow Warbler was well known to Clark Kennedy in 1868 and early this century it was described as generally distributed, H & R considering it as common as the Chiffchaff. This probably did less than justice to its status since it breeds in a wider spectrum of habitats than the other species, and there is little reason to think that it was not then, as it has been in post-war decades, the commonest warbler in the county. National Common Birds Census figures show a relatively stable index of population since 1965, though it seems to have been lower during 1962-64, the first years of census work.

Willow Warblers primarily frequent various types of scrubland. They require an open, initially not too tall, field layer such as grass, weeds, bracken or heather in which to breed. These conditions are frequently provided by chalk and downland, young plantations and regenerating woods, the surroundings of lakes and pools, heathland, and banks of railway lines. The bird also breeds in taller open woodland, old orchards, farmland spinneys, and tall hedge-lines with broad grassy verges. Pairs sometimes find large rural gardens attractive, and unsuspected nests can on occasion get pulled up in the course of weeding. During post-breeding dispersal and migration gardens are visited more extensively, as are riparian habitats. Many birds feed near water when newly arrived.

Nesting often commences about the second week of May. As a rule there is just one brood; nests with eggs which are found in June are presumably replacements. Willow Warblers are easily located by their song and call notes; sitting birds are not uncommonly flushed by chance from well concealed nests; and adults can often be watched carrying nest material or food for their young. So not surprisingly breeding was proved in a fair proportion of tetrads. The map shows the species to be the most widely distributed summer visitor in the county. The Swallow is almost as widespread but far less numerous. It even seems likely that fuller coverage would have furnished proof of breeding in many of the 22% of blank tetrads and also in many of those where possible or probable breeding was registered.

It may well be that singing birds quite frequently encountered in July and even later are already on passage. Adults undergo a complete moult before setting out for their African wintering grounds. Willow Warblers begin to migrate earlier than Chiffchaffs, though the passage of the two species overlaps considerably. Movement begins about mid July and is heaviest later that month and through August. There are several ringing recoveries, including a nestling from Lane End which had reached the E Kent coast on 2 Aug 1966 when no more than ten weeks old. A bird ringed at Moulsoe Old Wood in May 1983 was controlled well down the French coast on 22 Aug 1983, and a juvenile of uncertain origin which was caught near the Thames estuary in Essex on 9 Aug 1981 was controlled near Ashley Green on 5 Sep 1982. Two birds ringed at Weston Turville Reservoir went rather off course: an an adult ringed on 25 Jul 1966 was found in Lincolnshire 17 days later, while a juvenile ringed on 27 Aug 1966 was re-caught on Heligoland off NW Germany 15 days later.

Passage tails off rapidly in early September and in some years no birds are observed after mid month; but there is a scattering of October records, the latest in Buckinghamshire being at Hughenden on 20 Oct 1956. A bird showing characters of the large north European race *P. t. acredula* was caught by ringers at Wraysbury, now outside the county boundary, in Nov 1967 and again in Jan 1968.

20,000 pairs

The earliest spring observation was at Stoke Poges on 4 Mar 1959. First arrivals during the last ten days of March have been noted in at least twenty years since 1949, but in quite a few seasons the initial sighting is in the first week of April or even later (eg 11 Apr 1975). Up to this point only a few males are involved. Major influxes, sometimes in waves a week or two apart and evidently comprising both passage birds and local breeders, usually occur between mid and late April. Nestlings ringed in the county have been intercepted when returning in later springs in Spain (1 Apr 1966), France (30 Mar 1968) and Dorset (20 Apr 1985), while a bird ringed on the Hampshire coast on 15 Apr 1977 covered the 150 km to Stowe within about 24 hours. In contrast to these birds, one ringed at West Wycombe on 11 Aug 1956 was still only at Portland Bill, Dorset on 21 May 1957, suggesting that it might have belonged to a northern, late-breeding population.

HM-G

Goldcrest
Regulus regulus

Resident and winter visitor, common in suitable habitat but much reduced by hard winters.

Last century and in the early 1900s Goldcrests were regarded as not very widespread breeders, though frequently seen in winter. Since in 1883 the siting of a nest in ivy was (mistakenly) regarded as exceptional, it may be that scattered pairs breeding away from conifers were less often detected in the past than now. However, conifer woods constitute by far the most important habitat, and with the maturation of the relatively extensive plantings of the last few decades the numbers of breeding Goldcrests have multiplied; and this presumably also applies to wintering birds. The birds only begin to move in when the trees reach a moderate height. Few species can have benefited more from afforestation. Norway spruce plantations must hold a high proportion of the Buckinghamshire breeding population. Scots pines are also utilised, but stands of larch only rarely. All conifers, including exotic types from huge redwoods to smaller cypresses, will attract Goldcrests in virtually any situation, whether it be mixed woodland, small clumps, or scattered trees in parkland or gardens. Isolated pairs are quite often encountered in churchyard yews. Nesting also occurs, though at generally low densities, in deciduous woods, tall scrub and timbered hedgerows, especially where ivy is present. It is likely that habitats containing few or no conifers are occupied mainly when the species is at high abundance.

The distribution map reflects the bird's habitat preferences well, showing presence in nearly all tetrads over the generally well wooded country from the Chilterns southwards, but a more patchy distribution in the predominantly open areas to the north. Although a few records could have involved lingering winter visitors, it seems likely that the species bred in most tetrads in which possible or probable breeding was registered.

Apparent influxes are quite often recorded in the autumn. There is a single observation of an influx on 4-5 Sep 1965, but most arrivals have been recorded between 3-25 October. It is hard to guess at the numbers involved though counts of 40-50 birds at single sites are occasionally mentioned. These birds are generally presumed to come from N Europe, but ringing evidence hints that at least a few could be of N British stock. The Winter Atlas also mentions long-distance southward dispersal of British Goldcrests. On the other hand, Gladwin and Sage (1986) consider the winter flocks in Hertfordshire to consist of locally bred birds.

From autumn to spring the species is much more widespread than when breeding, and individuals may be observed feeding in gardens or hedgerows, as well as in woods. Numbers are reported to remain high during the winter in some years, but exceptionally cold spells often cause dramatic losses. This was first documented in the county after the severe frost of early 1917, when Goldcrests became rare and were only 'beginning to reappear in small numbers' in 1919. Comparable reductions were noted after arctic weather early in 1947 and 1963, followed by recoveries. In the latter case MTNHS members recorded increases up to at least 1966, though the national Common Birds Census showed that numbers in fact kept rising until the mid 1970s. After 1975 numbers dropped somewhat but remained moderately high before plummeting again in the rather severe winter of 1985/86. The sharp 1981/82 cold spell had caused only a small reduction, suggesting that only certain features of winter weather (probably including glazed frosts) pose a particular threat.

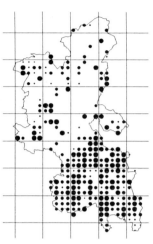

5,000 pairs

There are hardly any records concerning return migration. A flock of 24 at Old Slade on 14 Feb 1965 possibly falls into this category, and one observer reported a passage movement at the end of March 1967.

Ringing has tended to confirm that local birds are resident, with not infrequent retrapping of individuals where they were ringed (one was caught when at least 5 years old), whereas movements of even a few km are only occasional. A young male on passage at the Calf of Man on 24 Sep 1975 was controlled at Stony Stratford in January 1976.

HM-G

Firecrest
Regulus ignicapillus

Local summer visitor and rare migrant and winter visitor.

Prior to the chance discovery of a breeding colony in 1971 there were just 5 records:

1863: 1 killed, Great Marlow.
1941: 1 on 22 Mar, Gerrards Cross.
1967: 1 adult 9 Sep, Great Kingshill.
1969: 1 on 6 Apr, Latimer Park.
1969: 1 on 21 Apr, Oakley.

5 pairs

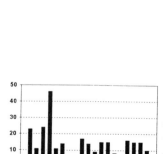

Territories 1971 - 1991

In 1971 at least two pairs bred in Wendover Woods, an event that was part of a continuing northward range expansion in southern England, where it had previously been known only from the New Forest. It is possible that the unfamiliarity most birders at this time had with the Firecrest song may have meant that many birds had remained undetected.

Firecrests have bred every year since 1971 in Wendover Woods. Numbers have varied considerably. In May 1975 there were 46 singing males but three years later this had fallen to only five. The maximum numbers of singing males located in the years 1971 to 1991 are shown on the histogram. During the 1980s the 5-16 territories in just 65 ha of Wendover Woods represented 9-23% of the known British population. The birds breed in a mature Norway Spruce plantation, part of which was destroyed by the storm of January 1990.

Since 1972 when a male was observed defending territory in N Buckinghamshire, there have been several other occupied sites in the county. These include Cliveden, Ashridge, and Chesham Bois Wood. Breeding birds normally appear at the end of April or in early May and are gone by mid-August. It is not known whether they leave Britain in winter.

There is a small passage in the county between March and May, and again in September. They have been seen in a number of sites in the county as far north as Willen, but they are most frequent in the Chilterns. During migration they inhabit a wider range of habitats than when they are breeding. One bird seen in a Chiltern beechwood was singing from the only large holly in the wood.

248

Since February 1976 birds have been occasionally seen in winter. Sites include Old Slade, Chalfont St Giles, Iver, Amersham, Weston Turville, and Calvert. In 1988/89 a bird wintered at Bradwell Common, while in the following two winters up to 2 birds were present. They are more likely to be in broad-leaved trees and bushes at this time, and particularly in the vicinity of water. It is probable that the increased number of wintering records is due to increased observer awareness.

DMF

Spotted Flycatcher
Muscicapa striata

Summer visitor, widespread and fairly common.

The old accounts speak of Spotted Flycatchers being abundant (Clark Kennedy 1868) or common (H & J 1920). While it would be unjustified to infer too much from such generalisations, they perhaps hint at a decline in abundance over the intervening period. Indeed, Fraser stated in 1967 that some observers had noted a decrease, and the national Common Birds Census has certainly shown a marked downward trend during the last 25 years. The year-to-year fluctuations which occur probably reflect the fortunes of the species on migration and in the African winter quarters, and they tend to obscure long-term changes unless counts of breeding pairs are maintained. In a garden at Frieth, 21 adults (including 7 ringed the year before) were mist-netted during May and June 1962, which seems a remarkable total even if it includes some passage birds.

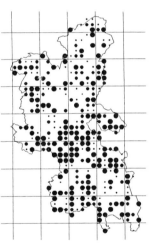

1986: 3,000 pairs
1991: 1,500 pairs

Generally thought of as birds of larger gardens, churchyards, orchards and parkland, Spotted Flycatchers also occur quite widely in tree-lines, clumps of trees in farmland, and larger woods with clearings. The preference is for sites with mature trees. While many territories are in quite dry habitats, birds do seem to like breeding near ponds or larger waters, drawn by the prolific insect life found there. As a rule territories are thinly scattered or isolated, though under ideal conditions densities of 10 pairs per sq km have been recorded by the CBC.

This species returns and breeds later than most. On first arrival birds are generally conspicuous, but quite often they soon move on even from seemingly suitable places. However, if they do settle they can become remarkably unobtrusive during the early stages of breeding despite their flycatching habits. Eggs are laid from late May onwards and there may be two broods. As the young mature, the parents react more noisily to human approach, and fledged broods are conspicuous. If a family party 'appears' in late summer, with young feeding independently, it may be uncertain whether the brood was reared locally. Clearly the odd breeding pair can easily be missed unless a tetrad is quite thoroughly covered, and local knowledge strongly suggests that the species was under-recorded. However, since open treeless country is avoided, the lack of records for some largely farmland tetrads probably reflects a genuine absence of birds. This is especially so as, with numbers declining, isolated pockets of suitable habitat may not always attract occupants. It is doubtful whether, during the fieldwork period, any tetrads were so totally urbanised as to offer no scope for a Spotted Flycatcher territory, though this might now be the case in parts of Milton Keynes until the young trees there mature.

Departure from breeding sites is virtually undocumented, but observations of birds on passage (not necessarily of local origin) are fairly frequent, occasionally beginning about 25 July and extending throughout August and sometimes well into September. There are several reports of 12-16 birds in one place, and an unprecedented one of about 70 along a fence near Hughenden on 25 Aug 1980. While final sightings are often in the last third of September, there are records in the first week of October for 5 different postwar years (3 birds in 1987), with the latest date being 17 Oct 1987. Two nestlings ringed in Buckinghamshire have been recovered during migration in Portugal, one in 1968 in its first autumn, the other on 4 Oct 1972 when it was 5 years old.

In many springs odd birds turn up well before the majority. The earliest Buckinghamshire dates are 17 Apr 1962 and 20 Apr 1975, both from the north of the county. More commonly the first arrival is seen during the first third of May, though it may occasionally be even later. Most birds probably reach the county during the second half of May. A 1955 nestling was found dead 88 km from its birthplace in June 1963 at Crowborough, Sussex, where it may well have bred in the intervening years.

HM-G

250

Red-breasted Flycatcher
Ficedula parva

Very rare vagrant. There are two records.

1943: 1 on 4 May, Boddington Hill, Wendover Woods.
1970: 1 male on 5 Jun, Statnalls Wood, Pitstone.

Only about 5% of records of this East European flycatcher have been recorded in spring. These two records are therefore rather unusual.

Pied Flycatcher
Ficedula hypoleuca

Scarce migrant. Has bred twice.

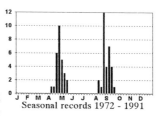
Seasonal records 1972 - 1991

The first record is of breeding. A female was killed sitting on 6 eggs in the 1870s at Berry Hill, Taplow (H & J). There were then a further 10 records to 1966, plus a pair that bred in the middle of the county in 1968. There have been 59 birds recorded since 1972, including a pair which was observed prospecting a tree-hole at Medmenham in late May 1976. Apart from this record and 3 birds together in Milton Keynes on 23 Aug 1983 all the records have been of single birds. They are shown on the histograms. 20 have been recorded in the north of the county, 28 in the middle, and 11 in the south. Birds are almost always seen just for a single day.

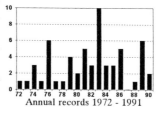
Annual records 1972 - 1991

Bearded Tit
Panurus biarmicus

Scarce winter visitor.

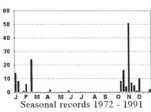
Seasonal records 1972 - 1991

The records prior to 1972 are:

1959: 1 on 15 Sep, Claydon Brook, near Winslow.
1959: 4 in early Nov, Buckinghamshire edge of Marsworth Res (later wintered in Hertfordshire).
1966: 4 on 1 Jan, Old Slade.
1967: 1 during Feb-Mar, Old Slade.
1971: max 8 from 17 Nov to 14 Mar 1972, Old Slade.

The records since 1972 are shown on the histograms. The localities are those wetland sites which have reedbeds. They include Weston Turville Res, Old Slade, Newport Pagnell GP, and Little Marlow GPs. Birds have not been recorded before

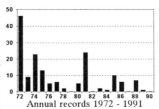
Annual records 1972 - 1991

251

early October or after mid February, although a female was trapped at Weston Turville on the remarkably late date of 25 May 1986 and was retrapped shortly afterwards at Poole Harbour.

The only indication of the origin of these birds is that one of the 1971 birds at Old Slade was wearing a colour ring, and was thought to have come from Minsmere.

Long-tailed Tit
Aegithalos caudatus

Resident, mainly in the south of the county.

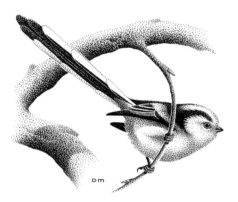

The Long-tailed Tit was recorded as common or very common in Buckinghamshire by Clark Kennedy and other earlier authors. Being largely insectivorous it is particularly susceptible to temporary decreases as a result of cold winters: 1917, 1947 and 1962/63 being noteworthy in this respect.

The population of the species in the county is generally resident. Though there is no indication of migration, there may be some short movements to escape severe weather. In the county breeding survey the Long-tailed Tit was recorded in 51% of the total tetrads. The corresponding figures for Hertfordshire and Oxfordshire are 43% and 61%. The Long-tailed Tit has a preference for woodland edges and larger hedgerows, and this probably accounts for the greater concentration of records in the south of the county. Virtually any type of woodland is acceptable but deciduous woods with an open canopy seem to be the most preferred. The Chiltern beechwoods are therefore near perfect.

The species starts nest building early, in March. The nest is so elaborate that it takes a long time to build and eggs are not usually laid until mid April. After breeding, family groups of anything up to 12 birds are often obvious and noisy as they move along hedgerows.

With the approach of autumn, Long-tailed Tits are more prone to leave the hedgerows and woodland borders and move towards the inner parts of woods. They often join up with other small birds which flock together and form the noisy parties so characteristic of woodlands in winter. They tend to be less often seen in gardens than many other small birds. The BBC Garden Bird Survey recorded the species from about 36% of gardens where a substantial number sampled food provided on tables and in feeders. Up to 6 have been seen on one peanut feeder with 4 others waiting their turn, and this was during a fairly mild winter. Flocks can be quite large; one of 64 was seen in Stockgrove Park on 23 Feb 1983.

There have been several hundred Long-tailed Tits ringed in the county but only very local movements have been shown. A 6-year-old bird was found at Weston Turville (F & Y).

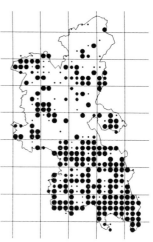

2,500 pairs

DBH

Marsh Tit
Parus palustris

Fairly common resident.

The Marsh Tit is not associated with marshes. It is essentially a bird of deciduous woodland and is found primarily in the more heavily wooded areas of the county, especially the Chiltern belt. F & Y described it as 'fairly common in wooded areas', which would be a reasonable summary of the bird's present status. The map shows that the species is present only in tetrads which have areas of woodland.

Earlier statements must be treated cautiously because they are likely to include Willow Tits, which were not identified as a separate species until 1897. There are, however, a few clues which suggest there has been a recent decline in numbers. In the fieldwork for the Breeding Atlas breeding was proved in all the county's 10-km squares, except one in which probable breeding was recorded. This is no longer the case. Several boundary 10-km squares have no records at all, and four or

600 pairs

five would now only qualify for probable or possible status. The national Common Birds Census shows an overall 12% drop in 10 years.

Marsh Tits begin prospecting for nest sites about March. They are hole nesters and will occasionally use nest boxes although they prefer natural sites. Breeding can be difficult to prove.

Unlike most other tits, paired adults remain together on their territories throughout the winter. Unpaired birds roam more widely in mixed parties, and are joined by the members of a pair when the party crosses their territory (the Winter Atlas).

The birds usually remain in woodland during the winter. However, the BBC Garden Bird Survey shows that they will visit gardens, but usually only those near woodland. They were recorded in 8% of gardens, with no more than 4 birds present at a time. They showed a marked preference for the food provided and could hold their own against the other smaller tits.

They are very sedentary birds and although over 100 have been ringed in the county, no recoveries of note have been reported. National records show that over 85% of recoveries are within 4 km of the ringing sites.

DBH

Willow Tit
Parus montanus

Uncommon resident.

As this species was only recognised as separate from the Marsh Tit in 1897, nothing can be determined about its status until relatively recently. Price and F & Y describe the Willow Tit as 'locally fairly common', but they then allude to identification difficulties. The map shows it is patchily scattered throughout the county. It appears to be more widespread than the Marsh Tit in the NE Chilterns, the Milton Keynes area and north-west of Buckingham. The population estimates suggest there are 200 pairs of Willow Tits compared to 600 for the Marsh Tit.

Unlike other tits the Willow Tit excavates a nest hole. For this it needs soft or rotting wood, which may explain its preference for damper areas. It is less likely to join mixed species flocks than other tits, and the adults usually seem to remain on their territories for longer (the Winter Atlas). It is also suggested that beech mast is not part of the winter diet, in contrast to the Marsh Tit, because its bill is thinner and less powerful. This would make beech woods less attractive to the species in winter.

Willow Tits are unusual in gardens. The BBC Garden Bird Survey shows they were only found in 5% of gardens, and that no more than 3 birds were seen at a time. This makes them somewhat rarer than Marsh Tits in gardens, and indeed they are only seldom encountered during the winter in the wider countryside.

Ringing records show that Willow Tits are very sedentary. Two Buckinghamshire recoveries involved the oldest birds reported to the national ringing scheme at the time. One ringed at Tring, Hertfordshire in May 1966 was retrapped at Weston Turville in April 1975, and another ringed at Weston Turville in May 1976 was retrapped there in May 1985.

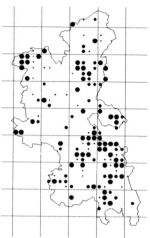

DBH

Coal Tit
Parus ater

200 pairs

Resident, mainly in the south of the county.

Early accounts suggest that the Coal Tit was widely dispersed though not as common as Blue, Great or Long-tailed Tits. Much the same applies today.

It is a widespread and well established woodland bird. Unlike other tits it is largely insectivorous and its beak is best adapted to extracting insects from conifer needles rather than deciduous trees. A preference for conifers may account for the concentration of records in the south of the county. The map shows the bird to be rather sparsely distributed over all the northern SP squares, and the 38% of tetrads recording the species is low compared to Hertfordshire (59%) but similar to Oxfordshire (41%) .

After the breeding season Coal Tits join other tits, Goldcrests, Nuthatches and other birds in flocks roaming the woodlands. Other than this they are highly sedentary. F & Y mention a bird trapped in West Wycombe being retrapped there seven years later, and the BBC report for 1984 reports a fully grown bird ringed at Great Brickhill in December 1977 retrapped there in 1978, 1979, 1983 and 1984. Both these seven-year-old birds are near the record age known from British ringing.

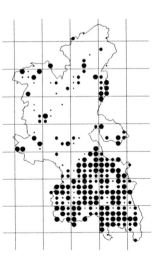

3,000 pairs

Coal Tits in winter will appear in gardens if they are not too far from woods. The BBC Garden Bird Survey recorded the birds in 62% of gardens. There is a preference for artificial food, with peanuts clearly an acceptable alternative to natural foods which in winter include beech mast and other seeds, as well as insects.

DBH

Blue Tit
Parus caeruleus

Resident throughout the county, with the possibility of winter visitors.

Since Clark Kennedy's time the Blue Tit has been one of the commonest and most widespread birds in the county, occurring wherever there are trees. Numbers fluctuate a little, largely as a consequence of particularly cold winters.

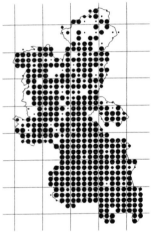

40,0000 pairs

In the county breeding survey the Blue Tit was the fourth most widely recorded bird, and as with many others there were fewer in the north of the county. Unlike in Hertfordshire and the Breeding Atlas it was not quite the most widespread tit species. It will use almost any hole for its nest and takes readily to nestboxes. There is one record in the county of a pair using the latch hole in an iron gate-post.

After fledging, Blue Tits join up with many other small birds to roam the woods, and it is usually the most numerous species in autumn flocks. However, they will move into gardens very early on and become increasingly common during the course of the winter. It is remarkable how many Blue Tits will visit a garden. The Winter Atlas suggests that 200 may visit a favoured bird table in a day, with over 1,000 during the course of a winter. A MTNHS report confirms this sort of number, with 300 birds being trapped in a Stony Stratford garden in the 1975/76 winter. In this case over 60% were adults, which is the reverse of the normal situation. There was no obvious explanation. The BBC Garden Bird Survey found the Blue Tit to be the commonest bird (in percentage of gardens visited) in all periods except one in the first two winters (98-100%), with a maximum of 30 at one time. Peanuts were the main attraction although there was also a fair amount of foraging for natural food.

Most birds seem to be sedentary, only a few having been recovered some little distance away. A bird ringed in Great Brickhill in March 1973 was recovered in December 1975 in Boston, Lincolnshire (120 km), one ringed in Stewkley in April 1958 had reached Maltby in S Yorkshire by October

256

1959, and others have moved to Sussex, Nottinghamshire and Somerset, the south-west being the direction favoured by two thirds of the longer distance ones reported. There is also a record of a seven-year-old bird in Oakley.

DBH

Great Tit
Parus major

Resident and widespread throughout the county.

The Great Tit is a very common bird in Buckinghamshire and widespread in the country as a whole. There is no evidence that there has been any great change in its status either locally or nationally since Clark Kennedy's time, though it is subject to occasional fluctuations caused by colder winters.

It is a woodland bird, preferring deciduous trees, but it is also found in conifers. Mature suburban gardens are also a favoured habitat. It is likely that Great Tits breed in every tetrad in the county and that the gaps are due to under-recording.

25,000 pairs

After fledging, the family group remains together for a while before the juveniles disperse. The adults continue to hold territory longer than other tits before joining flocks as autumn draws on. These flocks may also contain other species of tit, Goldcrests, Nuthatches, and even warblers early in the season. With the coming of winter there is a shift in their diet from insects to vegetable matter. A favourite is beech mast, so the Chilterns are ideal country. However, gardens are also used extensively and most, especially rural ones, will probably have a couple of pairs. The BBC Garden Bird Survey gives 12 birds as a maximum seen at any one time. Great Tits were seen in over 90% of the gardens and were one of the top ten most common species. It was clear that supplied food was the main attraction.

The Great Tit is generally sedentary in the British Isles. A few of the continental race are known to cross the Channel but there are no positive records as far inland as Buckinghamshire. There are, however, many recoveries of locally ringed birds, almost all of only very short range. The longest are of one ringed in Sheringham, Norfolk in July 1983 found in Moulsoe Old Wood the following March (160 km); one ringed at Tylers Green in 1981 found at Benhall, Suffolk (158 km); and one ringed in Margate on 21 Apr 1975 found

257

dead six days later at High Wycombe (154 km). Others have come from or gone to Essex, Gloucestershire and Wiltshire, and the counties adjacent to Buckinghamshire.

DBH

Nuthatch
Sitta europaea

Resident, mostly found in the south of the county.

There is no indication from early records that the status of the Nuthatch has changed much, if at all, in the county over the past 100 years. H & R and H & J note that it was especially common in Burnham Beeches.

The woods of the Chilterns provide well for its needs in terms of food and nest sites. It favours beech, oak, yew and hazel, as the fruits of these trees supply much of its diet. In the county breeding survey it was reported present in 32% of tetrads, which is slightly less than in Hertfordshire (39%) but similar to Oxfordshire (30%). In MTNHS and BBC reports it attracts little comment, except where it turns up in some less usual place; for example, one at Weston Turville Reservoir in 1983 was the first recorded at this well-watched site.

Nuthatches are less frequently seen in summer than in winter, when they join mixed flocks roaming the woods and appear at feeding stations. The BBC Garden Bird Survey reported them in 22% of gardens. They mainly came for the artificial food, especially peanuts which they are very adept at extracting from holders. They fly off to wedge the nuts into a crevice to be hammered into edible portions, in a very similar way to dealing with their natural food of acorns, beech mast and hazel nuts. They also regularly use bird baths.

Ringing in the county has provided no noteworthy recoveries, but the Nuthatch is the most sedentary of British birds. Only 2 recoveries of more than 5 km are known (the Winter Atlas).

An unusual individual was a bird without eye-stripes which frequented a garden in Lower Hartwell in 1985/86.

DBH

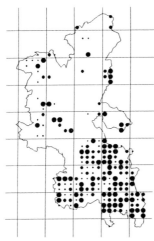

500 pairs

258

Treecreeper
Certhia familiaris

Resident in most wooded parts of the county .

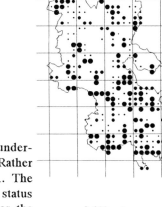

2,000 pairs

The Treecreeper is a widespread species but probably under-recorded due to its good camouflage and small size. Rather unusually, under-recording was also noted by H & R. The comments of these and other authors also suggest that its status in Buckinghamshire, has remained much the same over the years, though numbers can crash in cold winters. Recent years have shown a slight increase in the national population indices in both farmland and woodland.

Following dispersal in the late summer the adults tend to remain on their territory through the autumn and winter. It is not normally gregarious but will join mixed flocks of tits and Goldcrests roaming the woods. They were not common in the BBC Garden Bird Survey and none was seen to take artificial food. They were recorded in 13% of the gardens, with 2 being the largest number seen at a time. They fed on insects in trees.

The bird is no great wanderer. F & Y mention one ringed at Lane End in March 1964 recovered in Thame 18 days later, the 16 km movement being at the time the greatest distance of any national ringing recovery. Another ringed as a juvenile on Steps Hill on 15 Jul 1990 travelled 12 km to Bittam's Wood, near Wendover where it was trapped on 23 Jul 1990.

DBH

Golden Oriole
Oriolus oriolus

Rare vagrant which has bred.

The first record is by Clark Kennedy, who stated that a nest was found at Burnham, but he gives no details.

All other records are given:

1861: bred at Stoke.
1879: 1 male shot on 19 May, Stoke Mandeville.
1901: reported to have bred in the middle of the county.
1925: female on 9 Sep, Haddenham.
1933: 1 on 25 May, Burnham.
1936: 1 in Apr, Beaconsfield.
1949: 1 on 1 Aug, Burnham.
1972: 1 on 30 Apr to first week of May, Ivinghoe.
1979: male heard on 17 Jun, Linford Wood, Little Linford.
1983: male on 5 Jun, Ellesborough.
1988: 1 adult female on 22 and 25 May, Wendover Woods.
1989: first-summer male from 9-11 Jul, Cholesbury.

The increase in the number of records may be related to the establishment of a small breeding population in East Anglia in the 1970s.

Red-backed Shrike
Lanius collurio

Formerly a local summer visitor and rare passage migrant, now extinct.

H & J, writing in 1920, described the population as 'rather local and less common during the last 12 years than it used to be'. The birds must have suffered a substantial decrease since Clark Kennedy's time, who wrote that the species was 'numerous and breeds abundantly'. Sites mentioned ranged from Buckingham and Newport Pagnell to the Thames Valley, where it was described as local. By 1947 they were 'breeding in small and decreasing numbers' (Price).

During the 1950s the population had decreased to 3-6 pairs around High Wycombe and Farnham Royal. In 1959 a bird was seen at Wolverton and in 1960 a pair bred at Halton, but in the following year three of the sites near Wycombe were built on. In 1963 there were pairs at Little Chalfont and Haversham, and birds were seen at Gerrards Cross and Bletchley. Only one pair bred in 1968, none in 1969, although one bird was seen, while in 1970 two pairs bred near High Wycombe and Princes Risborough, and a male was seen near Olney. In 1971 two pairs successfully raised young at Grangelands and Dancersend, while another pair may have been successful. A single male was present in the south of the county. The following year marked the end: birds were seen at Steps Hill, and at two sites in N Buckinghamshire, the last being seen on 22 Jun 1972.

The events in the county were part of a national extinction of the species. The decline began in the middle of the 19th century and continued until 1988, when the last pair bred in Britain. It is difficult to find a single cause. The obvious factor is the lowering of mean summer temperatures which has taken place during the 20th century, but even during the short periods when the climate warmed the decline still continued. The bird had always been a target for egg-collectors - indeed Clark Kennedy mentions the eggs being on sale in Eton, and this may have been a factor. Much of one of its prime habitats - heathland - has been destroyed, but there is still plenty of apparently suitable areas of bushes in the Chilterns. Indeed the two last breeding sites, both nature reserves, still seem much as they were when shrikes bred there. But undoubtedly the habitat has degraded in some way. The large insects that shrikes feed on are now much rarer than they used to be, probably because of the increased use of pesticides. All these factors have undoubtedly contributed to the extinction of one of the county's finest birds.

DMF

Great Grey Shrike
Lanius excubitor

Scarce and decreasing winter visitor.

Clark Kennedy gives an undated record for Hampden.

The first dated record is:

1778: 1 shot on 8 Jan, Dinton Hall.

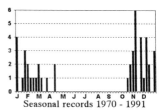

Seasonal records 1970 - 1991

There were a further 13 records to 1969. Since 1970 about 45 birds have been recorded. They are shown on the histograms. From being an annual winter visitor, Great Grey Shrikes have become very rare with only five birds recorded during the 1980s.

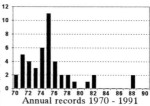

Annual records 1970 - 1991

Woodchat Shrike
Lanius senator

Very rare vagrant. There have been two records:

1974: 1 on 5 Jun, Padburyhill Farm, Padbury.
1976: 1 on 16 May, Little Marlow.

Jay
Garrulus glandarius

Resident, breeding throughout the county.

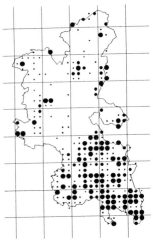

1,000 pairs

In 1905 H & R considered Jays to be 'very numerous residents', and 'anxiously kept down by keepers'. By 1920 the species was 'more or less common in all wooded districts' and had 'increased in numbers considerably since 1914' (H & J), presumably because keepering had declined during the First World War. Since then there is little evidence of any dramatic change. National Common Birds Census data show that the breeding population throughout the country has been more or less stable since 1966.

From the map it can be seen that the distribution of Jays in Buckinghamshire parallels that of woodland in the county, with the majority of birds nesting in the Chilterns or to the south. Other favoured areas include the Brickhill Woods, the woods south of the Claydons, the Buckinghamshire part of Salcey Forest, Whaddon Chase and the areas west of Oakley. Jays were probably under-recorded during the survey, being more secretive than the other corvids and more difficult to prove breeding. In Buckinghamshire, the Jay breeds in mature woodland of all types, including well wooded parks and suburban gardens.

In Chiltern beechwood CBC plots, breeding densities of about 10 territories per sq km have been found, with about 25 per sq km in the oaks of Church Wood in 1963 and 26 per sq km in the spruces of Wendover Woods in 1974. In the north, Shenley Wood in Milton Keynes held 21 per sq km in 1980. Jays often occur in gardens. The BBC Garden Bird Survey has shown that Jays have been recorded in 30% of the participating gardens. A maximum of 12 have been seen at a time.

In autumn Jays can be much more visible and are more often seen away from woodland. Acorns are an important food source at this time. In some autumns Jays are more plentiful than usual. This happened in 1975 and in 1983 when there was a huge influx nationally, probably due to a shortage of acorns

262

both in this country and on the continent. Some of this movement was seen in Buckinghamshire, with flocks of up to 45 seen moving west across the county in October.

The Winter Atlas recorded the species in all the county 10-km squares with a slight concentration in the north-west of the county.

RJT

Magpie
Pica pica

Resident, breeding throughout the county.

H & R and H & J regarded the Magpie as widely distributed in Buckinghamshire, though fairly scarce and local. This was partly because it was tightly controlled by keepering. H & J pointed to an apparent increase after the First World War, but clearly the species has undergone a vast expansion since then as it is now abundant everywhere in the county. The increase since the 1960s has been shown by the national Common Birds Census and locally.

The Magpie occurs in a variety of habitats, usually within range of thick cover of bushes or trees. It is found in woodland (mostly near the edge), in farmland (especially if the hedges are tall), and increasingly this century in parks and suburban gardens. The BBC Garden Bird Survey has shown that they occurred in 75% of participating gardens with a maximum flock size of 27. A small sample of BTO nest record cards for S Buckinghamshire show that many nested in hawthorn and a few in blackthorn, with nests often 5-10 m from the ground. Typically, the young hatched in late April or early May. Magpies breed in most parts of the county, gaps in the north probably being mainly due to under-recording.

1986: *6,000 pairs*
1991: *8,000 pairs*

CBC plots in the county show the highest breeding densities to be in small woods. Haleacre Wood, Little Kingshill has held up to 40 territories per sq km between 1977 and 1983; there were 20 per sq km in Shenley Wood, Milton Keynes and 25 per sq km in 1977 in Cowcroft Wood, Ley Hill. Most farmland plots had no more than 5 territories per sq km and some plots in large woods such as Burnham Beeches (1982-85) and Monkton Wood, Speen (1970-72) were devoid of Magpies.

After breeding, birds can be seen in parties of up to 20 or 30, often in hedgerows or scrub. During winter some roost communally. In February 1984 some 50 birds were seen at a pre-roost gathering in a young thicket-stage conifer plantation near Ashley Green. The Winter Atlas recorded Magpies in all the county's 10-km squares, with an indication of more in the middle and south of the county than in the north. Indeed N Buckinghamshire was more or less on the edge of an area extending through East Anglia in which there is a paucity of Magpies.

RJT

Nutcracker
Nucifraga caryocatactes

Very rare vagrant. There have been three records.

1911: 1 killed on 7 Oct, Whitchurch.
1968: 1 on 22 Sep, Penn.
1968: 1 from Sep-6 Oct, in the county near Berkhamsted.

The 1968 records were part of a large invasion into Britain of the Siberian slender-billed race. A further record at Ringshall on 13 Dec 1970 (F & Y) was never submitted to the British Birds Rarities Committee and cannot be substantiated.

Jackdaw
Corvus monedula

Resident, breeding throughout the county.

To H & R the species was 'by no means rare' in the county. H & J state that the bird was 'common in many places, especially where there is much old timber'. Both refer to much persecution by keepers. Since their time the persecution has perhaps declined, and if there have been any changes at all Jackdaw numbers have probably increased slightly. The national Common Birds Census index for farmland shows no great change from 1963 until the mid 1970s, since when there has been a steady rise. If this increase has occurred in Buckinghamshire it has not been large enough for the casual observer to notice.

The county breeding survey map shows a patchy distribution with many small gaps. The greatest concentrations of records largely correspond to the areas of best coverage. The pattern is also quite similar to that of the Rook with the birds shunning some of the higher parts of the Chilterns and some of the denser woodland areas such as Burnham Beeches.

4,000 pairs

As hole nesters Jackdaws prefer old trees. They occur frequently in small woods or in hedgerows and not so commonly in large woods. They also nest in buildings, sometimes in towns, and the nests are often in small colonies. Breeding Jackdaws usually feed in small flocks on open ground, often with Rooks.

Outside the breeding season, Jackdaws wander and disperse but seldom travel very far. The longest distances shown by ringing recoveries are to Devon and Worcestershire. From August until March they usually roost communally with Rooks and are often found feeding with them in flocks on farmland. The Winter Atlas shows that the Jackdaw was recorded in all the 10-km squares in the county but in relatively small numbers compared to some other parts of the country.

RJT

Rook
Corvus frugilegus

Resident, breeding throughout the county.

Writing early this century both H & R and H & J were agreed that the Rook was very numerous, and that most parks had a rookery. There was little change until after the 1940s. In recent years there have been two censuses, by Fisher in 1945/46 and by the BTO in 1975/76, and comparisons were reported by Sage and Vernon (1978). In the Thames Valley part of Buckinghamshire (using the pre-1974 boundary) there

12,000 pairs

was an increase of about 30% in nests counted compared with a national decrease in England and the Isle of Man of around 45%. In 1980 a census taken in a random selection of 10-km squares did not reveal any net change in the county.

In Buckinghamshire, Rooks start to incubate eggs in March. During the fieldwork for the county breeding survey young could be heard calling in some nests by mid April, although a few nests were still being added to in the rookeries (R. J. Tomlin). In 1973-75 most rookeries were in farmland with a scattering of hedgerow trees and small copses. Large areas of woodland such as Burnham Beeches were shunned as were built-up areas. The nests were almost always in the crowns of large trees. In the north of the county almost all were in English elms but in the Chilterns beech was the favoured tree (Tomlin & Youngman 1981). This is probably explained by the relative abundance of each tree species rather than any preference of Rooks for one or the other.

The Breeding Atlas shows proved breeding in every 10-km square in the county, but the more detailed county breeding survey gives a patchy distribution. The map shows many clusters of rookeries and many areas with none. Rooks are particularly widespread and abundant in the Vale of Aylesbury, but less so in the higher parts of the Chilterns. However, the Rivers Chess, Misbourne and Wye can be traced on the map, since many of the Chiltern rookeries were in small copses on the sides of the valleys. Breeding was recorded in few tetrads in the north-east where coverage was sparse, and in the far south where there is much dense woodland and urban development.

The local figures from the 1975 census provide another view of the bird's distribution. The largest densities of nests were recorded in 10-km squares in the Vale. SP61 (Brill) had about 9 per sq km, SP71 (Waddesdon) and SP72 (Winslow) both had about 12 per sq km, and other high densities were 9.5 in SP83 (Milton Keynes) and 10 in SU99 (Amersham). Overall, the density in the county was 6.4 per sq km. The largest individual rookeries were at Coleshill (c180) and at Newton Longville (c190).

In the autumn and winter, Rooks continue to feed near their rookeries which they often visit during the day. In the evening they gather in larger flocks at a roost, usually accompanied by about half their number of Jackdaws. In the early autumn of 1971 there were three such roosts in the Amersham/Chesham area, in small copses at Shardeloes, Botley and The Lee. The first two were also the sites of rookeries of around 100 nests. In late October the birds abandonded the Shardeloes and

Botley roosts, but they continued to gather at them in late afternoon before flying off to the main roost at The Lee at which c5,000 Rooks and c3,000 Jackdaws spent each night until early March. During the winter of 1971/72 there were other roosts at Winchendon (c1,000 Rooks) and Wing (c2,000). Also there were three large roosts just outside the county at Sonning in Berkshire, and at Studham and Woburn in Bedfordshire. Many Rooks and Jackdaws were seen to fly to each of these from Buckinghamshire (R J Tomlin).

RJT

Carrion Crow
Corvus corone corone

Resident, breeding throughout the county.

In 1905 H & R considered that Carrion Crows were widespread throughout the county, scarce in well keepered country, but common in 'the grass country' of NE Buckinghamshire and north-west of Aylesbury. They considered that the bird was declining. While largely agreeing with this, H & J thought there had been an increase since the intervening war when keepering had diminished. Apparently crows are now appreciably more numerous than earlier in the century, and the national Common Birds Census index has shown a continuation of this since the early 1960s.

The county breeding survey map shows a fairly widespread distribution in most types of country. If any area is favoured, it is a broad belt including the farmland of the Vale of Aylesbury, the Stewkley area and Milton Keynes, the very area mentioned by H & R. During a survey in April 1975 in the area around Waddesdon, Quainton and the Claydons, quite a large proportion of hedgerow trees were seen to contain used nests. Some of the gaps shown on the map are no doubt due to under-recording, but there are others especially at the north-east end of the Chilterns where there is much woodland and several built-up areas. Perhaps it is easier to prove breeding in open country with scattered hedgerow trees than it is in dense woodland or in urban areas. Local farmland CBC plots seemed to follow the national increase in the 1970s and some woodlands also showed an increase, although most plots only contained two or three territories. A Burnham Beeches plot contained no Carrion Crows in the late 1960s, but regularly one or two territories in the early 1980s. Two notable densities were 12 territories per sq km in Stowe Park in 1974 and a

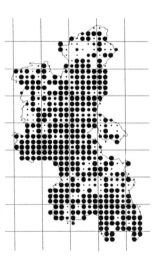

6,000 pairs

267

remarkable 47 per sq km near Claydon in 1986 in a small wood that also contained a large rookery.

Outside the breeding season Carrion Crows are less gregarious than Rooks or Jackdaws. However they often form night-time roosts of several hundreds. In the early 1970s there was regularly one at Bellingdon and one near Dancers End. Both of these were occupied in the late autumn and winter and contained 200-300 birds. Carrion Crows were not much in evidence at the large Rook/Jackdaw roosts watched. During the Winter Atlas period Carrion Crows were recorded in all the county's 10-km squares, with the largest numbers in the Vale of Aylesbury. It appears that in winter the species showed much more of a preference for low-lying farmland than it did in the breeding season.

RJT

Hooded Crow
Corvus corone cornix

Very rare vagrant. Formerly a regular winter visitor.

There has evidently been a change in the status of the Hooded Crow since 1868 when Clark Kennedy wrote 'may be observed on the banks of the Thames every winter'. Apparently it was common in winter near Drayton Beauchamp and found near Chesham in frosty weather. In 1920 H & J stated 'Winter visitor. Generally more or less scarce, but sometimes occurs in fair numbers. More common along the Thames Valley and on the plains near Cheddington, Mentmore, and Leighton Buzzard.'

Since 1946 there have been only four records:

1951: 1 on 18 Mar, Pinewood.
1953: 1 on 8 and 22 Mar, Marlow.
1953: 1-3 wintered at Wendover, one remaining until 12 Apr.
1964: 1 on 1 Jan, Stone.

The UK boundary between Hooded and Carrion Crows has retreated northwards this century and this may account for the status change, although it is believed that most Hooded Crows wintering in England originate from Scandinavia (the Winter Atlas).

DMF

Raven

Corvus corax

Very rare vagrant. All records are given.

1828: 1 shot on 25 Mar, Dinton Hall.
1829: 1 shot on 16 Dec, Dinton Hall.
1887: 1 on 14 Aug, Farnham.
1932: 1 probable on 12 Nov, Boveney.
1947/48: 1 seen at Ravenstone mobbed by Rooks.
1982: 1 on 25 Jan, Willen.

Starling

Sturnus vulgaris

Resident and winter visitor, very common and breeding throughout the county.

The Starling was once considered rare as a resident, following a large drop in numbers in the early nineteenth century. This may have been due to changes in agricultural practices, a period of abnormally severe winters, or a combination of the two. An increase was well under way by the middle of that century, as Clark Kennedy states it to be a 'very plentiful resident by 1860'. In 1920 H & J reported that there had been a huge increase in the preceding 50 years.

Given a hole and cavity of suitable size the Starling may use it as a nest site. Hence it can be found in almost any habitat, urban or rural. The county breeding map shows the bird's versatility; it was the fourth most widespread bird recorded,with breeding proved in more tetrads than any other species. The distribution in the north of the county appears rather thin in parts but this is probably due to under-recording.

20,000 pairs

After a breeding season starting in mid April, young birds start to appear in flocks from early June, and from then on some quite large flocks can be seen roaming the fields. However, it is not until autumn and winter that the really large flocks appear, when residents are joined by many thousands from N and E Europe. The largest numbers are usually seen early and late in the day when the birds are going to or leaving their roosts.

In Buckinghamshire a number of large roosts have been reported consistently over the last two decades. The MTNHS report for 1972 mentioned two: one at Aston Clinton containing over one million birds had attracted publicity in local newspapers in March, while one at Wicken Wood near

Deanshanger reportedly holding around half a million birds in November 1971 was considered to have doubled in size by mid January 1972. In early 1975 the Aston Clinton roost had built up to a total 'in excess of a million birds'. Others have included one of over 50,000 at Drayton Parslow in March 1978 and another of similar size near Chesham at the same time. In 1981 there were possibly as many as a quarter of a million at Calvert (C Fisher counted 17,000 arriving between 16.20 and 16.45 on 22 January).

Recoveries of birds ringed locally show that many of the winter visitors are from breeding populations in E Europe and that they do not necessarily return to the same wintering areas each year. One ringed at Bletchley in November 1971 was shot on the Black Sea coast of Bulgaria in January 1979, and others have been found in the USSR (4), Latvia (3), Poland (4), Denmark (3), Finland (2), Sweden (1), Norway (1), Germany (12), the Netherlands (10) and Belgium (2). In addition, birds ringed in some of these countries have been found in Buckinghamshire. Most of the winter visitors have left for their breeding grounds by mid March.

DBH

Rose-coloured Starling
Sturnus roseus

Very rare vagrant. There have been two records.

There is an undated record in Gould's *Birds of Europe* of a bird shot at Iver Court.

1978: adult on 7 Nov, Bletchley.

Birds have been recorded in Britain in every month of the year, but November is one of the least likely for a genuinely wild individual to be found.

House Sparrow
Passer domesticus

Resident throughout the county.

All the older records name the House Sparrow as the commonest bird in the county and in recent reports it seldom rates more than a bare mention. It is probably safe to assume that in Buckinghamshire, as elsewhere, the House Sparrow has been a resident in towns and villages and around farms and homesteads, indeed part of the everyday scene, for many generations past. In that sense it is very common, and it was the second most widespread species in the county breeding survey. However, it is easy to walk in the Chiltern woodlands and never see it, so it is probable that the tetrads in the south of the county which show a dearth of the species do reflect those woodland areas where it is less than plentiful. Common Birds Census data indicate a population decline since the late 1970s, although there are no local surveys to support this. The reasons for the decline are likely to be a reduction in food supply caused by crop-spraying, and the change to autumn sowing of cereals which has reduced the area of stubble available for winter feeding.

50,000 pairs

The bird is a prolific breeder and is adept at finding its way through tiles and loose bricks to find a dry spot in the roof or eaves of a building. Later on in the season it will dispossess House Martins given half a chance. In towns it also has a liking for lamp posts, particularly the older sort where presumably it derives some warmth from the lamp itself. This can be important as it uses the nest all the year round as a roost site.

With breeding over, House Sparrows can be seen in considerable numbers in hedgerows and shrubberies. They fly out in numbers to whatever food is available and can cause problems if this happens to be a cereal crop. The Handbook suggests that, during winter, cattle and horse feeds help nourish the House Sparrow. This no doubt still occurs but rural and urban bird tables are also a common substitute. The BBC Garden Bird Survey shows the House Sparrow to be among the commonest birds, coming to feed in 90% of gardens. Although showing a preference for the foods put out for them, and rapidly learning to rival tits and finches clinging to nut feeders, the House Sparrows still did a lot of foraging for natural food. One report speaks of 94 being present at one time.

F & Y mention a fully grown female ringed at Taplow in January 1957 being recovered there in May 1965. There are two long-distance recoveries. A bird ringed in the county in May 1977 was found at Ryton-on-Dunsmore, Warwickshire in April 1983, while an adult male ringed at Aston Abbots on 21 May 1987 was found at Ewell, Surrey on 12 Mar 1990.

DBH

Tree Sparrow
Passer montanus

Resident, with local colonies more widespread in the north of the county.

The Tree Sparrow is a bird of fluctuating fortunes whose whereabouts vary considerably, both countrywide and locally. Earlier authors suggest that it was distinctly local in the middle and late nineteenth century but had increased by the 1930s, a situation which remained until the mid 1970s. Since then there has been a major decline, paralleled by the national population (Summers-Smith 1989). The MTNHS report for 1979 mentions the bird as becoming 'uncommon in the area (or under-recorded)'. It is certainly unobtrusive, especially in the breeding season, and when it flocks in the winter it may do so in the company of House Sparrows, finches and buntings. If there are only a few Tree Sparrows in a large mixed flock they can easily be overlooked.

As the map shows, the north-east of the county held a high proportion of the population, although there were pockets of birds in other places. The decline in recent years is noticed here, too. In 1968-1972 Hertfordshire recorded the species in 90% of its tetrads compared to 31% in Buckinghamshire. The Oxfordshire figure was 32%. It now appears to be mainly a bird of hedgerows and small woods in the county, and not of denser woods. However, Williamson (1972) reported that a small area of mature deciduous woodland in the Chilterns held 62 pairs per sq km.

Both MTNHS and BBC reports frequently mention sizeable flocks in autumn and winter. During the 1970s these often exceeded 100, but in the 1980s they were usually much smaller. The birds wander quite extensively but the reports indicate that a few areas always seem to hold some. Bishopstone, for example, had a flock of 300 on stubble in December 1980, 50 in September 1982, 45 in March 1983 and 50 in September 1984. Leckhamstead is also mentioned twice in the 1980s.

The BBC Garden Bird Survey shows that the species is only a rare visitor to gardens, and mainly rural ones. The maximum reported at any one time was 4, but more often it was only single birds - odd for a bird which is so gregarious in winter. It was reported in only 2% of gardens, in some of which it concentrated on the food provided, to the exclusion of all else.

A few local ringing recoveries suggest small scale movements. F & Y mention local birds found in Kent and Essex, and one ringed at Wheathamstead, Hertfordshire in July 1982 was found in Moulsoe Wood 6 months later.

DBH

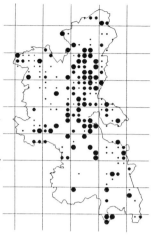

1986: 3,000 pairs
1991:   500 pairs

Chaffinch
Fringilla coelebs

Very common resident, passage migrant and winter visitor.

H & R considered the Chaffinch to be one of the most common birds in Buckinghamshire, if not the most numerous species, and nesting virtually everywhere.

The county breeding survey showed it still to be present as a breeding bird throughout the area, and it was the third most widespread species after the Blackbird and House Sparrow. It is thought that there was a national decline in late 1950s, probably due to the effects of toxic chemicals used in agriculture, but national Common Birds Census figures suggest that this trend was reversed during the early 1960s. Since the early 1970s, the CBC shows the species to be slowly on the increase.

Chaffinches occupy a wide range of habitats, breeding wherever there are trees or bushes. Numbers tend to be highest in broad-leaved woodland but just about all habitats within the county will be utilised, including scrub, farmland hedgerows and gardens, even those in suburban areas. The Chaffinch is easily detected as it is strongly territorial and has

50,000 pairs

a distinctive song and call-note, which means recording is quick even in less well covered areas, but the breeding season is rather short with usually only one brood being raised. The characteristic, neat nest is usually built in a hedge or tree from mid April onwards. During the breeding season, Chaffinches are insectivorous, feeding their young largely on caterpillars. At other times the diet is predominantly seeds. In winter they are common in gardens, the BBC Garden Bird Survey recording them in 92% of gardens, with a maximum flock size of 200 birds. The considerable majority were taking artificial food.

Breeding birds within the county appear to be very sedentary, moving only short distances and tending to remain in the breeding area for most of their life. However, the population is swollen in late autumn and winter by immigrants from Scandinavia, N Germany and Finland. Most arrive in October and only leave again between March and mid April. This movement has been shown by ringing recoveries. For example, several birds ringed at High Wycombe in February or March have been recovered in Norway and Sweden in April, May and June, while others have been found in Germany and the Benelux countries at this time and in October. These continental birds, of the race *F.c.coelebs*, are slightly larger and paler than the resident British birds.

Winter flocks which may number 250-400 birds can often be found in beechwoods in the Chilterns, where they feed on the fallen mast. The largest flock recorded is one of 750 at Ford in March 1981.

PAW

Brambling
Fringilla montifringilla

Winter visitor in low numbers scattered across the county.

The Brambling was reported by H & R to be a regular winter visitor, although numbers were variable between years and higher when beech mast was plentiful. For example, flocks of several hundreds were seen in Chiltern beechwoods in the winter of 1905/06.

The first birds to arrive in Buckinghamshire are usually recorded during the second week of October, often from Steps Hill on the Chiltern escarpment near Ivinghoe. Most reports in winter though come from the south-central part of the county between Amersham and Aylesbury, associated with the

Chiltern beechwoods. Beech mast forms the principal food of the species in the county, and birds will move around until they find an adequate source. If mast is in short supply or exhausted, they will utilise other habitats and food, such as cereal and weed seeds in open fields, and they will also visit gardens and take peanuts, particularly in late winter. In the BBC Garden Bird Survey they were recorded in 4% of gardens with a maximum of 8 birds at a time, and were recorded taking both natural and artificial food.

The birds wintering in Britain come mainly from breeding areas in Scandinavia, although ringing recoveries show that they may arrive via other NW European countries. A bird recovered at Cheddington in December 1983 had been ringed in Antwerp, Belgium 66 days previously.

The number of birds wintering within the county is probably largely dependent on the size of the beech mast crop. In recent years, flock sizes have tended to be fairly small, the largest recorded being 70 at Kingswood on 6 Apr 1984, except for one flock of over 600 recorded at Woburn Sands in January 1981. The wintering area of individuals varies from year to year, as shown by some local ringing recoveries. Birds wintering in Buckinghamshire in one year have been recovered as far apart as the Netherlands, Denmark, France and Italy in subsequent winters. Hard weather may force Bramblings to move out of the county, usually towards the south and west.

The last birds are normally recorded in the last week of April, with the latest a female which stayed at Bradenham Woods until 4 May 1986.

PAW

Serin
Serinus serinus

Very rare vagrant. There has been one record.

1971: pair from 12-14 Mar, Bourne End. Only the male was seen on the second date.

Greenfinch
Carduelis chloris

Common resident and winter visitor.

8,000 pairs

Specific historical information on the status and distribution of the Greenfinch within Buckinghamshire is somewhat sketchy. It seems to have been a very common resident and winter visitor since records began, occupying a range of habitats including gardens, farmland hedgerows and orchards.

The present distribution is little changed. Breeding was confirmed over the majority of the area by the county breeding survey. The gaps that exist on the map correspond with the areas where coverage was poorest. Breeding birds occur in small, loose colonies of a few pairs in a variety of habitat types where suitable shrub cover for nesting is available. National Common Birds Census data show the population on farmland over the country as a whole to have been fairly stable since the mid 1960s, although the woodland data suggest a slight decrease over this period.

Greenfinches are easily detected during the breeding season by the characteristic song, a nasal 'dzwee' followed by a short trill. There is also a butterfly-like display flight, during which the male continues to sing. The nest is built in a bush, usually in April. There may be from two to four broods, which can extend the breeding season until as late as August.

There is no known regular movement of birds from their breeding areas in Buckinghamshire to any specific wintering grounds. However, birds do tend to wander and others come into the county as winter visitors. One bird ringed in France in January 1960 was recovered at Chesham in April 1961, another was ringed in Wexford (Ireland) in January 1982 and found at Mentmore that April, and birds ringed in the county in October have been found as far south-west as Cardiff and Exeter during the winter. A female ringed at Lowton, Greater Manchester in December 1982 journeyed to High Wycombe, where it was controlled 29 days later, before turning up at Lowton again in March 1983. There are also several records of birds travelling to and from East Anglia, suggesting perhaps a regular movement.

The Greenfinch enjoys a varied diet of seeds ranging from those of chickweed and dandelion to cultivated cereals, hornbeam and yew. Its main food in winter is the seed of agricultural weeds, although peanuts at garden feeding stations are also a significant food source. It was always in the top ten of most widespread birds in the BBC Garden Bird Survey, being recorded in over 88% of all gardens, where it favoured

276

artificial food. More visit gardens in late winter, especially during severe weather. Flocks of 100 or more occur in most winters in Buckinghamshire and may reach up to 400 in some years if there are good food supplies in one place.

PAW

Goldfinch
Carduelis carduelis

Common resident and summer visitor.

At the beginning of the present century H & R stated that the Goldfinch was nowhere common, although it was more regular in winter and on passage than as a breeding bird. It was seen occasionally and bred in limited numbers, but was decreasing in many places. H & R laid the blame for this squarely at the door of professional bird-trappers, as the species was a very popular cage-bird. The trappers were said to be particularly active in the hills above Wendover. By 1920, however, numbers of Goldfinches had increased considerably and the species could frequently be seen near Chesham, Beaconsfield, Cholesbury, Aylesbury, Wendover, Cheddington and Aston Abbots (H & J), and by 1947 it was considered by Price to be a common resident and passage bird.

The county breeding survey shows the Goldfinch to be well distributed throughout the county, especially in the centre and south, but the population may have decreased somewhat since. National Common Birds Census data show a peak in the late 1970s, followed by a steady decrease, bringing the level in the mid 1980s back to that of the early 1960s. A range of habitats is occupied during the breeding season including farmland, gardens, parkland, scrub and woodland edge as well as areas of wasteground, provided there are tall bushes or trees for nesting. The birds will travel some distance from their nest to find food, which is mainly weed seeds, especially those of thistles and other *Compositae*.

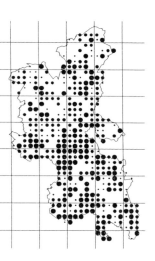

5,000 pairs

Feeding flocks are a familiar sight in August and September when birds visit wasteland, allotments, and rough pasture to feed on the seeds of dandelion, groundsel, ragwort, and particularly thistles. The birds' long, sharp beaks are well suited to extracting these seeds. The largest flocks tend to be recorded in October. Recent flocks of up to 100 were seen in that month at Drayton Parslow and at Willen in 1985, and one of 150 on Pitstone Hill in 1984.

It is likely that up to 80% of the summer population leaves

the county by late October. Ringing recoveries show that most of the birds travel to France or Spain. For example, two ringed at Lane End on 26 Sep 1964 were recovered in Spain in January and February 1965, while one ringed there in August 1967 was found in France in January 1968. A less distant recovery concerns a bird ringed at Marlow STW in August 1984 and recovered in Dorset in February 1985.

Winter flocks rarely exceed 50 birds, but over 200 were present at Loudwater in February 1981.

PAW

Siskin
Carduelis spinus

A regular winter visitor which may occasionally breed.

H & R considered the Siskin to be an irregular winter visitor, being more frequent in cold winters, for example that of 1866/67.

The county breeding survey shows the Siskin to be present in suitable habitat in four tetrads, two in the centre and two in the south of the county. The preferred habitat in the breeding season is coniferous woodland, the main food at that time of year being seeds of spruce and pine. There does not appear to be any sign of birds holding territory in Wendover Woods during the survey period, despite the fairly large expanse of apparently suitable habitat, although odd ones have been seen there subsequently.

The commercial planting of conifers has allowed the species to extend its breeding range from its original stronghold in the Scottish pine forests to Ireland and parts of England and Wales. The Siskin's nest is difficult to find, and although its song and calls are distinctive, the odd pair in extensive suitable habitat could easily be overlooked.

Siskins are more familiar in Buckinghamshire as winter visitors. The first usually arrive around mid September, though they may appear towards the end of August or not until late October. Ringing recoveries have shown these birds to be a mixture of British breeding birds and continental migrants, with perhaps the majority being Scottish bred. One male was ringed in Hertfordshire in February 1982, controlled at Chalfont St Peter in March 1983 and again at Bonar Bridge, Highland two months later. Other British birds found wintering in Buckinghamshire had been ringed in N England and Dyfed, Wales during the summer. Continental immigrants

seem mainly to arrive via Belgium and the Netherlands. Their countries of origin are indicated by ringing recoveries to be Norway, Sweden, Germany and Austria, and one bird was found bearing a Lithuanian ring.

This is an irruptive species, and the number of birds wintering within the county varies from year to year. In some winters they seem plentiful and widespread while in others they can be hard to find. Flocks of up to 150 are not unusual, the larger flocks tending to occur in the later part of the winter. However, 13 Dec 1981 proved to be a particularly good day, with 500 at Old Slade and 170 at Denham. Siskins were reported to be particularly widespread in early 1986. This was largely due to a big continental influx, which also resulted in several records of summering birds.

Birds may winter in widely separated places from one year to the next. Individuals caught in Britain in one winter have been found the following winter in the Netherlands, Belgium, France, Spain and Austria. Local movements during the winter and spring of up to 20 km are common. A male ringed at Uxbridge, Middlesex on 1 Apr 1986 was controlled at Seer Green the following day, a distance of 11 km, and it was subsequently found dead at Fort William, Highland 43 days later.

In winter, the main habitat is alder woods and copses, although Siskins can also be found in birches or larches. Their habit of visiting gardens was first noticed in the 1960s and is more a feature of late winter and early spring. They will readily take peanuts (sometimes showing a preference for those in red containers) and fat, and they are also attracted to feed on the seeds of ornamental cypresses. This has made them easy to catch and ring, thereby enabling more to be learnt about their movements. The BBC Garden Bird Survey recorded Siskins in 11% of gardens, although the percentage varied from winter to winter.

The last birds are usually recorded towards the end of April, although a few remain later, and song is often heard as late as mid May.

PAW

Linnet
Carduelis cannabina

Common resident and summer visitor.

The Linnet was described by H & R as very common in the early part of this century, but it has shown a major national decline especially since the mid 1970s (national Common Birds Census data).

Breeding was confirmed during the county breeding survey over much of the county, with the main gaps occurring in the north where coverage was poorest. A range of habitats is occupied during the breeding season including farmland, downland, heath, woodland edge, young plantations and areas of scrub. The Breeding Atlas estimated a mean of 7 pairs per sq km (using CBC data) in 1972, and densities were found to be especially high in chalk grassland scrub and young conifer plantations. The basic requirements of the birds are bushes for nesting, and weed seeds which comprise the bulk of their food. They usually nest in small colonies of about half a dozen pairs, where their song and display flights make them easy to locate. Eggs are laid from mid April, to take advantage of the seasonal crop of fresh seeds, and breeding extends into early August which allows some pairs to raise as many as four broods.

The national Common Birds Census has recorded a major decrease in numbers both on farmland and in woodland habitats since the mid to late 1970s. This has been caused in the main by the increased use of herbicides, which has reduced the amount of weed seeds available for food. Birds have also been affected on their breeding grounds in France and Iberia where most of our birds winter. There is some reason to believe that the increase in the area of oil-seed rape may be beneficial to the birds.

Although some birds remain to winter in the county, the species is generally scarce between the end of September and the end of March. Ringing recoveries indicate that most go south, taking a similar route to the county's Goldfinches, although the Linnets probably leave a few weeks earlier. Their destinations have been shown to be the Low Countries, W France and Spain. Some southerly movement within Britain may also occur during hard weather.

Those birds that do remain form flocks which feed mainly on farmland and wasteground, wherever weed seeds, particularly brassicas, persicaria and fat hen, are available. The largest gatherings tend to occur in autumn when they often number 200-300, but a flock of 600 was recorded on stubble fields at Dorney in August 1984. Winter flocks generally do not exceed more than about 100 birds, a notable exception being one of about 800 just outside the county boundary at Bray, Berkshire. Roosts within the county may number up to 400 birds, one such being recorded at Willen in January 1984. Birds tend to return from the Continent during April and early May.

PAW

1986: 4,000 pairs
1991: 2,000 pairs

Twite
Carduelis flavirostris

Rare vagrant. All records are given.

1893: 21 Nov, caught by bird-catcher near Aston Clinton.
1893: 5 Dec, as above.
1898: 11 Nov, as above.
1902: 3 caught Feb, near Skirmett.
1962: c25 on 1 Apr, Shardeloes.
1964: 5 on 27 Sep, Weston Turville Res. One was caught and ringed.
1966: 1 on 21 Mar, Old Slade.

The lack of records since 1966 is surprising. If the above records are all correct identifications then the status within Buckinghamshire of this species has changed markedly.

281

Redpoll
Carduelis flammea

Uncommon resident, summer and winter visitor.

When H & R published their account of birds in Buckinghamshire in 1905, there had been no authenticated record of Lesser Redpolls nesting within the county, although they were thought to breed occasionally and had been found nesting nearby in Hertfordshire. The species was known principally as a winter visitor. Price still recorded the Lesser Redpoll as a winter visitor but also as breeding locally in small numbers. F & Y stated that it bred regularly in small numbers 'which appear to be increasing'.

The county breeding survey confirmed breeding in only 6 tetrads, with probable or possible breeding in ten times that number. These were scattered throughout the county although more numerous on the eastern side. The pattern is broadly similar to that discovered by the Breeding Atlas in 1968-72. Most breeding season reports seem to be associated with commons and wooded areas such as those around Burnham Beeches, the Chiltern escarpment and Wendover, although some records were from tetrads with little or no woodland at all, particularly in the north of the county.

The breeding population of the Redpoll is subject to an eruptive strategy, which, in Europe, depends upon the quantities of seed crops of birch and spruce. The local population also seems to be subject to considerable fluctuations. Breeding records for the early 1990s seem rather sparse, and the map may show a wider distribution than is now the case.

Because of these factors, calculating the breeding population with any accuracy is even more difficult than usual. A density of five pairs per 100 ha for mixed broad-leaved/coniferous woodland and 10 pairs per 100 ha for pure coniferous woodland, gives a population of 400 pairs. Even this figure is likely to be an over-estimate.

Traditionally, the birds favour birch woodland or scrub, tree-lined streams and chalk downland where scrub has invaded. They will also take to overgrown field hedgerows and have benefited in recent years from the growth in commercial forestry, favouring young conifer plantations with trees up to six metres high. Eggs are laid between late April and late May, with the breeding season extending to mid July, allowing two or three broods to be raised. The diet at this time consists of seeds and flowers of sallows, and seeds of a variety of herbaceous plants, as well as insects.

In autumn and winter Lesser Redpolls are largely reliant on birch and alder seeds for their food, and their movements are largely governed by the abundance of these. Birds from N Britain move into S England around late September and October. Some may then cross into the Netherlands, Belgium, France or West Germany, stopping when they reach an abundant food source. If the birch seed crop in England is good, more birds tend to overwinter. There are 3 instances of birds ringed in Buckinghamshire in April or October, being found in Belgium during the winter months. Wintering flocks within the county tend to be small, only occasionally numbering over 100.

The nominate race of the Redpoll, the Mealy Redpoll *C. f. flammea* which originates in Fenno-Scandia, was thought by earlier authors to occur in Buckinghamshire, but this was not proved until December 1921 when a flock of 20 birds was present at Weston Turville Reservoir until February 1922. Subsequent records include 2 at Old Slade in December 1972 and a male showing the characters of this race at Newport Pagnell in April 1982.

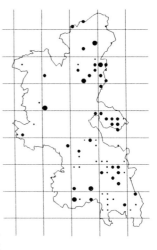

1986: 400 pairs
1991: 100 pairs

PAW

Crossbill
Loxia curvirostra

Irregular winter visitor and occasional breeding bird.

H & R considered the Crossbill to be a frequent winter visitor, rare or absent in some years but numerous in others. They also made reference to what may have been the first breeding record in the county, at Dinton Hall in 1791. The first definite record of breeding came from a Mr R. Bulstrode who was shown a nest with four eggs near Gerrards Cross on 1 Apr 1910. The young were still in the nest on 23 April.

The Crossbill is an irruptive species, and most breeding reports relate to birds which irrupted in the previous summer and stayed on. The breeding season is early, usually from February to April, but is dependent on an adequate food supply and can be at almost any time of the year. The habitat occupied is dictated by the Crossbill's food of conifer seeds. Coniferous plantations of pine, larch, spruce and fir are all utilised. The nest is placed in thick foliage high up in a tree, and hence it is difficult to prove breeding.

Movements of birds usually occur when the new crop of seeds is forming. In the case of European birds, which feed

largely on spruce, this happens in late June and July. Birds will move from areas where the new crop is poor and settle where it is good. In some years large numbers of birds move out of their normal range, travelling anything up to 4,000 km. The reason for such irruptions is not fully understood, but they probably arise from the combination of a high population of birds and a poor food crop.

In recent years there have been a number of large country-wide invasions. Birds appeared in the county in mid June 1985, and again in the following October. There were flocks of up to 34 at Wendover Woods and 60 at Woburn golf course at this time. A number of these birds stayed on until at least 1989. Then 1990 saw the largest invasion recorded. The first birds were seen on 27 May 1990 and by July birds were found at 40 sites within the county, though only 5 of these were in the north. The largest flocks were 74 at Wendover Woods on 10 Jul 1990, 40+ near Kingsash on 20 Nov 1990, and 40 at Seer Green Railway Station on 2 Dec 1990.

Between 1985 and 1990 a number of pairs were proved to have bred. A pair was seen with nest material at Black Park, Iver on 15 Mar 1984, and a pair bred at Wendover Woods in 1985. In 1986 pairs were seen in the Brickhill Woods and Wendover Woods, and a female and 2 juveniles at Bernwood. In 1988 3 pairs bred in Wendover Woods but the birds had gone by February 1989. The huge invasion of 1990 did not lead to any proved breeding in 1991 although it almost certainly took place.

PAW

Bullfinch
Pyrrhula pyrrhula

Common resident.

Reference to historical literature shows that the Bullfinch has long been a common resident in the county, despite some persecution from gardeners due to its liking for fruit buds. It was considered by F & Y to be showing signs of an increase. This would seem to be supported by national Common Birds Census data, although the CBC suggests that it has decreased considerably since 1976, especially on farmland.

The county breeding survey showed the species to be breeding over much of the county, particularly in the centre just north of the Chiltern escarpment. It occupies a range of habitats, provided there are sufficient bushy thickets for nesting. Woodland edge, scrub, and overgrown churchyards and gardens are typical.

As far as is known, the species is very sedentary and birds are unlikely to move more than a few kilometres. However, a male ringed at West Wycombe in May 1961 was recovered at Chichester in January 1962, a distance of about 125 km, and one found wintering on 31 Dec 1969 at Sherington, Newport Pagnell had been ringed four months earlier at Gibraltar Point, Lincolnshire.

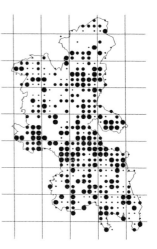

4,000 pairs

The complete lack of information about this species in recent Buckinghamshire bird reports, would suggest that there is still ample opportunity to increase our knowledge of this common county resident.

PAW

Hawfinch
Coccothraustes coccothraustes

Scarce resident.

The distribution of the Hawfinch within the county seems to have changed little over the past century. It was known to breed at Burnham Beeches and near Chesham, Aylesbury, Langley, Stowe Park and Marlow in the latter part of the 19th century, and it had also been noted at Halton, Wendover, Beaconsfield, Cholesbury, Cheddington and Aston Abbots.

The county breeding survey produced reports of confirmed breeding in only two tetrads, and of probable or possible breeding in another fourteen. These came from similar areas to those mentioned above, such as the Ashridge estate near

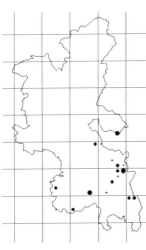

50 pairs

Tring, the Chesham/Amersham area, Beaconsfield, Great Missenden, High Wycombe and Marlow. However, there was a noticeable absence of records from Burnham Beeches, despite reasonable coverage in that area. The species is, however, likely to be under-recorded as the birds are unobtrusive and easily overlooked. They are usually located during the breeding season by their call note, a Robin-like 'tic', and may be seen among the topmost branches of a tree or, more likely, as they fly away. They are most easily located in early April, when they seem to call more frequently, and pairs can sometimes be observed chasing through the treetops.

Their favoured habitat within the county, as elsewhere, is mature deciduous woodland, especially where hornbeam or beech are prominent, such as at Chesham Bois and parts of the Ashridge estate. They will sometimes breed in orchards, parks or large gardens, and a pair was recorded nesting in a garden at Great Marlow in 1891.

Within the county, the birds are almost exclusive to the Chilterns. Given the elusive nature of the birds, the population is even more difficult to estimate than usual, but assuming 3 pairs per occupied tetrad, may be around 50 pairs.

Very little is known about the movements of Hawfinches. It would seem likely that the birds in Buckinghamshire are mainly sedentary, although a bird ringed in November 1968 at High Wycombe, was retrapped at Tunbridge Wells, Kent in May 1974, a distance of about 100 km. Their habitat use in winter is much the same as in the breeding season, although wintering sites are not regularly used. Sites at West Wycombe and Flackwell Heath may be used regularly one winter but are deserted the next, presumably due to a variable food supply. In winter small flocks usually build up and the birds become marginally easier to find. Maximum flock sizes vary from 6 to about 20, most reports coming from the Chesham area. While the British population of the Hawfinch seems to be sedentary, N European populations migrate regularly, so it is possible that a continental bird could eventually be recorded wintering within the county.

PAW

Lapland Bunting
Calcarius lapponicus

Very rare vagrant and winter visitor. All records are given.

1982: male from 21-22 Apr, Willen.
1984: 2 on 11 Oct, with Skylarks on Dorney Common.
1987: of 3 present at Slough SF (Berks) different individuals strayed to Dorney Common on 21 Jan and 10 Feb.
1990/91: 1 on 24 Nov, Drayton Parslow rising to 5 on 31 Dec. Between 1 and 3 birds were seen to 2 Feb 1991 when a single bird was seen.
1991: 1-3 birds from 9-17 Feb, Boveney.

Although typically found on the coast in winter, Lapland Buntings occasionally winter inland. The unobtrusive nature of the species must make it difficult to detect. Indeed little was seen of the birds at Drayton Parslow on the ground, and identification was based almost entirely on their distinctive flight-calls.

Snow Bunting
Plectrophenax nivalis

Rare vagrant. All records are given.

1776: 1 on 8 Jan, Dinton Hall.
1895: large flocks near Tring Res.
1901: male shot on 4 Nov, Drayton Lodge.
1903: 1 Ivinghoe Beacon.
1956: male on 23 Feb, Ballinger.
1960: 1 on 8 Nov, Foxcote Res.
1973: male from 8 Nov-early May 1974, Fulmer.
1976: 2 on 31 Jan, Willen.
1976: female on 23 and 25 Nov, Oakley.
1981: 1 on 24 Mar and 1 Apr, Willen.
1981: 1 on 15 Nov, Willen.
1983: female on 16 Oct, Linford.
1984: first-winter female on 27 Jan, Pitstone Hill.
1987: 1 on 1 Feb, Hulcott.

Unusually, the long-staying bird at Fulmer frequented a garden.

Yellowhammer
Emberiza citrinella

Very common resident.

15,000 pairs

The population of Yellowhammers has probably remained fairly constant this century. H & J described the status of Yellowhammers as 'common', while Price wrote 'very common'. The map shows a bird widely distributed throughout the county. The gaps are almost certainly due to under-recording.

Yellowhammers are virtually the type-species for agricultural land with hedges, but they are also found in scrub, young conifer plantations, and woodland clearings. It is likely that there has been some reduction in population due to the destruction of hedges, but the species seems to have survived the changes in agricultural practices well. National Common Birds Census indices have been remarkably consistent since recording began in 1962 and there is no reason to suppose these do not apply locally. Although some species of finch and bunting have been adversely affected by crop spraying with herbicides, particularly the species which depend upon weed seeds, Yellowhammers, with their larger bills, tend to rely more upon cereal grain, and have remained largely unaffected.

Scrub areas in the Chilterns can hold high densities of breeding Yellowhammers. A study on Steps Hill (Williamson 1975) showed that there were an average of 42.5 pairs per 100 hectares in hawthorn scrub. This compares with a national population density of 10.8 pairs per 100 hectares for farmland. Using these two figures and the mapping data, gives a county population of 15,000 pairs.

During winter Yellowhammers form flocks. One of 500 feeding on stubble at Bishopstone on 7 Dec 1980 is the largest recorded. There were flocks of 400 at Latimer on 19 Jan 1985 and at Drayton Parslow in Dec 1989 and Jan 1990.

There have been 10 ringing recoveries, all within the county. None has involved a movement of more than 10 km. This is consistent with national ringing recoveries which indicate that 70% of adult Yellowhammers winter within 5 km of their breeding territories.

DMF

288

Cirl Bunting
Emberiza cirlus

Formerly a local resident, no records since 1985.

H & J described the Cirl Bunting as breeding regularly in the Chilterns, and list localities from Ivinghoe to Princes Risborough, the birds being commonest between Wendover and Princes Risborough. Elsewhere it occurred at Ashley Green, Drayton Beauchamp, and occasionally near Marlow. The decline that has occurred since is hinted at by their disappearance from the Tring area since 1917.

In 1947 Price described the population as only a few pairs, a situation which remained until the early 1980s. The main centre of population was still the Chiltern escarpment, and there were also records for Bourne End, Burnham, Turville, Downley, and the Ivinghoe area. Two pairs were proved to breed at an isolated site at Haversham in 1961. They were last seen there in 1963.

The 1982 BTO survey resulted in birds being found at four sites, with breeding proved at only one. The following year the range had decreased to a single locality at West Wycombe, where the last bird was seen on 13 May 1985. The County Breeding Survey found birds to be probably breeding in only two tetrads: SU89H and SP80G.

The decline in Buckinghamshire is part of a national decline which began in the mid 19th century and has resulted in the British population becoming restricted to S Devon, where there are now thought to be about 3-400 pairs.

The birds bred in open country with scattered trees, usually on or near the Chilterns escarpment. In winter some dispersal took place, with birds being found in neighbouring areas such as the canal at Wendover.

The reasons for the extinction are certainly based upon climatic change. During the 1980s West Wycombe was probably the most northerly breeding site in the world. Undoubtedly these birds, whose population centre is the Mediterranean, were at the extreme edge of their climatic tolerance, so that any small unfavourable changes could easily bring extinction. The northern limit of the European range approximately coincides with the 3 C -5 C January isotherm, which suggests that winter temperatures are a significant factor (the Winter Atlas).

A recent study in Devon suggests that another factor may have been the increase in the planting of winter cereals at the expense of leaving arable fields as stubble, which deprives the birds of a source of winter seeds. Spraying with herbicides was probably another cause.

If Cirl Buntings had managed to hang on for a few more years, they may have survived. Set-aside may have proved an adequate substitute for stubble and the warmer climate of the late 1980s would surely have helped this southern species.

DMF

Little Bunting
Emberiza pusilla

Very rare vagrant. There has been one record.

1987: male from 17 Mar-26 Apr, Woodlands Park, near Iver Heath. It was in song towards the end of its stay.

Only 15% of the British records are for the spring, so this is a rather unusual record. It is possible that the bird wintered in the area.

Reed Bunting
Emberiza schoeniclus

Local resident and migrant.

H & J described the status of Reed Buntings as 'not rare in suitable places on rivers and reservoirs', while Price described it as 'a common resident'. The map shows a wide distribution north of the Chilterns with gaps which are likely to be due to under-recording. Within the Chilterns there are very few records, except for a cluster associated with the River Misbourne and Shardeloes Lake, while in the Thames Valley the species is widespread.

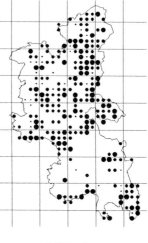

3,000 pairs

This distribution has probably remained constant throughout this century, though there have been some changes in habitats. Typically, Reed Buntings nest in marshy areas, including. small reed-filled ditches. During the 1960s a population increase occurred, probably because of a succession of mild winters, and the excess population moved into drier habitats. Examples of sites include the dry slopes of Ivinghoe Beacon and young conifer plantations in the Chilterns. A decline occurred in the 1970s, probably because of more severe winters and the increased use of herbicides, so that the species reverted to more traditional habitats.

The CBC gives an average density of 50-70 pairs per square km in typical wetland habitats, but Glue and Bodenham (1974) recorded 208 pairs per square km at Aylesbury Sewage Farm.

In winter the birds tend to form small flocks which are often found in hedges in agricultural areas. In severe winters they also move into gardens. This is the time when the species is most at risk as a long period of snow cover can have a detrimental effect on this ground-feeding bird. The largest flock recorded is one of 144 birds in Central Milton Keynes on 21 Sep 1982. The species may roost communally. The roost at Dadford held 100 birds on 27 Sep 1986, while that at Weston Turville Res had at least 170 birds on 22 Jan 1989. A small passage occurs at the end of March and early April.

Four county ringing records support the view that winter flocks comprise birds from a wide area. A bird ringed in the county on 31 Dec 1971 was recovered in Cambridgeshire on 14 Jun 1973; another bird ringed in the county on 19 Jan 1975 was recovered in Hampshire on 16 Dec 1975; a bird ringed in Norfolk on 12 Jul 1970 was recovered in the county on 27 Dec 1971; and a bird ringed at Rutland Water on 23 May 1988 was recovered at Dadford on 2 Oct 1988.

DMF

Corn Bunting
Miliaria calandra

Uncommon and decreasing resident.

Until recenty the status of Corn Buntings in the county seems to have changed little since H & J described it as 'not actually rare in arable districts, but nowhere numerous'. The map shows a curiously patchy distribution with concentrations in the Vale of Aylesbury and parts of the south. The patchiness is a reflection of its national distribution but on a more detailed scale.

1986: 700 pairs
1991: 200 pairs

There is no doubt that Corn Buntings live up to their name, though Barley Bunting would be even more accurate. The birds are strongly associated with this crop, from a national scale down to individual farms (O'Connor and Shrubb 1986). In areas where barley is comparatively rare, such as the Chilterns, they are uncommon. There is evidence on a national scale that there has been a decrease in the Corn Bunting population since about 1980. It is possible that the modern farming practice of early harvesting, which coincides with the rather late nesting period, has had a detrimental effect on their breeding success. The national population decrease is being reflected in the county. The number of singing birds at Dorney Common has reduced from 8 birds in 1987 to a single bird in 1991. A similar decrease has been noted in the Marlow area.

The average population density given by the national Common Birds Census and the mapping data gives a population for the county of 700 pairs in 1986. It is likely that the 1991 population is lower than this, perhaps around 200 pairs. These figures are even more inaccurate than usual owing to the very small sample sizes.

In winter Corn Buntings form flocks. The largest recorded in the county is of a roosting flock of c300 birds at Weston Turville on 3 Jan 1972. Since then there has been a decrease in the maximum flock sizes. In 1979 the maximum was 120 birds at a roost at Dadford, a figure which has remained fairly constant apart from a feeding flock of 250 at Dorney Common in Jan 1987. Regular roosts have occurred at Weston Turville Reservoir, Dadford, Drayton Parslow, and Mursley.

DMF

292

INTRODUCED AND ESCAPED SPECIES

A number of deliberate attempts have been made at introducing species not native to Buckinghamshiree. Some have involved birds native to other parts of Britain, while others have been of exotic species. All of them have quickly failed and are usually poorly documented.

In addition a number of species have escaped from captivity. Escaped wildfowl may survive for many years and may wander around the county quite extensively, but smaller birds usually quickly succumb to the hostile conditions. The species involved can be fairly bizarre, and some can present challenging identification problems.

Accounts of feral species were not published until 1982, and there is no doubt that many observers do not bother to report observations. The following list is therefore likely to be very incomplete. However the list includes firstly all species identified as seeming to be in a feral condition but which are not on the British list and, secondly, birds on the British list records of which are known only to refer to individuals introduced into the county.

Rufous Tinamou
Rhynchotus rufescens

This native of South America was first introduced into Britain in the 1880s. In July 1901 one was shot near Olney, some 30 km from Woburn where the Duke of Bedford had turned down a number that did fairly well for 'a good many years' before finally capitulating to the cold, wet climate and the foxes which killed the sitting hens.

Sacred Ibis
Threskiornis aethiopicus

An example of this African species was seen at Willen on 20 Sep and 2 Oct 1989.

Greater Flamingo
Phoenicopterus ruber

A bird showing characters of Caribbean race roseus was seen between 3 and 5 Apr 1982 at Willen.

Whistling Duck species
Dendrocygna sp

A bird seen at Stony Stratford on 11 Oct 1989 was probably a Fulvous Whistling Duck Dendrocygna bicolor.

Black Swan
Cygnus atratus

Single birds have been recorded on 10 occasions between 1982 and 1991. In addition 1 or 2 juveniles were recorded at Marlow between Sep and Dec 1989 and an adult and juvenile on the Thames at Marlow on 27 Jan 1991.

Lesser White-fronted Goose
Anser erythropus

Single birds were recorded at Emberton between Sep and Nov 1986, and at Marlow between 28 May and 2 Jun 1989. The birds had clearly escaped from captivity.

Bar-headed Goose
Anser indicus

Single birds have been recorded every year between 1982 and 1991, mostly on Milton Keynes waters and Emberton. In addition 2 birds were recorded in Aug and Sep 1982 at Linford and in Apr and Aug 1990 at the same site.

Snow Goose
Anser caerulescens

Small numbers of clearly feral birds are regularly seen in the north of the county. 2 young were seen in 1986, but the breeding locality is not known.

Ross's Goose
Anser rossi

There have been 3 records of single birds between 1983 and 1990, including one of the rare blue phase. An apparent blue phase bird at Linford and Willen between Feb and Jun 1991 had a dark centred tail and was presumably a hybrid of some kind.

Magellan Goose
Chloephaga picta

A male was seen on 21 Aug 1988 at Emberton.

Egyptian Goose
Alopochen aegyptiacus

Very rare vagrant. All records refer to feral birds.

H & R noted a report by J W Owen in *The Field* of 19 Nov 1859 that 'A fine specimen was shot on November 1 at Marlow' and commented that 'It is supposed to have been driven there during preceding gales, as it presented no appearance of ever having been in confinement. We are inclined to think that it must have escaped from some pond.'

All other records are given:

1867:   1 at Dorney Common.
1972:   1 on 4 Jul, Foxcote.
1983:   1 from 15 Apr-4 May, Haversham, Linford, Cosgrove.
1985:   1 on 5 May, Pitstone.
1989:   2 on 19 Feb, Willen.
1991:   1 on 25 Dec, flew from Wilstone Res into the county.

Ruddy Shelduck
Tadorna ferruginea

A bird was shot at Wotton Lakes in Dec 1908. There were 4 records of single birds between 1983 and 1991 at Willen and Medmenham. In addition 3 males were seen with 3 Shelducks at Willen on 8 Sep 1987. All were probably escapes.

Cape Shelduck
Tadorna cana

There were 3 records of single birds between 1988 amd 1990 at Linford, Weston Turville Res, and Marlow.

Muscovy Duck
Cairina moschata

1 on 26 Oct 1983 at Willen.

Wood Duck
Aix sponsa

The following records are known:

1973: a female from 7-15 Mar, Medmenham. It was very tame.
1976: 3 males and 2 females on 4 Jan, and a pair 18 Jan, Little Missenden.
1985: 2 pairs from 12-13 Jan, Dorney Reach.
1985: 2 males, 1 female on 10 Mar, and 2 males on 20 Mar, Coleshill Pond.
1987: 1 male on 15 Nov, Tongwell.
1991: 1 male 18 May, Cliveden Reach.

This is one exotic species which may form a truly feral breeding population, for it is closely related to the Mandarin, which thrives in some parts of Britain and is increasing in the south of the county.

Chiloë Wigeon
Anas sibilatrix

1 on 3 Jan 1982 at Bourne End; 2 on 15 Jan 1986 at Caldecotte; and 1 on 6 and 20 Jun 1988 at Newport Pagnell.

White-cheeked Pintail
Anas bahamensis

1 on 14 Sep and 18-20 Oct 1990 at Willen; 1 on 1 Dec 1990 at Linford; 1 on 31 Aug 1991 at Furzton; and 2 on 6 Sep 1991 at Willen.

Versicolor Teal
Anas versicolor

A pair was seen on 18 Dec 1983 at Bourne End.

Cinnamon Teal
Anas cyanoptera

A male was seen on 23 Apr 1984 at Weston Turville Res.

Hooded Merganser
Mergus cucullatus

A female or immature seen at Willen on 28-29 December 1983 and accepted by the BBRC has recently been reviewed by the same body. It is no longer considered more likely to be wild than other recent occurrences in Britain.

White-backed Vulture
Gyps africanus

A bird seen in late June 1984 over Dagnall was an escape from Whipsnade Zoo.

Black Grouse
Tetrao tetrix

Single males were shot at Hyde Heath in 1852 and near Penn House, near Amersham in 1863. Birds were introduced into Surrey in 1815 from where they apparently spread. It is not known where the Buckinghamshire birds came from.

Capercaillie
Tetrao urogallus

In the autumn of 1855 a pair was shot at Burnham Beeches. These birds were certainly escapes or releases.

Greater Prairie-chicken
Tympanuchus cupido

This native of the plains of North America was introduced into the county in June 1903, when 'a good many' pairs were put down. Of these a hen was shot at Wing in October of the same year.

Northern Bobwhite
Colinus virginianus

Birds going under this name or California Quail were introduced at Marlow in 1867 and bred there for a short time.

Chukar
Alectoris chukar

A recent introduction.

Chukars, which are natives of SE Europe and the southern Palaearctic, were first introduced into Britain in 1894 in Peeblesshire. Between the wars they were kept fully-winged at Woburn and Whipsnade but they died out. Releases of game farm birds began in 1971 but they were not recorded in the county until 1990. The lateness of the first records may be due to a lack of awareness by observers. Since 1990 records have become more frequent, although numbers seem small compared to the Red-legged Partridge population.

Some alarm has been expressed by the introduction of Chukars as they hybridise with Red-legged Partridges to produce 'Ogridges'. Eventually, it is thought this may eliminate the population of pure Red-legged Partridges which, although also an introduction, are now generally regarded as a native species, and one which has a rather restricted world distribution.

This potential degradation of the Red-legged Partridge population has resulted in the release of Chukars being prohibited from 1993. However, Red-legged Partridges prefer to breed with each other and pure Chukars seldom breed successfully in our climate, being adapted to much hotter conditions. Hybrids have genetic problems and low breeding success. *Alectoris* partridges will only survive in the long term if there is sufficient pure Red-leg blood in the population (Game Conservancy Trust, pers comm). It seems likely that the Red-legged population will revert to its original state once the introduction of Chukars ends

SC

Reeves' Pheasant
Syrmaticus reevesii

A bird was seen on 29 Oct 1989 at Stokenchurch.

Sarus Crane
Grus antigone

A bird which flew over the county near Wilstone on 4 Apr 1937 was an escape from Whipsnade Zoo. Another was seen at Edgecott on 25 Apr 1975.

Cockatiel
Nymphicus hollandicus

Single birds were recorded on 5 occasions between 1983 and 1990 in the Milton Keynes area and at Marlow. In addition 6 birds on 3 Aug 1990 seen at Hughenden Valley were presumably escapes from the same cage.

Budgerigar
Melopsittacus undulatus

One was seen on 11 Sep 1990 at Marlow, and another at the same locality on 22 Mar 1991.

Snowy Owl
Nyctea scandiaca

One was seen from 31 Jul-c4 Aug, 1912 at Yewdon Manor, Hambleden. The time of year suggests that the bird was an escape.

White-eye species
Zosterops sp

One was seen in a garden at The Lee in April 1990.

Red-vented Bulbul
Pycnonotus cafer

One was seen in gardens at Chesham from Dec 1980 to Feb 1981.

Glossy Starling species
Lamprotornis chalcurus or *chalybaeus*

A Bronze-tailed or Greater Blue-eared Glossy Starling was seen on 21 Jan 1984 at Mentmore.

Chough
Pyrrhocorax pyrrhocorax

There is one problematical record of a female found dead on 29 Dec 1991 by the road between Beaconsfield and Gerrards Cross.

It had been ringed as a nestling on Islay on 31 May 1986 and had bred at Islay in 1990 but did not reappear in 1991. When it was found, the three colour rings it had been wearing were missing. It is very unlikely that this bird was a genuine vagrant. It is more likely that it reached southern England as a captive and subsequently escaped or was released. Consequently the record has not been admitted to the county list.

Somali Sparrow
Passer castanopterus

One was present at Willen between Oct and Nov 1983.

White-winged Widow
Euplectes albonotatus

A male was seen with Tree Sparrows from 5-8 Dec 1991 near Padbury.

Zebra Finch
Taeniopyga guttata

One was seen in Feb and Mar 1990 at Marlow.

Canary
Serinus canaria

One was seen on 18 Sep 1987 at Willen.

Trumpeter Finch
Bucanetes githagineus

One seen between 2 and 4 Jul 1990 at Haverfield, Great Missenden was believed to be an escaped cage bird.

SPECIES NO LONGER RETAINED
ON THE COUNTY LIST

Assessing the validity of old records of rare birds is beset with problems. Sight records do not always have written descriptions, and for those that do, the details recorded typically fall far short of today's requirements of the county and national records committees and leave room for doubt that sufficient care was taken over the identification. Even the best of 19th-century ornithologists can hardly have had the experience and field skills, and certainly not the powerful optical equipment, that is commonplace nowadays.

According to the epigram, what's hit is history: but even specimen records often leave doubt that the finding circumstances were exactly as recorded or that, if the whereabouts of the specimen are still known, it is the same one referred to in the original literature. Apart from the famous 'Hastings rarities', there are many cases where specimen records of British birds are known or believed to be invalid - because the corpse was imported from abroad, or because the specimen was not continuosly in responsible hands. Even where identification and provenance are clearly established, knowledge of escape likelihood of many species in earlier decades is insufficient for a proper assessment to be made of the bird's likely origin.

A review of old Buckinghamshire rarity records has been begun by the Records Committee of the Buckinghamshire Bird Club, and is continuing. Despite the very poor documentation of many of the records, we believe it would not be right to reject all those not meeting present-day standards. Rather, we wish to re-examine the records in the context of our present knowledge of the status of the species in Buckinghamshire and in Britain as a whole. Some claims are clearly not worthy of any serious attention. No credence can be placed, for different reasons, in claims of Great Auk (W. Macgillivray, 1852, *A History of British Birds*, page 361) or Rufous Tinmaou (A Allen, *The Field*, 1st March 1902) (see page 293). These records have been ignored, clearly deliberately, by earlier authors.

The following species have been included in previous lists and reports of Buckinghamshire birds but, after review, the Records Committee now finds all records unacceptable and has deleted the species from the county list.

Great Shearwater
Puffinus gravis

1911: 1 killed by striking telegraph wires, Olney.

The Great Shearwater is not rare in the Western Approaches between July and October, but it is seldom seen from land anywhere in the British Isles and there are exceptionally few inland records. H & J record the following:
'Mr Archibald Allen, writing in *The Field* (October 28, 1911, p.968), records a Greater Shearwater *Puffinus major* as having been killed by striking telegraph wires "a few weeks since" near Olney. No investigation appears to have been made as to whether the specimen in question was correctly identified, and the date

suggests the probability of confusion with the Manx Shearwater, which frequently occurs inland during September, though, curiously enough, there appears to be no record of this species from Bucks.'

The Countryman also carried an article about this bird on 29 Oct 1911. The later sequence of Manx Shearwater records in Buckinghamshire lends support to H & J's conclusion.

Little Crake
Porzana parva

1954: 1 calling on 3 Jun, Marlow.

. No details are recorded of this record. Confusion may perhaps have arisen with Water Rail, since the repertoire of that species is not fully described in The Handbook or in the then new Peterson field guide.

Scops Owl
Otus scops

1833: 1 shot near Brill.

There is no published description of this bird, and no indication that the specimen was ever seen by a competent ornithologist. Further, the bird was said to have been taken on the county border and may in fact relate to Oxfordshire. The date is 1833 in the original reference, not 1838 as quoted in H & R.

Black Woodpecker
Dryocopus martius

Clark Kennedy claims he watched one in Ditton Park for half a minute at close range, busily engaged on a tall elm till it flew off with an undulating flight, in March 1867. No details are given. Like all other British claims of this species this record is widely believed to be erroneous.

Savi's Warbler
Locustella luscinioides

1897: 1 in May, Olney.

No details are recorded to support this difficult identification. The species was not recorded breeding in Britain between the middle of the 19th century and 1960 (BOU 1971).

EXTRA SPECIES RECORDED WITHIN THE PRE-1974 COUNTY BOUNDARY

These species additional to the present county list have been recorded in that part of Berkshire which, before the boundary revisions of 1974, lay in Buckinghamshire. Important sites for birds which lie in this region include Slough SF and Wraysbury. These additions complete the avifauna for the Watsonian vice-county number 24 (Buckinghamshire).

Marsh Sandpiper
Tringa stagnatilis

1940: 1 in May, Slough SF.

Alpine Swift
Apus melba

1983: 1 from 9-at least 22 May, Wraysbury GPs.

Short-toed Lark
Calandrella brachydactyla

1985: 1 from 29-30 April, Wraysbury Reservoir.
1987: 1 from 2-at least 16 Jan, Slough SF.

Dartford Warbler
Sylvia undata

1991/92: juvenile during winter, Slough SF.

Arctic Redpoll
Carduelis hornemanni

1991: 1 from 21-28 Mar, another from 23-24 Mar, New Wavendon Heath.

REFERENCES

Many records and information about individual species are taken from the series of reports covering the county, published by the Oxford Ornithological Society until that for 1953, the Middle Thames Natural History Society (1954 to 1979 inclusive) and the Buckinghamshire Bird Club from 1980 to the present. Specific references to the accounts in the systematic species accounts in these are rarely referred to individually and do not appear in the following list of references. However specific papers and notes published separately as part of the reports are noted here.

ALEXANDER, W.B. and D. LACK. 1944. Changes in status among British breeding birds. Brit. Birds 38:42-45,62-69,82-88.

ASTLEY, H.D. 1900. My Birds in Freedom and Captivity. Dent, London.

BAILLIE, S.R. 1990. Integrated population monitoring of breeding birds in Britain and Ireland. Ibis 132:151-166.

BAINBRIDGE, I.P. and C.D.T. MINTON. 1978. The migration and mortality of the Curlew in Britain and Ireland. Bird Study 25: 39-50.

BERTHOLD, P. and S.B. TERRILL. 1988. Migratory behaviour and population growth of Blackcaps wintering in Britain and Ireland: some hypotheses. Ringing & Migration 9:153-159.

BONHAM P.F. and J.T.R. SHARROCK. 1974. Sedge Warblers singing in fields of rape. Brit. Birds 67:389-390.

BOU. 1971. The status of birds in Britain and Ireland. Blackwell Scientific Publications, Oxford.

BOU. 1992. Checklist of birds of Britain and Ireland. British Ornithologists' Union, Tring.

BRADSHAW, A.D. 1983. The reconstruction of ecosystems. J. Appl. Ecol. 20:1-17.

BRADSHAW, A.D. and M.J. CHADWICK. 1980. The Restoration of Land. Blackwell, Oxford.

BROWN, A.F. and N.H.F. STONE. 1991. Mute Swan census in Buckinghamshire 1990. Buckinghamshire Bird Report 1990:8-13.

BROWN, L. 1976. British Birds of Prey. Collins, London.

BRUCKER, J.W., A.G. GOSLER and A.R. HERYET (eds). 1992. Birds of Oxfordshire. Pisces, Newbury.

BURTON, P.J.K. 1986. Ringing recoveries of Chilterns Sparrowhawk. Buckinghamshire Bird Report 1984:3-5.

BURTON, P.J.K. 1993. Nest-boxes as a monitoring tool for Kestrel (*Falco tinnunculus*) breeding performance. Biology and Conservation of Small Falcons (M.K.Nicholls & R.Clarke, eds). Hawk and Owl Trust, London.

CADBURY, C.J. 1980. The status and habitats of the Corncrake in Britain 1978-79. Bird Study 27:203-218.

CADWALLADR, D.A. and J.V. MORLEY. 1973. Sheep grazing preferences on a saltings pasture and their significance for wigeon (*Anas penelope* L.) conservation. Journal of the British Grassland Society 28:235-242.

CAMPBELL, B. 1960. The Mute Swan census in England and Wales 1955-56. Bird Study 7:208-223.

CASSELDEN, P. 1986. Chartridge and Pednor hedgerows: a landscape study. Records of Buckinghamshire 28:182-210.

CAVÉ, A.J. 1968. The breeding of the Kestrel, *Falco tinnunculus* L., in the reclaimed area Oosterlijk Flevoland. Neth. J. Zool. 18:313-407.

CHANDLER, R.J. 1981. Influxes into Britain and Ireland of Red-necked Grebes and other water-birds during winter 1979/79. Brit. Birds 74:55-81.

COOK, A. 1984. Winter wildfowl at Weston Turville Reservoir. Buckinghamshire Bird Report 1982:2-6.

CRAMP, S. and K.E.L.SIMMONS (eds). 1977-1992. The BIrds of the Western Palearctic. Vols 1-6. University Press, Oxford.

DAVIS, P. 1966. The movement of Pied Wagtails as shown by ringing. Bird Study 13:147-162.

DOBINSON, H.M. and A.J. RICHARDS. 1964. The effects of the severe winter of 1962-63 on birds in Britain. Brit. Birds 57:373-434.

DYMOND J.N., P.A. FRASER, and S.J.M. GANTLETT. 1989. Rare Birds in Britain and Ireland. Poyser, Calton.

FERGUSON-LEES, I.J., I. WILLIS and J.T.R. SHARROCK. 1983. The Shell Guide to Birds of Britain and Ireland. Michael Joseph, London.

FITTER, R.S.R. 1959. The Ark in our Midst. Collins, London.

FRASER, A.C. 1954. The Birds of the Middle Thames. Middle Thames Natural History Society, Slough.

FRASER, A.C. and R.E. YOUNGMAN. 1976. The Birds of Buckinghamshire and East Berkshire. Middle Thames Natural History Society, Slough.

FULLER, R.J. 1981. Aspects of counting Lapwings and Curlews breeding on lowland grasslands. Wader Study Group Bulletin 33: 14-16.

FULLER, R.J. 1982. Bird Habitats in Britain. Poyser, Calton.

FULLER, R.J. 1986. Breeding bird communities on downland at Pitstone Hill before and after scrub clearance. Buckinghamshire Bird Report 1984:5-12.

FULLER, R.J. 1988. A comparison of breeding bird assemblages in two Buckinghamshire clay vale woods with different histories of management. Research and Survey in Nature Conservation 15:53-65. (Proceedings of a symposium on 'Woodland conservation and research in the clay vales of Oxfordshire and Buckinghamshire', edited by K.J. Kirby and F.J. Wright. Nature Conservancy Council, Peterborough.)

FULLER, R.J. 1990. Wintering Golden Plovers in central Buckinghamshire: annual variation in numbers and distribution. Buckinghamshire Bird Report 1988:4-8.

FULLER, R.J., J.K. BAKER, R.A. MORGAN, R. SCROGGS and M. WRIGHT. 1985. Breeding populations of the Hobby on farmland in the southern midlands of England. Ibis 127: 510-516.

FULLER, R.J. and D.E. GLUE. 1978. Seasonal activity of birds at a sewage-works. Brit. Birds 71:235-244.

FULLER, R.J. and D.E. GLUE. 1980. Sewage works as bird habitats in Britain. Biol. Conserv. 17:165-181.

FULLER, R.J. and R.E. YOUNGMAN. 1979. The utilisation of farmland by Golden Plovers wintering in southern England. Bird Study 26:37-46.

GIBBONS, D.W., J.B. REID and R.A. CHAPMAN. 1993. The New Atlas of Breeding Birds in Britain and Ireland: 1988-1991. Poyser, Calton.

GILES, N. and R.WRIGHT. 1986. Reproductive success of Canada and Greylag Geese on gravel pits. Game Conservancy Annual Review 18:142-145.

GLADWIN, T. and B. SAGE. 1986. The Birds of Hertfordshire. Castlemead, Ware.

GLUE, D.E. (ed.) 1982. The Garden Bird Book. MacMillan, London.

GLUE, D.E. and D. BODENHAM. 1974. Bird-life at a modern sewage farm. Bird Study 19:81-90.

GLUE, D.E. and D. BODENHAM. 1985. Changes in the breeding bird community of Aylesbury sewage works during 1970-1983. Buckinghamshire Bird Report 1983:2-9.

GLUE, D.E. and R.A. MORGAN. 1972. Cuckoo hosts in British habitats. Bird Study 19:187-192.

GLUE, D.E. and D. SCOTT. 1980. Breeding biology of the Little Owl. Brit. Birds 73:167-180.

GRANT, P.J. 1986. Gulls. A Guide to Identification. 2nd edn. Poyser, Calton.

HARDING, A. 1982. Waders at Willen Lake. Buckinghamshire Bird report 1981:2-6.

HARRISON, G. 1934. A Bird Diary. Dent, London.

HARRISON, G.R., A.R. DEAN, A.J. RICHARDS and D. SMALLSHIRE. 1982. The Birds of the West Midlands. West Midlands Bird Club.

HARTERT, E. and W. ROTHSCHILD. 1905. Birds. Pp. 128-152 in A History of Buckingham (ed. W. Page). Constable & Co., London.

HARTERT, E. and F.C.R. JOURDAIN. 1920. The birds of Buckinghamshire and the Tring reservoirs. Novitat. Zool. 27:171-259.

HAYWARD, H.H.S. 1947. The birds of the Tring reservoirs. Records of Buckinghamshire 15:51-62.

HEATH, J., E. POLLARD, and J. THOMAS. 1984. Atlas of Butterflies in Britain and Ireland. Viking, Harmondsworth.

HIBBERT-WARE, A. 1937-8. Report of the Little Owl food inquiry, 1936-7. Brit. Birds 31:162-187, 205-229, 249-264.

HILL, D.A. 1984. Laying date, clutch size and egg size of the Mallard *Anas platyrynchos* and Tufted Duck *Aythya fuligula*. Ibis 126:484-495.

HÖHN, E.O. 1943. Some observations on the Common Pochard. Brit. Birds 37:102-107.

HORNBY, R.J. 1987. Nature conservation in Chiltern woodlands - a Nature Conservancy Council view. Quart. J. For. 81:116-121.

HUDSON, R. 1972. Collared Doves in Britain and Ireland during 1965-1970. Brit. Birds 65:139-155.

HUDSON, R. 1973. Early and late dates for summer migrants. British Trust for Ornithology, Tring.

HUGHES, S.W.M., P. BACON, and J.J.M. FLEGG. 1979. The 1975 census of the Great Crested Grebe in Britain. Bird Study 26:213-226.

HUTCHINSON, C.D. and B. NEATH. 1978. Little Gulls in Britain and Ireland. Brit. Birds 71:563-582.

IMBODEN, C. 1974. Zug, Fremdansiedlung und Brutperiode des Kiebitz *Vanellus vanellus* in Europa. Orn. Beob. 71:5-134.

JENKINS, J.G. 1967. Chequers. A History of the Prime Minister's Buckinghamshire Home. Pergamon Press, Oxford.

JUILLARD, M. 1984. La chouette chevêche. Nos oiseaux. Société Romande pour l'étude et la protection des oiseaux.

KENNEDY, A.W.M. CLARK. 1868. The Birds of Berkshire and Buckinghamshire, a Contribution to the Natural History of the two Counties. Eton and London.

KENWARD, R.E. 1979. Winter predation by Goshawks in lowland Britain. Brit. Birds 72:64-73.

KIRBY, J. 1988. Westerly movement of Buckinghamshire Ringed Plovers. Buckinghamshire Bird Report 1987:3-4.

KNIGHT, J. and N.H.F. STONE. 1988. Census of the Mute Swan in Buckinghamshire 1983. The Buckinghamshire Bird Report 1986:3-4.

LACK, P. 1986. The Atlas of Wintering Birds in Britain and Ireland. Poyser, Calton.

LEACH, I.H. 1981. Wintering Blackcaps in Britain and Ireland. Bird Study 28:5-15.

LEVER, C. 1987. Naturalised Birds of the World. Longman Scientific & Technical, Harlow.

LLYN-ALLEN, E. 1956. A Partridge Year. A.W.P. Robertson.

LLOYD, C., M.L.TASKER and K.PARTRIDGE. 1991. The status of seabirds in Britain and Ireland. T & A D Poyser, London.

MARCHANT, J.H., R. HUDSON, S.P. CARTER and P. WHITTINGTON. 1990. Population Trends in British Breeding Birds. British Trust for Ornithology, Tring.

MARCHANT, J.H. and P.A. HYDE. 1980. Aspects of the distribution of riparian birds on waterways in Britain and Ireland. Bird Study 27:183-202.

MEAD, C.J. and K.W. SMITH. 1982. Hertfordshire Breeding Bird Atlas. HBBA, Tring.

MILSOM, T.P. 1984. Diurnal behaviour of Lapwings in relation to moon phase during winter. Bird Study 31:117-120.

MORGAN, R.A. 1980. The 1978 Mute Swan Survey in Buckinghamshire. Buckinghamshire Bird Report 1980:5-7.

MORGAN, R.A. and D.E. GLUE. 1977. Breeding, mortality and movements of Kingfishers. Bird Study 24:15-24.

MORRIS, F.O. 1970. A History of British Birds. Vol.5. Groombridge & Sons, London.

MURTON, R.K. 1966. Natural selection and the breeding seasons of the Stock Dove and Wood Pigeon. Bird Study 13:311-327.

NEWTON, I. 1972. Finches. Collins, London.

NEWTON, I. 1986. The Sparrowhawk. Poyser, Calton.

O'CONNOR, R.J. and C.J. MEAD. 1984. The Stock Dove in Britain 1930-80. Brit. Birds 77:181-201.

O'CONNOR, R.J. and M. SHRUBB. 1986. Farming and Birds. University Press, Cambridge.

OGILVIE, M.A. 1967. Population changes and mortality of the Mute Swan in Britain. Wildfowl Trust Annual Report 18:64-73.

OGILVIE, M.A. 1977. The number of Canada Geese in Britain, 1976. Wildfowl 28:27-34.

OSBORNE, P. 1982. Some effects of Dutch elm disease on nesting farmland birds. Bird Study 29:2-16.

OWEN, M., G.L. ATKINSON-WILLES and D.G. SALMON. 1986. Wildfowl in Great Britain, 2nd ed. University Press, Cambridge.

OWEN, M. and D.G. SALMON. 1988. Feral Greylag Geese *Anser anser* in Britain and Ireland, 1960-86. Bird Study 35:37-45.

PARSLOW, J. 1973. Breeding Birds of Britain and Ireland. Poyser, Berkhamsted.

PETERKEN, G.F. 1981. Woodland Conservation and Management. Chapman & Hall, London.

POLLARD, E., M.D. HOOPER and N.W. MOORE. 1974. Hedges. Collins, London.

PRICE, K. 1947. The Birds of Buckinghamshire. Records of Buckinghamshire 15:20-31.

RACKHAM, O. 1986. The History of the Countryside. J.M. Dent & Sons, London.

RADFORD, M.C. 1966. The Birds of Berkshire and Oxfordshire. Longman, Green & Co., London.

REDFERN, C.P.F. 1982. Lapwing nest sites and chick mortality in relation to habitat. Bird Study 29:201-208.

REED, M. 1979. The Buckinghamshire Landscape. Hodder & Stoughton, London.

RICHARDSON, P.W. 1982. Northamptonshire Bird Report 1982.

RIDDIFORD, N. 1983. Recent declines of Grasshopper Warblers at British observatories. Bird Study 30:143-148.

RIDDIFORD, N. and P. FINDLAY. 1981. Seasonal movements of summer migrants. BTO Guide no.18. British Trust for Ornithology, Tring.

RODEN, D. 1968. Woodland and its management in the medieval Chilterns. Forestry 41:59-71.

SAGE, B.L. 1959. A History of the Birds of Hertfordshire. Barrie & Rockliff, London.

SAGE, B.L. and J.D.R. VERNON. 1978. The 1975 national survey of Rookeries. Bird Study 25:64-86.

SHRUBB, M. 1980. Farming influences on the food and hunting of Kestrels. Bird Study 27:109-115.

SIBLEY, C.G. and B.L. MONROE, Jr. 1990. Distribution and Taxonomy of Birds of the World. Yale University Press, New Haven.

SHARROCK, J.T.R. 1976. The Atlas of Breeding Birds in Britain and Ireland. Poyser, Berkhamsted.

SHAWYER, C.R. 1987. The Barn Owl in the British Isles: its Past, Present and Future. The Hawk Trust, London.

SMITH, C.J. 1980. Ecology of the English Chalk. Academic Press, London.

SMITH, K.W. 1983. The status and distribution of waders breeding on wet lowland grasslands in England and Wales. Bird Study 30:177-192.

SMITH, K.W. and N.H.F. STONE. 1984. Survey of breeding waders of wet meadows. Buckinghamshire Bird Report 1982:8-10.

SMYTHE, W.H. 1864. Aedes Hartwelliana. Nicholls & Son, London.

SNOW, D.W. 1968. Movements and mortality of British Kestrels. Bird Study 15:65-83.

SNOW, B. and D.W. SNOW. 1988. Birds and Berries. Poyser, Calton.

SPENCER, J. 1982. Buckinghamshire inventory of ancient woodlands. Nature Conservancy Council, Huntingdon.

SOVON. 1987. Atlas van de Nederlandse Vogels. SOVON, Arnhem.

STUTTARD, P. and K. WILLIAMSON. 1971. Habitat requirements of the Nightingale. Bird Study 18:9-14.

SUMMERS-SMITH, J.D. 1989. A history of the Tree Sparrow *Passer montanus* in the British Isles. Bird Study 36:23-31.

SWANN, R.L. 1971. Birds of Shardeloes lake. Records of Buckinghamshire 19:73-88.

TAYLOR, K. 1985. Crossbill Invasion. BTO News 140:1.

TAYLOR, K. and J.H. MARCHANT. 1983. Population changes for waterways birds, 1981-82. Bird Study 30:121-126.

TAYLOR, K., R. HUDSON and G. HORNE. 1988. Buzzard breeding distribution and abundance in Britain and Northern Ireland in 1983. Bird Study 35:109-118.

TOMLIN, R.J. and R.E. YOUNGMAN. 1982. Rookeries in Buckinghamshire. Buckinghamshire Bird Report 1981:8-11.

TRODD, P. and D. KRAMER. 1991. The Birds of Bedfordshire. Castlemead, Ware.

VILLAGE, A. 1990. The Kestrel. Poyser, Calton.

WARD, C. 1992. The American Golden Plover at Broughton, Milton Keynes. Buckinghamshire Bird Report 1991:12-14.

WATT, A.S. 1934. The vegetation of the Chiltern Hills, with special reference to the beechwoods and their seral relationships. J. Ecol. 22:230-270, 445-507.

WHITE, T.H. 1953. The Goshawk. Jonathan Cape, London.

WILLIAMSON, K. 1972. The conservation of bird life in the new coniferous forests. Forestry 45:87-100.

WILLIAMSON, K. 1974. Habitat changes in a young Forestry Commission plantation. Bird Study 21:215-217.

WILLIAMSON, K. 1975. The breeding bird community of chalk grassland scrub in the Chiltern Hills. Bird Study 22:59-70.

WITHERBY, H.F., F.C.R. JOURDAIN, N.F. TICEHURST and B.W. TUCKER. 1938-1941. The Handbook of British Birds. Vols 1-5. Witherby, London.

WORTHINGTON, T.R. and D.R. HELLIWELL. 1987. Transference of semi-natural grassland and marshland onto newly created landfill. Biol. Conserv. 41:301-311.

WRIGHT, R.M. and N. GILES. 1988. Breeding success of Canada and Greylag Geese (*Branta canadensis* and *Anser anser*) on gravel pits. Bird Study 35:31-36.

YOUNGMAN, R.E. 1977. Great Crested Grebes breeding on rivers. Brit. Birds 70:544-545.

ARRIVAL AND DEPARTURE DATES OF MIGRANTS

The tables that follow contain information on the arrival and departure of migrant species based upon data collected for the years 1971 to 1991.

The species concerned have been split into three groups :-

1) Summer visitors
2) Winter visitors
3) Spring and autumn migrants

Not all migrant species seen in the county are included in the tables. Where possible the commoner migrant species are included. The rarer species are not usually included as there are often insufficient data to make arrival and departure dates meaningful. Where a histogram showing the occurrence of the species has been provided then that species is not usually included in these tables. In addition it has not been possible to include some species that are normally regarded as common summer visitors (eg Blackcap) because of the regular winter sightings of this species.

Apart from giving the earliest arrival date (EAD) and the latest departure date (LDD), the average arrival date (AAD) and average departure date (ADD) are also quoted along with the standard deviation (SD) of the data used in calculating the averages. The SD gives an indication of the consistency in arrival/departure from year to year. It is noticeable that visually obvious birds such as Swifts and Swallows have a low SD while more skulking species such as Grasshopper Warbler have a high SD. Species may also have a high SD if they are sufficiently scarce to be seen only infrequently (eg Garganey).

The data used as the basis for the tables has been obtained from the annual reports published by the Middle Thames Natural History Society (MTNHS - up until 1979) and the Buckinghamshire Bird Club (from 1980). The MTNHS reports covered an area of east Berkshire and the whole of Buckinghamshire. On occasion only dates for Berkshire birds are given. As it was the intention to only use Buckinghamshire records in the compilation of these tables, wherever Buckinghamshire dates have not been given, the numbers of dates used as the basis for determining the earliest arrival date, latest departure date or the SD, may vary. A similar problem occurs when the editor of the annual report may omit, for some reason, vital data for a species that is normally covered in depth. Referring back to the original records was considered but found to be impractical.

For some species normally regarded as strict summer visitors, winter visitors, or passage migrants it has not always been possible to quote the EAD and LDD due to the occasional summer or winter records for those species (eg Fieldfare, Chiffchaff and Common Sandpiper). In some cases this may even refer to species that have bred in the county on occasion (eg Whinchat). Where this situation occurs the dates have been excluded from the calculations for AAD and ADD.

	Earliest Arrival Date	Average Earliest Date	Std dev Earliest Dates	Average Latest Date	Std Dev Latest Dates	Latest Date
Summer visitors						
Garganey	18 Mar	7 Apr	16	6 Oct	27	22 Dec
Hobby	10 Apr	24 Apr	7	6 Oct	15	12 Nov
Quail	9 May	31 May	16	24 Jul	21	4 Sep
Little Ringed Plover	10 Mar	23 Mar	6	17 Sep	13	2 Oct
Ringed Plover		27 Feb	24	8 Oct	25	17 Nov
Common Tern	6 Apr	16 Apr	7	25 Sep	18	23 Oct
Turtle Dove	20 Mar	20 Apr	10	26 Sep	9	17 Oct
Cuckoo	31 Mar	11 Apr	6	29 Aug	15	19 Sep
Swift	15 Apr	24 Apr	4	25 Sep	15	2 Nov
Sand Martin	24 Feb	22 Mar	10	5 Oct	11	18 Oct
Swallow	15 Mar	30 Mar	6	5 Nov	11	2 Dec
House Martin	29 Mar	8 Apr	5	5 Nov	12	4 Dec
Tree Pipit	3 Apr	11 Apr	5	23 Sep	12	19 Oct
Yellow Wagtail	23 Mar	2 Apr	6	22 Oct	18	29 Nov
Nightingale	13 Apr	23 Apr	5			2 Aug
Redstart	17 Mar	15 Apr	11	27 Sep	24	6 Nov
Grasshopper Warbler	10 Apr	19 Apr	5	19 Aug	19	23 Sep
Sedge Warbler	5 Apr	12 Apr	6	27 Sep	11	22 Oct
Reed Warbler	11 Apr	21 Apr	7	1 Oct	13	13 Nov
Lesser Whitethroat	10 Apr	21 Apr	4	27 Sep	16	8 Nov
Whitethroat	11 Apr	20 Apr	6	24 Sep	6	18 Dec
Garden Warbler	13 Mar	20 Apr	11	22 Sep	9	11 Oct
Wood Warbler	14 Apr	26 Apr	8	24 Aug	7	2 Sep
Willow Warbler	13 Mar	29 Mar	8	26 Sep	9	16 Oct
Chiffchaff		13 Mar	7	21 Oct	9	
Spotted Flycatcher	20 Apr	3 May	6	28 Sep	8	17 Oct

	Earliest Arrival Date	Average Earliest Date	Std dev Earliest Dates	Average Latest Date	Std Dev Latest Dates	Latest Date
Spring and Autumn migrants						
Spring arrival dates						
Greenshank		24 Apr	12	22 May	17	
Common Sandpiper		8 Apr	13	31 May	7	
Whinchat	11 Apr	26 Apr	8	17 May	6	
Wheatear	6 Mar	17 Mar	8	25 May	12	28 Jun
Return passage dates						
Greenshank		11 Jul	11	4 Oct	12	
Common Sandpiper		28 Jun	6	9 Oct	11	
Whinchat		4 Aug	16	4 Oct	9	29 Sep
Wheatear	11 Jul	31 Jul	10	18 Oct	12	5 Nov
Winter Visitors						
Bewick's Swan	19 Oct	9 Nov	15	17 Mar	22	30 Apr
Whooper Swan	6 Oct	7 Nov	16	14 Mar	28	20 Apr
Wigeon		16 Aug	17	16 May	18	
Pintail	15 Aug	3 Oct	37	14 Mar	25	13 May
Scaup	18 Sep	2 Nov	33	10 Mar	25	16 Apr
Goldeneye	10 Oct	19 Oct	6	1 May	8	15 May
Smew	18 Nov	13 Dec	14	2 Mar	19	6 Apr
Goosander	24 Oct	6 Nov	10	9 Apr	14	4 May
Golden Plover	25 Jun	18 Aug	23	25 Apr	12	22 May
Green Sandpiper		27 Jun	12	4 May	10	
Short-eared Owl		26 Oct	17	24 Apr	19	
Fieldfare		28 Sep	16	1 May	9	
Redwing		24 Sep	17	20 Apr	8	
Brambling	5 Oct	15 Oct	7	25 Apr	6	8 May

THE POPULATION ESTIMATES

An attempt has been made to estimate the populations of most of the regular breeding birds of Buckinghamshire. It should be said at once that these estimates are not accurate, but should be regarded as conjectures based upon the best available information. Each estimates is given as a single figure. Ranges are not shown as this implies that the limits of the range are accurate, which would not be the case.

Bird populations vary from year to year (see Marchant et al 1990). For most species the annual variation is masked by the inaccuracies of the estimates, but the populations of some birds have changed significantly since the mapping period (1980-1986). In these cases two population estimates are given, one for 1986 and another for 1991. The estimates are given in pairs, even when this is known to be inappropriate (eg Woodcock), and are shown under the maps.

For each species, an estimate was made of the breeding population using the tetrad maps. Three sets of data are required

1. The area of each broad habitat type in every tetrad in the county

    This was estimated using already available habitat data and by calculating areas using OS maps. It was not possible to differentiate between the different types of agricultural land, but woodland was divided into three broad types: broad-leaved, mixed broad-leaved/coniferous, and coniferous.

2. Population densities for each broad habitat type

    These were estimated using CBC data. Where figures were not available then informed guesses were made.

    The BTO are very circumspect about using the absolute population densities calculated from CBC data because of the small sample sizes. Furthermore, they do not distinguish between the various types of woodland. It is likely that beechwood has lower densities of birds than oakwood and that as a consequence Buckinghamshire has densities of woodland birds which are below the national average. The population densities of conifer-nesting birds are usually not known.

3. The BBC maps

    Most species have been under-recorded, which results in lower population estimates. No differentiation has been made between the three levels of breeding.

The population of each species was calculated using a computer program which worked in the following way:

Each species map was scanned tetrad by tetrad. If the species occurred in the tetrad then it was assumed to be present in every habitat in the tetrad which has a population density figure for that species, and at those densities. If the species did not occur in that tetrad then its population was taken as zero. The calculated tetrad populations for each species were then totalled to given the county population.

THE GARDEN BIRD SURVEY

Arthur Brown

The Buckinghamshire Bird Club Garden Bird Survey commenced on 9 Nov 1986 and covered 25 weeks to 2 May 1987. Subsequent years covered 27 weeks comprising three 9 week periods from October to March. In certain years the periods included the last few days in September or the first few days in April.

Participants provide details of the maximum number of a species seen at one time in each week, and also note which species have taken artificial food (peanuts, seeds, kitchen scraps, etc), natural food (berries, seeds, fruit on trees, windfalls, etc) and whether the species has been seen drinking or bathing. These categories are listed below under the letters A, N, D, and B.

The average number of participating gardens is 89 with 53% in suburban areas (S), 47% in rural (R), and less than 1% in urban areas. 90 native species and 2 escapes have been recorded.

The statistics for the 40 most frequently occurring species in the period 1986/87 - 1991/92 are given below.

		Max flock size		% of total gardens	% taking food		% using water	
					A	N	D	B
1	Blue Tit	30	R	98.7	94.4	73.4	20.4	10.9
2	Blackbird	22	R	98.7	84.3	67.0	57.5	45.9
3	Robin	8	R	98.5	89.9	76.4	42.2	26.2
4	Starling	300	S	96.0	90.7	59.4	50.1	45.8
5	Chaffinch	200	R	91.7	85.0	65.9	35.3	9.3
6	House Sparrow	94	U	90.5	95.9	67.5	59.0	36.0
7	Great Tit	12	R	90.2	90.9	57.8	23.6	12.3
8	Dunnock	11	S	89.2	84.2	80.5	19.9	8.0
9	Greenfinch	270	R	88.3	92.0	40.0	37.5	9.3
10	Song Thrush	6	R	78.5	59.1	77.1	24.6	21.7
11	Collared Dove	122	R	75.8	78.0	47.1	43.7	8.9
12	Magpie	27	R	75.2	66.4	49.0	15.8	4.2
13	Wren	4	R	75.0	18.1	83.4	7.8	5.4
14	Coal Tit	10	R	62.4	84.7	39.4	14.0	3.2
15	Woodpigeon	52	R	53.0	47.6	63.8	30.1	6.2
16	Long-tailed Tit	30	R	35.6	44.6	66.5	3.4	1.2
17	Carrion Crow	10	R	31.1	47.3	39.1	7.3	1.0
18	Gt Sp Woodpecker	3	R	30.3	75.8	45.5	2.4	0.0
19	Jay	12	R	29.6	54.8	52.3	9.8	1.5
20	Pied Wagtail	12	R	25.1	48.6	58.3	8.0	4.4

		Max flock size		% of total gardens	% taking food A	N	% using water D	B
21	Mistle Thrush	5	R&S	25.0	32.7	55.7	13.0	7.6
22	Bullfinch	8	R	23.6	12.3	75.4	17.4	7.4
23	Nuthatch	3	R&S	21.8	84.0	37.2	6.8	4.1
24	Goldfinch	60	R	18.3	14.4	75.0	15.7	8.2
25	Redwing	40	R	18.0	20.9	68.1	12.5	7.0
26	Goldcrest	9	S	17.5	4.9	80.8	3.4	6.8
27	Green Woodpecker	4	R	15.4	3.4	85.4	2.4	0.0
28	Jackdaw	12	R&S	13.7	71.6	21.2	9.1	0.0
29	Pheasant	12	R	13.7	63.0	72.5	21.8	0.0
30	Treecreeper	2	R	13.2	6.5	86.0	1.0	2.0
31	Fieldfare	210	R	12.9	30.6	61.7	11.4	3.0
32	Siskin	50	R&S	11.0	78.7	26.5	18.5	2.2
33	Sparrowhawk	2	R&S	10.8	1.8	39.6	0.0	0.0
34	Rook	28	R	9.1	60.9	25.4	2.4	0.0
35	Marsh Tit	4	R	8.0	73.6	37.2	9.0	0.0
36	Reed Bunting	12	R	7.9	70.8	29.2	9.4	4.7
37	Blackcap	6	R	7.6	41.7	40.0	11.8	5.9
38	Black-headed Gull	25	R	7.5	84.8	4.4	1.5	0.0
39	Willow Tit	3	R	5.1	74.0	36.4	8.5	0.0
40	Brambling	8	R	4.3	64.6	30.8	19.2	7.7

BREEDING LOSSES AND GAINS THIS CENTURY

The 20th century has seen significant changes in the fortunes of many of the county's birds which has resulted in a number of breeding birds becoming lost to the county. These losses have been more than matched by the number of gains, but it should be noted that many of these are of introduced species. The losses and gains are summarised below.

Losses	Year last bred
Corncrake	c1947
Stonechat	c1947
Wheatear	1954
Stone-curlew	1964
Woodlark	1971
Red-backed Shrike	1971
Whinchat	1983
Cirl Bunting	1984
Wryneck	1985

Gains	Year first bred
Lady Amherst's Pheasant	c1905
Woodcock	1926
Mandarin	1955
Little Ringed Plover	1955
Collared Dove	1961
Black Redstart	1965
Common Tern	1968
Firecrest	1971
Greylag Goose	1972
Ring-necked Parakeet	1974
Shelduck	1975
Ringed Plover	1975
Ruddy Duck	1980
Gadwall	1985

It should also be noted that numbers of many other species have changed significantly during the course of the century although not actually gained or lost.

LIST OF BREEDING SPECIES IN ORDER OF NUMBER OF OCCUPIED TETRADS

	Species	Poss	Prob	Conf	Total	%
1	Blackbird	19	68	424	511	88.4
2	Starling	39	9	452	500	86.5
3	Woodpigeon	65	176	259	500	86.5
4	Chaffinch	16	201	281	498	86.2
5	Carrion Crow	89	67	336	492	85.1
6	Robin	20	97	371	488	84.4
7	Blue Tit	38	45	402	485	83.9
8	House Sparrow	63	31	391	485	83.9
9	Wren	18	193	271	482	83.4
10	Song Thrush	29	139	312	480	83.0
11	Great Tit	40	77	363	480	83.0
12	Dunnock	30	204	244	478	82.7
13	Yellowhammer	25	250	194	469	81.1
14	Magpie	93	63	305	461	79.8
15	Skylark	33	326	90	449	77.7
16	Willow Warbler	11	227	210	448	77.5
17	Swallow	112	106	224	442	76.5
18	Greenfinch	57	217	164	438	75.8
19	Collared Dove	96	212	117	425	73.5
20	Blackcap	20	251	126	397	68.7
21	Pheasant	120	156	112	388	67.1
22	Stock Dove	143	169	74	386	66.8
23	Mistle Thrush	82	67	220	369	63.8
24	Goldfinch	79	173	131	383	66.3
25	Linnet	105	166	112	383	66.3
26	Cuckoo	52	288	29	369	63.8
27	Kestrel	201	78	89	368	63.7
28	Bullfinch	120	123	124	367	63.5
29	House Martin	96	31	230	357	61.8
30	Jackdaw	139	68	146	353	61.1
31	Whitethroat	25	215	110	350	60.5
32	Swift	218	51	71	340	58.8
33	Moorhen	56	30	253	339	58.6
34	Chiffchaff	24	220	74	318	55.0
35	Rook	81	10	226	317	54.8
36	Pied Wagtail	107	25	170	302	52.2
37	Turtle Dove	61	205	34	300	51.9
38	Mallard	101	32	166	299	51.7
39	Spotted Flycatcher	81	73	141	295	51.0
40	Long-tailed Tit	70	35	188	293	50.7

	Species	Poss	Prob	Conf	Total	%
41	Lapwing	61	119	102	282	48.8
42	Green Woodpecker	103	131	47	281	48.6
43	Great Spotted Woodpecker	102	76	89	267	46.2
44	Goldcrest	40	129	89	258	44.6
45	Jay	129	51	74	254	43.9
46	Lesser Whitethroat	25	147	74	246	42.6
47	Tawny Owl	88	69	88	245	42.4
48	Reed Bunting	32	136	75	243	42.0
49	Treecreeper	98	60	82	240	41.5
50	Coal Tit	43	73	106	222	38.4
51	Red-legged Partridge	93	80	49	222	38.4
52	Garden Warbler	28	137	51	216	37.4
53	Grey Partridge	70	86	60	216	37.4
54	Little Owl	90	43	79	212	36.7
55	Corn Bunting	17	164	29	210	36.3
56	Yellow Wagtail	66	42	101	209	36.2
57	Sparrowhawk	115	31	54	200	34.6
58	Nuthatch	54	62	68	184	31.8
59	Tree Sparrow	75	50	57	182	31.5
60	Coot	19	13	139	171	29.6
61	Marsh Tit	51	45	57	153	26.5
62	Willow Tit	42	45	59	146	25.3
63	Sedge Warbler	7	73	50	130	22.5
64	Tufted Duck	42	25	38	105	18.2
65	Mute Swan	28	9	63	100	17.3
66	Little Grebe	19	15	62	96	16.6
67	Lesser Spotted Woodpecker	54	23	11	88	15.2
68	Tree Pipit	5	49	28	82	14.2
69	Canada Goose	28	4	50	82	14.2
70	Kingfisher	40	16	21	77	13.2
71	Redpoll	35	34	6	75	13.0
72	Reed Warbler	12	24	37	73	12.6
73	Great Crested Grebe	9	10	38	57	9.9
74	Grasshopper Warbler	2	49	5	56	9.7
75	Woodcock	12	35	8	55	9.5
76	Grey Wagtail	25	11	19	55	9.5
77	Meadow Pipit	18	15	19	52	9.0
78	Curlew	12	26	4	42	7.3
79	Wood Warbler	6	26	5	37	6.4
80	Snipe	15	13	1	29	5.0
81	Sand Martin	13	0	13	26	4.5
82	Redshank	10	8	8	26	4.5
83	Nightingale	4	17	3	24	4.1
84	Barn Owl	11	1	8	20	3.5
85	Little Ringed Plover	6	1	10	17	2.9

	Species	Poss	Prob	Conf	Total	%
86	Hawfinch	6	8	3	17	2.9
87	Teal	11	2	2	15	2.6
88	Pochard	12	0	2	14	2.4
89	Greylag Goose	5	1	7	13	2.2
90	Common Tern	7	1	5	13	2.2
91	Ringed Plover	3	1	8	12	2.1
92	Water Rail	9	0	1	10	1.7
93	Redstart	1	3	5	9	1.6
94	Whinchat	6	1	2	9	1.6
95	Grey Heron	0	0	8	8	1.4
96	Shoveler	7	0	1	8	1.4
97	Firecrest	3	3	2	8	1.4
98	Nightjar	2	2	3	7	1.2
99	Shelduck	2	2	2	6	1.0
100	Quail	0	5	0	5	0.9
101	Mandarin	0	2	2	4	0.7
102	Black Redstart	2	0	1	3	0.7
103	Lady Amherst's Pheasant	0	4	0	4	0.7
104	Gadwall	2	1	0	3	0.5
105	Garganey	0	2	0	2	0.3
106	Cirl Bunting	0	2	0	2	0.3
107	Long-eared Owl	0	1	0	1	0.2
108	Stonechat	0	1	0	1	0.2
109	Wryneck	0	0	1	1	0.2

Hobby is the only species known to have bred in the county during the breeding survey period which is not listed.

THE BUCKINGHAMSHIRE LIST

The 270 species recorded in the present county are as follows.

Red-throated Diver	Rare vagrant. 11 records.
Black-throated Diver	Rare vagrant. 8 records.
Great Northern Diver	Rare vagrant. 10 records.
Little Grebe	Fairly common resident and winter visitor.
Great Crested Grebe	Local resident.
Red-necked Grebe	Scarce migrant and winter visitor.
Slavonian Grebe	Scarce migrant and winter visitor.
Black-necked Grebe	Scarce migrant.
Fulmar	Very rare vagrant. 4 records.
Manx Shearwater	Rare vagrant. 7 records.
Storm Petrel	Rare vagrant. 6 records. Last record in 1929.
Leach's Petrel	Rare vagrant. 10 records.
Gannet	Rare vagrant. 10 records.
Cormorant	Regular winter visitor. A few summer.
Shag	Scarce but increasing migrant and winter visitor.
Bittern	Scarce winter visitor.
Little Bittern	Rare vagrant. 5 records.
Night Heron	Very rare vagrant. 4 records.
Little Egret	Very rare vagrant. 2 records.
Grey Heron	Local resident and winter visitor.
Purple Heron	Very rare vagrant. 2 records.
Glossy Ibis	Very rare vagrant. 1 old record.
White Stork	Very rare record. 1 old record.
Spoonbill	Very rare vagrant. 4 records.
Mute Swan	Local resident.
Bewick's Swan	Scarce winter visitor.
Whooper Swan	Scarce winter visitor.
Bean Goose	Rare vagrant. All records may be of feral birds.
Pink-footed Goose	Scarce migrant.
White-fronted Goose	Scarce migrant.
Greylag Goose	Introduced local resident.
Canada Goose	Introduced locally common resident.
Barnacle Goose	Feral flocks present. Not certainly known to have occurred wild.
Brent Goose	Scarce migrant.
Shelduck	Scarce resident and regular migrant.
Mandarin	Very local but increasing resident.
Wigeon	Locally common winter visitor.
Gadwall	Very local resident and regular winter visitor.
Teal	Scarce resident and regular winter visitor.
Mallard	Common resident and winter visitor.
Pintail	Scarce migrant and winter visitor.

Garganey	Scarce migrant and summer visitor.
Shoveler	Scarce resident and local migrant and winter visitor.
Red-crested Pochard	Scarce migrant. Origin of birds uncertain.
Pochard	Scarce resident and regular winter visitor.
Ring-necked Duck	Very rare vagrant. 4 records.
Ferruginous Duck	Very rare vagrant. 4 records. All may be escapes.
Tufted Duck	Local resident and common winter visitor.
Scaup	Rare vagrant and winter visitor.
Eider	Very rare vagrant. 1 record.
Long-tailed Duck	Rare vagrant and winter visitor. 9 records.
Common Scoter	Scarce migrant.
Velvet Scoter	Very rare vagrant. 3 records.
Bufflehead	Very rare vagrant. 1 record.
Goldeneye	Regular winter visitor.
Smew	Scarce winter visitor.
Red-breasted Merganser	Rare vagrant and winter visitor.
Goosander	Local winter visitor.
Ruddy Duck	Very local resident and scarce migrant.
Honey Buzzard	Very rare vagrant. 5 records. May have bred in 19th century.
Red Kite	Scarce vagrant. Recent increase due to released birds.
White-tailed Eagle	Very rare vagrant. 3 records.
Marsh Harrier	Scarce migrant.
Hen Harrier	Scarce migrant.
Montagu's Harrier	Very rare vagrant. 3 records.
Goshawk	May be resident in very small numbers.
Sparrowhawk	Fairly common resident.
Buzzard	Very rare resident and scarce migrant.
Rough-legged Buzzard	Very rare vagrant. 6 records.
Osprey	Scarce migrant.
Kestrel	Common resident.
Red-footed Falcon	Very rare vagrant. 1 record.
Merlin	Scarce winter visitor and migrant.
Hobby	Scarce breeding summer visitor.
Peregrine	Rare winter visitor.
Red-legged Partridge	Fairly common introduced resident.
Grey Partridge	Fairly common but decreasing resident.
Quail	Scarce summer visitor; occasionally breeds.
Pheasant	Common introduced resident.
Golden Pheasant	Introduced or escaped in very small numbers.
Lady Amherst's Pheasant	Very local introduced resident.
Water Rail	Rare resident and local winter visitor.
Spotted Crake	Very rare vagrant. 3 records.

Corncrake	Very rare migrant. Formerly a breeding summer visitor.
Moorhen	Common resident and winter visitor.
Coot	Common resident and winter visitor.
Crane	Very rare vagrant. 1 record.
Oystercatcher	Scarce migrant.
Black-winged Stilt	Very rare vagrant. 1 record.
Avocet	Very rare vagrant. 6 records.
Stone-curlew	Very rare vagrant. Former local breeding summer visitor.
Little Ringed Plover	Scarce breeding summer visitor and migrant.
Ringed Plover	Scarce breeding summer visitor and migrant.
Kentish Plover	Very rare vagrant. 1 record.
Dotterel	Very rare vagrant. 3 records.
American Golden Plover	Very rare vagrant. 1 record.
Golden Plover	Locally common winter visitor.
Grey Plover	Scarce migrant and very rare winter visitor.
Lapwing	Common resident and winter visitor.
Knot	Scarce migrant.
Sanderling	Scarce migrant.
Little Stint	Scarce migrant.
Temminck's Stint	Rare migrant.
Pectoral Sandpiper	Very rare vagrant. 2 records.
Curlew Sandpiper	Scarce migrant.
Purple Sandpiper	Very rare vagrant. 2 records.
Dunlin	Locally common migrant and rare winter visitor.
Ruff	Locally common migrant and rare winter visitor.
Jack Snipe	Uncommon winter visitor.
Snipe	Rare resident and uncommon winter visitor.
Great Snipe	Very rare vagrant. 2 records.
Woodcock	Uncommon resident and winter visitor.
Black-tailed Godwit	Scarce migrant.
Bar-tailed Godwit	Scarce migrant.
Whimbrel	Scarce migrant.
Curlew	Scarce breeding summer visitor and uncommon migrant.
Spotted Redshank	Scarce migrant.
Redshank	Scarce breeding summer visitor, and winter visitor.
Greenshank	Local migrant.
Lesser Yellowlegs	Very rare vagrant. 1 record.
Green Sandpiper	Local winter visitor and migrant.
Wood Sandpiper	Scarce migrant.
Common Sandpiper	Regular migrant. Has bred.
Turnstone	Scarce migrant.
Red-necked Phalarope	Very rare vagrant. 2 records.

Grey Phalarope	Rare vagrant. 7 records.
Pomarine Skua	Very rare vagrant. 4 records.
Arctic Skua	Very rare vagrant. 2 records.
Long-tailed Skua	Very rare vagrant. 1 record.
Great Skua	Very rare vagrant. 2 records.
Mediterranean Gull	Scarce but increasing migrant and winter visitor.
Little Gull	Scarce migrant.
Sabine's Gull	Very rare vagrant. 4 records.
Black-headed Gull	Common migrant and winter visitor.
Ring-billed Gull	Very rare vagrant. 3 records.
Common Gull	Common winter visitor.
Lesser Black-backed Gull	Common migrant and winter visitor.
Herring Gull	Locally common migrant and winter visitor.
Iceland Gull	Rare winter visitor. 12 records.
Glaucous Gull	Scarce winter visitor.
Great Black-backed Gull	Uncommon winter visitor.
Kittiwake	Scarce migrant.
Caspian Tern	Very rare vagrant. 1 record.
Sandwich Tern	Scarce migrant.
Roseate Tern	Very rare vagrant. 2 records.
Common Tern	Local breeding summer visitor and locally common migrant.
Arctic Tern	Local migrant.
Little Tern	Scarce migrant.
Black Tern	Local migrant.
Little Auk	Rare vagrant. 11 records.
Guillemot	Very rare vagrant. 1 record.
Puffin	Rare vagrant. 11 records.
Pallas's Sandgrouse	Very rare vagrant. 3 records, none since 1908.
Feral Pigeon	Common resident.
Stock Dove	Common resident.
Woodpigeon	Very common resident.
Collared Dove	Common resident.
Turtle Dove	Fairly common breeding summer visitor.
Ring-necked Parakeet	Scarce vagrant which has bred.
Cuckoo	Common breeding summer visitor.
Barn Owl	Scarce resident.
Little Owl	Fairly common introduced resident.
Tawny Owl	Fairly common resident.
Long-eared Owl	Rare resident and scarce winter visitor.
Short-eared Owl	Scarce winter visitor.
Nightjar	Rare summer visitor. May no longer breed.
Swift	Common breeding summer visitor.
Kingfisher	Local resident.
Bee-eater	Very rare vagrant. 4 records.
Hoopoe	Scarce migrant.

Wryneck	Scarce migrant. Former breeding summer visitor.
Green Woodpecker	Fairly common resident.
Great Spotted Woodpecker	Fairly common resident.
Lesser Spotted Woodpecker	Uncommon resident.
Woodlark	Rare vagrant. Former resident.
Skylark	Common resident, migrant, and winter visitor.
Sand Martin	Very local breeding summer visitor.
Swallow	Common breeding summer visitor.
House Martin	Common breeding summer visitor.
Richard's Pipit	Very rare vagrant. 2 records.
Tree Pipit	Uncommon breeding summer visitor.
Meadow Pipit	Scarce resident, uncommon migrant, and winter visitor.
Water Pipit	Scarce migrant.
Rock Pipit	Scarce migrant.
Yellow Wagtail	Fairly common breeding summer visitor.
Grey Wagtail	Scarce resident and winter visitor.
Pied Wagtail	Common resident.
Waxwing	Scarce winter visitor.
Dipper	Rare migrant.
Wren	Very common resident.
Dunnock	Very common resident.
Robin	Very common resident.
Nightingale	Scarce breeding summer visitor.
Bluethroat	Very rare vagrant. 2 records.
Black Redstart	Rare resident, migrant, and winter visitor.
Redstart	Rare breeding summer visitor.
Whinchat	Migrant. Former breeding summer visitor.
Stonechat	Migrant and winter visitor.
Wheatear	Migrant. Former breeding summer visitor.
Black-eared Wheatear	Very rare vagrant. 1 record.
Ring Ouzel	Migrant.
Blackbird	Very common resident and winter visitor.
Fieldfare	Common winter visitor.
Song Thrush	Common resident and winter visitor.
Redwing	Common winter visitor.
Mistle Thrush	Common resident.
Cetti's Warbler	Rare vagrant. 6 records.
Grasshopper Warbler	Scarce breeding summer visitor.
Moustached Warbler	Very rare vagrant. 1 record.
Aquatic Warbler	Very rare vagrant. 2 records.
Sedge Warbler	Fairly common breeding summer visitor.
Marsh Warbler	Very rare vagrant. 3 records including one of breeding.
Reed Warbler	Local breeding summer visitor.
Great Reed Warbler	Very rare vagrant. 1 record.

Lesser Whitethroat	Common breeding summer visitor.
Whitethroat	Common breeding summer visitor.
Garden Warbler	Common breeding summer visitor.
Blackcap	Common breeding summer visitor and scarce winter visitor.
Yellow-browed Warbler	Very rare vagrant. 1 record.
Wood Warbler	Rare breeding summer visitor.
Chiffchaff	Common breeding summer visitor and scarce winter visitor.
Willow Warbler	Very common breeding summer visitor.
Goldcrest	Common resident.
Firecrest	Rare summer visitor and winter visitor.
Spotted Flycatcher	Fairly common breeding summer visitor.
Red-breasted Flycatcher	Very rare vagrant. 2 records.
Pied Flycatcher	Scarce migrant. 2 breeding records.
Bearded Tit	Scarce winter visitor.
Long-tailed Tit	Common resident.
Marsh Tit	Fairly common resident.
Willow Tit	Uncommon resident.
Coal Tit	Common resident.
Blue Tit	Very common resident.
Great Tit	Very common resident.
Nuthatch	Fairly common resident.
Treecreeper	Fairly common resident.
Golden Oriole	Rare migrant. 11 records including 1 breeding.
Red-backed Shrike	No records since 1972. Former scarce breeding summer visitor.
Great Grey Shrike	Scarce and decreasing winter visitor.
Woodchat Shrike	Very rare vagrant. 2 records.
Jay	Common resident.
Magpie	Common resident.
Nutcracker	Very rare vagrant. 3 records.
Jackdaw	Common resident.
Rook	Common resident.
Carrion Crow	Common resident.
Raven	Very rare vagrant. 5 records, last 1932.
Starling	Very common resident and winter visitor.
Rose-coloured Starling	Very rare vagrant. 2 records.
House Sparrow	Very common resident.
Tree Sparrow	Uncommon resident.
Chaffinch	Very common resident.
Brambling	Uncommon winter visitor.
Serin	Very rare vagrant. 1 record.
Greenfinch	Common resident and winter visitor.
Goldfinch	Common resident and summer visitor.
Siskin	Uncommon winter visitor that occasionally

	summers.
Linnet	Common but decreasing resident.
Twite	Rare vagrant. 7 records.
Redpoll	Uncommon resident; winter visitor.
Crossbill	Irregular visitor and breeder.
Bullfinch	Common resident.
Hawfinch	Scarce resident.
Lapland Bunting	Very rare but increasing vagrant. 5 records.
Snow Bunting	Rare winter visitor. 13 records.
Yellowhammer	Very common resident.
Cirl Bunting	Last record 1985. Former scarce resident.
Little Bunting	Very rare vagrant. 1 record.
Reed Bunting	Locally common resident.
Corn Bunting	Uncommon and decreasing resident.

SCIENTIFIC NAMES OF PLANT SPECIES MENTIONED IN THE TEXT

Alder	*Alnus glutinosa*
Ash	*Fraxinus excelsior*
Barley	*Hordeum* spp
Beech	*Fagus sylvatica*
Birch	*Betula* spp
Black Poplar	*Populus nigra*
Blackthorn	*Prunus spinosa*
Bracken	*Pteridium aquilinum*
Bramble	*Rubus fruticosus*
Cedar	*Cedrus* spp
Cherry	*Prunus avium*
Chickweed	*Stellaria* spp
Common reed	*Phragmites communis*
Dandelion	*Taraxacum* spp
Deadly nightshade	*Atropa belladonna*
Dogwood	*Cornus sanguinea*
Elm	*Ulmus* spp
Erect Brome	*Bromus erectus*
False Oat Grass	*Arrhenatherum elatius*
Fat Hen	*Chenopodium album*
Field Maple	*Acer campestris*
Fir	*Abies* spp
Fumitory	*Fumaria* spp
Gorse	*Ulex europaeus*
Groundsel	*Senecio vulgaris*
Hawthorn	*Crataegus monogyna*
Hazel	*Corylus avellana*
Hornbeam	*Carpinus betulus*
Horse chestnut	*Aesculus hippocastanum*
Ivy	*Hedera helix*
Juniper	*Juniperus communis*
Larch	*Larix* spp
Norway Spruce	*Picea abies*
Oak	*Quercus* spp
Pendunculate Oak	*Quercus robur*
Persicaria	*Polygonum persicaria*

Privet	*Ligustrum vulgare*
Ragwort	*Senecio jacobaea*
Rhododendron	*Rhododendron ponticum*
Rose	*Rosa* spp
Rowan	*Sorbus aucuparia*
Sallow	*Salix caprea*
Scots pine	*Pinus sylvestris*
Spruce	*Picea abies*
Sycamore	*Acer pseudoplatanus*
Thistle	*Cirsium* or *Carduus* spp
Traveller's joy	*Clematis vitalba*
Wayfaring tree	*Viburnum lantana*
Wheat	*Triticum aestivum*
Willow	*Salix* spp
Yew	*Taxus baccata*

GAZETTEER

The sites listed below are either mentioned in the text of this book or are of local interest. Against each site is given the 4-figure OS National Grid reference, the nearest town, its bearing, and its distance from the town in kms.

Site	Grid ref	Town	Bearing	Km
ARC Wildfowl Centre	SP 84 42	Great Linford	NW	1
Ashridge Commons and Woods	SP 98 13	Tring	ENE	5
Aston Clinton Ragpits	SP 88 10	Aylesbury	ESE	4
Aston Sandford	SP 75 07	Thame	ENE	4
Aylesbury STW	SP 79 14	Aylesbury West		
Bacombe Hill	SP 86 07	Wendover	SW	1
Balham's Wood	SU 73 88	Stokenchurch	SSW	7
Beacon Hill (Ellesborough)	SP 83 06	Wendover	SW	3
Bergers Hill	SU 91 87	Beaconsfield	SSW	2
Bernwood Forest	SP 61 10	Thame	WNW	10
Bernwood Meadows	SP 60 11	Thame	WNW	11
Berryfields	SP 78 16	Aylesbury	WNW	2
Bishopstone	SP 80 10	Aylesbury	SSW	2
Black Park Country Park	TQ 01 06	Slough	NE	3
Bledlow Ridge	SU 79 97	High Wycombe	NNW	2
Bletchley Brick Pits	SP 86 31	Bletchley		
Bletchley STW	SP 88 34	Bletchley		
Blue Lagoon	SP 86 32	Bletchley		
Boarstall Duck Decoy	SP 62 15	Thame	NW	12
Bockmer End	SU 81 86	Marlow	W	3
Booker	SU 83 91	High Wycombe	SW	1
Botolph Claydon	SP 73 24	Aylesbury	NW	12
Bottom Wood	SU 79 95	Stokenchurch	E	3
Boveney	SU 93 77	Slough	WSW	3
Bradenham Woods	SU 82 98	High Wycombe	NW	3
Buckingham Canal	SP 72 35	Buckingham	ENE	2
Burnham Beeches	SU 95 85	Slough	NNW	3
Buttlers Hangings	SU 81 96	High Wycombe	WNW	4
Caldecotte Lake	SP 89 35	Milton Keynes E		
Calvert Jubilee Reserve	SP 68 25	Buckingham	S	8
Campbell Park	SP 85 38	Milton Keynes, Central		
Castlethorpe Mill	SP 78 44	Wolverton	NW	4
Chairborough	SP 84 92	High Wycombe		
Chalfont Common	TQ 00 92	Beaconsfield	ENE	5
Chalfont Park	TQ 01 89	Beaconsfield	ENE	5
Chartridge	SP 93 03	Chesham	NW	3
Chearsley	SP 71 10	Thame	N	4
Chelmscote (3 Locks)	SP 89 28	Bletchley	SSE	4

Site	Grid ref	Town	Bearing	Km
Chequers	SP 84 05	Wendover	SW	3
Chesham Bois Woods	SU 96 00	Chesham	S	1
Chesham Cress Beds	SU 96 00	Chesham	SSE	0.5
Chesham Moor	SU 96 00	Chesham	SSE	1
Chesham STW	SU 97 99	Chesham	SSE	2
Chesham Waterside	SP 96 00	Chesham	SSE	0.5
Chess Valley	SU 99 98	Amersham	E	2
Cholesbury	SP 93 07	Chesham	NNW	4
Church Wood	SU 97 87	Beaconsfield	SE	4
Claydon Lakes	SP 71 25	Buckingham	SSE	8
Cliveden	SU 91 85	Beaconsfield	SSW	5
Coleshill	SU 94 95	Beaconsfield	N	3
College Lake	SP 93 13	Tring	NNE	1
Common Wood (Tylers Green)	SU 91 94	High Wycombe	ENE	3
Coombe Hill	SP 84 06	Wendover	SW	2
Cosgrove	SP 79 42	Wolverton	WNW	2
Dadford	SP 66 38	Buckingham	NW	5
Dancersend	SP 90 09	Wendover	ENE	3
Dagnall	SP 99 16	Tring	ENE	7
Denham Country Park	TQ 04 86	Slough	NE	8
Dinton Hall	SP 77 11	Aylesbury	WSW	5
Dipple Wood	SU 93 87	Beaconsfield	S	2
Doddershall Wood	SP 69 20	Thame	N	14
Dorney Common	SU 93 79	Slough	WSW	2
Dorney Reach	SU 91 79	Slough	WNW	3
Dorney Wood	SU 93 84	Slough	NW	3
Dorton	SP 68 12	Thame	NNW	12
Downley Common	SU 84 95	High Wycombe	NW	3
Drayton Beauchamp	SP 89 12	Tring	WNW	1
Drayton Parslow	SP 84 28	Bletchley	SSW	5
Dropmore	SU 92 86	Beaconsfield	S	4
East Claydon	SP 74 25	Aylesbury	NW	12
Edgecott	SP 68 22	Buckingham	SSW	11
Egypt Woods	SU 95 86	Beaconsfield	SSE	3
Ellesborough & Kimble Warrens	SP 83 05	Wendover	WSW	3
Emberton Country Park	SP 88 50	Great Linford	NNE	8
Eythrope	SP 77 14	Aylesbury	W	3
Fawley	SU 75 86	Marlow	WSW	7
Finemere Wood	SP 71 21	Aylesbury	NW	11
Foxcote Reservoir	SP 71 36	Buckingham	NNE	2
Frame Wood	SU 98 84	Slough	NNE	3
Frieth Meadows	SU 79 90	High Wycombe	WSW	4
Fulmer Mere	SU 99 86	Slough	N	5
Gomm Valley	SU 89 92	High Wycombe	ESE	1
Gomm's Wood	SU 89 92	High Wycombe	ESE	1

Site	Grid ref	Town	Bearing	Km
Grangelands & Pulpit Hill	SP 82 04	Wendover	SW	5
Great Brickhill	SP 90 30	Bletchley	ESE	4
Great Hampden	SP 84 01	High Wycombe	N	7
Great Wood (Hambleden)	SU 76 87	Marlow	W	7
Grebe Lake (Calvert)	SP 68 25	Buckingham	SSW	8
Grendon Wood	SP 69 21	Thame	N	13
Ham Home cum Ham Grn Wd	SP 69 18	Thame	N	12
Hangar Wood (Cadmore End)	SU 78 91	High Wycombe	W	6
Hambleden	SP 78 86	Marlow	W	5
Hampden Bottom	SP 86 02	High Wycombe	N	8
Hartigan's GP **	SP 88 38	Milton Keynes E		
Haversham	SP 83 43	Wolverton	NNE	2
Hedgerley	SU 97 87	Beaconsfield	SE	4
Hockeridge & Pancake Woods	SP 97 06	Chesham	NNE	3
Hodgemoor Woods	SU 95 94	Beaconsfield	NE	3
Homefield Wood	SU 81 86	Marlow	NE	3
Howe Park Wood	SP 83 34	Milton Keynes W		
Hughenden Park and Manor	SU 86 95	High Wycombe	N	1
Hulcott	SP 81 28	Aylesbury	NW	3
Hyde Lane Lake	SP 72 35	Buckingham	ENE	2
Iver GP	TQ 03 80	Slough	E	3
Iver STW	TQ 04 80	Slough	E	4
Ivinghoe Hills	SP 96 15	Tring	NE	4
Kings Wood (Tylers Green)	SU 89 94	High Wycombe	ENE	1
Langley Park Country Park	TQ 00 84	Slough	NNE	2
Latimer Park/Lake	SU 99 98	Amersham	E	2
Lenborough	SP 70 31	Buckingham	S	1
Linford Wood (MK)	SP 84 40	Milton Keynes N		
Linford/Newport Pagnell Lakes	SP 84 43	Great Linford	NNW	1
Little Britain Country Park	TQ 05 81	Slough	E	5
Little Linford Wood	SP 83 45	Great Linford	NNW	3
Little Marlow GPs	SU 87 87	Marlow	ENE	2
Little Marlow STW	SU 87 87	Marlow	ENE	2
Littleworth Common	SU 93 86	Beaconsfield	S	4
Lodge Hill	SP 79 00	Stokenchurch	NW	5
Loughton Valley Park	SP 83 37	Milton Keynes W		
Marlow Low Grounds	SU 83 84	Marlow	SSW	1
Marsworth Reservoir	SP 92 13	Tring	N	2
Medmenham	SU 80 84	Marlow	SW	4
Millfield Wood	SU 87 95	High Wycombe	N	1
Moorend Common	SU 80 90	Marlow	NW	5
Mousloe	SP 91 42	Willen	ENE	3
Mursley	SP 81 28	Bletchley	SW	6
Naphill Common	SU 84 97	High Wycombe	NNW	3
Newport Pagnell	SP 86 43	Great Linford	NE	2

Site	Grid ref	Town	Bearing	Km
Newton Longville	SP 83 41	Bletchley	SSE	2
North Dean	SU 84 98	High Wycombe	NNW	4
Oakley	SP 64 12	Thame	NW	9
Old Rectory Meadows	TQ 03 87	Slough	NE	8
Old Slade (South Iver)	TQ 03 77	Slough	ESE	3
Olney	SP 88 50	Great Linford	NNE	9
Padbury	SP 72 31	Buckingham	SE	3
Park Wood	SU 82 98	High Wycombe	NW	4
Penn Wood	SU 91 96	High Wycombe	ENE	4
Philipshill Wood	TQ 00 94	Amersham	ENE	4
Pickeridge Quarry(WDS)	SU 98 85	Slough	N	5
Pitstone Fen	SP 93 14	Tring	NNE	3
Pitstone Hill	SP 95 14	Tring	NE	3
Quainton	SP 74 20	Aylesbury	NW	8
Ravenstone	SP 84 50	Great Linford	N	7
Ringshall	SP 98 14	Tring	ENE	7
Rushbeds Wood	SP 66 15	Thame	NNW	10
Salcey Forest (The Straits)	SP 81 50	Wolverton	N	9
Shabbington Wood	SP 61 10	Thame	NNW	10
Shardeloes	SU 94 98	Amersham	W	2
Sheephouse Wood	SP 70 23	Buckingham	S	10
Skirmett	SU 77 90	High Wycombe	WSW	6
Startops End Reservoir	SP 92 13	Tring	N	1
Steps Hill	SP 95 15	Tring	NE	4
Stockgrove Country Park	SP 91 29	Bletchley	SE	5
Stoke Common	SU 98 85	Slough	N	4
Stoke Hammond	SP 88 29	Bletchley	S	2
Stony Stratford NR	SP 78 41	Milton Keynes N		
Stowe	SP 67 37	Buckingham	NNW	4
Taplow Court	SU 90 82	Slough	WNW	3
Taplow GP	SU 91 81	Slough	W	3
Temple Island Meadows	SU 76 84	Marlow	WSW	7
The Lee	SP 91 04	Chesham	WNW	6
Three Locks	SP 89 28	Bletchley	SSE	4
Tilbrook	SP 89 35	Milton Keynes E		
Tilehouse GPs	TQ 03 89	Slough	NNE	10
Tongwell	SP 87 41	Milton Keynes E		
Tyringham Park	SP 85 46	Great Linford	N	4
Wapseys Wood WDS	SU 97 88	Beaconsfield	ESE	3
Watermead	SP 82 15	Aylesbury	N0.5	
Wavenden Wood	SP 91 35	Bletchley	ENE	4
Wendover Canal	SP 88 10	Wendover-Tring		
Wendover Woods	SP 89 08	Wendover	ENE	1
West Wycombe Park	SU 82 94	High Wycombe	WNW	1
Westbury Wild	SP 62 37	Buckingham	WNW	7

Site	Grid ref	Town	Bearing	Km
Westcott	SP 71 17	Aylesbury	WNW	8
Weston Turville Reservoir	SP 86 09	Wendover	NNW	1
Whitecross Green Wood	SP 60 14	Thame	NW	13
Willen Lake	SP 88 40	Milton Keynes E		
Wilstone Reservoir	SP 90 13	Tring	NW	2
Winchbottom	SU 86 90	High Wycombe	S	1
Windsor Hill	SP 82 02	Wendover	SW	6
Woodrow	SU 93 96	Amersham	SW	3
Wotton Lakes	SP 67 16	Thame	NNW	10
Wycombe Rye	SU 87 92	High Wycombe		
Yiewsley GP	TQ 04 80	Slough	E	3

Abbreviations: GP   - Gravel Pit
NR   - Nature Reserve
STW - Sewage Treatment Works
WDS - Waste Disposal Site
**   - site no longer exists

ATLAS FIELDWORKERS

Listed below are the names of those who took part in the fieldwork for the Buckinghamshire Atlas with apologies to those we have inadvertently left out.

Alderman, P J	Glue, D E	Marchant, J H	Snell, N
Baillie, S R	Halton, S	Marsh, G J F	Snow, D W
Bardsley, A (Mrs)	Hamley, D B	Mayer-Gross, H	Sterry, D
Bell, D P	Hammond, D	KcKeown, M	Stevens, P
Bodenham, D	(Mrs)	Mead, R	Stone, N H F
Boyd, M A	Harding, A V	Money, N	Taylor, J
Bream, R	Harris, A J	Morgan, R A	Timms, D
Brooks, T J L	Harris, E (Mrs)	Muldal, S	Tomlin, R J
Brown, C	Havers, M W	Murphy, J	Tunnicliffe, W F
Bubb, P J	Hawkins, B	Newell, W	Torry, C
Bubb, R (Mrs)	Heap, P	Newman, L & H	Towerton, J
Buisson, R S K	Hemmings, P	Newton, N	Tubby, J
Bunning, C J	Hill, B (Mrs)	Ogle, J R	Tucker, C
Burton, P J K	Horton, D	Orr-Ewing, D C	Turner, E
Catlett, P & E	Humphrey, C	Parker, T N	Veale, C
Clements, A	Hunt, M	Petts, R	Ward, C
Cogswell, A S	Hurst, R	Plant, C	Ward, R M
Coles, E	Jacoby, P	Phillips, J	Webb, V
Cook, A H	James, G	Prince, P & G	Wege, D C
Cook, J	Parker-Jervis, D	Read, R	Whitehouse, A
Correy, B C	Keen, J	Rear, D	Williams, P
Cowdy, S	Keen, S	Richards, G	Wilson, P & E
Crombie, D C	Kent, M	Robinson, J F	Windett, R V
Crathorne, B	Knight, J & E	Roddis, S J	Young, C E
Dean, T	Knox, A M (Mrs)	Rodwell, S	Youngman, R E
Denby, P (Mrs)	Knox, A G	Rose, J E	
Devas, D (Mrs)	Lack, P C	Rowe, C	
Elder, I D	Leby, P	Schofield, F & M	
Emary, C	Lee, D	Seabrook, J	
Evans, D E	Lewis, D R	Seymour, M	
Ferguson, D M	Lewis, P	Shepherd, S	
Fisher, C	Levy, R	Showler, D	
Freed, M	Lovatt, R	Sledge, B	
Fuller, R J	(Mr/Mrs)	Smallwood, D	
Gladwin, C G	Lukes, M	Smith, D	
Glover, A (Mrs)	Mandale, R	Smith, K	

INDEX OF BIRD NAMES

This index does not include references to the birds mentioned in the tables towards the end of the book as almost all species are listed there.

Map of Buckinghamshire

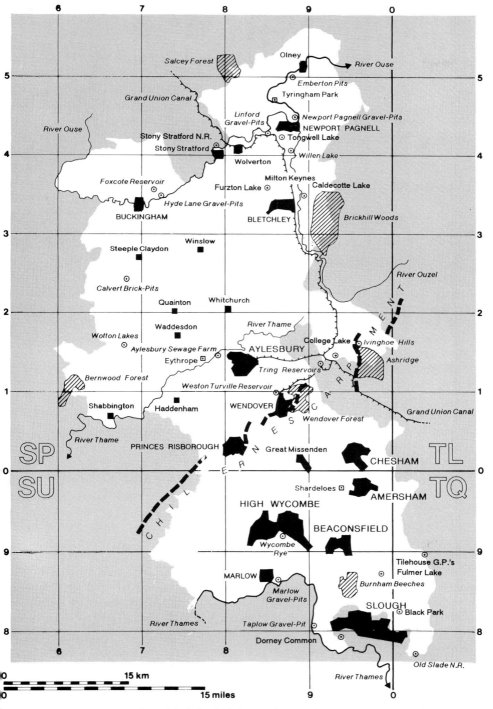

SP   SU   TL   TQ

0   15 km

0   15 miles

The inclusion of a site on this map does not imply the right of access: for most of them written permission to visit is required.